CORPORATE ABORIGINAL RELATIONS

Copyright

Corporate Aborginal Relations: Best Practice Case Studies.
Copyright © 1995 Hill Sloan Associates Inc.

Cover design and typesetting by Rick Eskins, Toronto, Ontario.

Printed by Friesen Printers, Altona, Manitoba.

Canadian Cataloguing in Publication Data

Sloan, Pamela, 1952-
Corporate aboriginal relations

ISBN 0-9699600-0-0

1. Native peoples - Canada - Services for - Case studies.* 2. Industry - Social aspects - Canada - Case studies. 3. Social responsibility of business - Canada - Case studies. 4. Native peoples - Canada - Economic conditions.* 5. Native peoples - Canada - Social conditions.*
I. Hill, Roger, 1945-   . II. Hill Sloan Associates. III. Title.

E78.C2S56 1995   362.84'97071   C95-931352-4

CONTENTS

Part Three: Employment Opportunities   *127*

Introduction

Relationships with Aboriginal people are increasingly important to corporate Canada. Aboriginal people are the fastest-growing part of the Canadian population. Aboriginal leaders in all parts of the country are seeking fairness for their people and opportunities for them to become economically self-reliant. Land claims and self-government are redefining the role that Aboriginal people play in Canadian society.

These developments translate into opportunities and challenges for organizations all across Canada. An increasing number are responding by putting in place active corporate Aboriginal relations programs that are designed to build constructive partnerships with communities and expand employment and business opportunities for Aboriginal people.

This book was written to document how leading corporations in all parts of the country are implementing Aboriginal policies and programs. Over the past four years, we have researched "best practices" in corporate Aboriginal relations for several clients. Some have wanted examples of tested practices that they can learn from, replicate and adapt. Others have wanted advice on benchmarks that they could use to evaluate their own initiatives. Our experience suggests that practical information about corporate Aboriginal relations programs is needed and wanted by many, yet there is very little reference material that is comprehensive, detailed and readily available.

This book is designed to fill that gap. We invited leading companies across Canada to share their experiences. The result is this compilation of 38 case studies describing actual policies and programs, as well as the results achieved. As such the book provides a unique insight into the actions that are being taken by corporate Canada to develop effective Aboriginal relations programs and offers a rich source of practical experience that can guide others.

A Growing Trend

Successful corporate Aboriginal relations initiatives are taking place all across Canada, in urban centres, rural communities and remote hamlets. The case studies document a variety of programs. Some are national in scope; most are regional or local initiatives. They take place in all major regions including British Colum-

Canada's Aboriginal Population (1993)		
	Number of People	% of Total
Status Indians	553,000	46%
- on reserve	326,000	27%
- off reserve	227,000	19%
Non-Status Indians	405,000	34%
Metis	192,000	16%
Inuit	41,000	4%
Total Aboriginal Population	1,191,000	100%

Source: Department of Indian Affairs and Northern Development

bia, the Prairies, Ontario, Quebec, Atlantic Canada, as well as the Yukon and Northwest Territories.

The number of Aboriginal relations programs in Canada has grown significantly in each of the past three decades, with the greatest growth in activity taking place in the last five years.

- The book includes three long-standing programs started in the mid-1970s that continue to grow and flourish today.

- The 1980s saw an increased number of Aboriginal programs introduced by organizations in the prairie provinces and northern territories, reflecting expanding oil and gas activity in these regions. The proclamation of the federal *Employment Equity Act* in 1986 caused federally-regulated companies, such as banks, transportation companies and crown corporations, to review their Aboriginal employment policies and procedures.

- The greatest growth and most widespread activity has taken place in the 1990s. Almost two-thirds of the programs in this book were introduced in the past five years. Across Canada, more and more organizations are taking steps to build constructive relationships with Aboriginal communities and people.

The case studies also illustrate that partnerships with Aboriginal people are being developed by a diverse range of organizations in a large number of sectors.

- In the resource sector, Aboriginal relations programs have been initiated by oil and gas companies, electric utilities, mining companies and forestry operations.

- The case studies include many examples from the service sectors of the economy, including banking, transportation, telecommunications, education and retailing.

- Crown corporations and government departments, at both the federal and provincial level, also have been active in developing comprehensive Aboriginal relations programs.

The breadth and depth of the programs clearly indicate that constructive relationships with Aboriginal people have become an important corporate issue.

The Business Imperative

The increased emphasis on corporate Aboriginal relations is a response to fundamental changes in the business environment. While many of the companies have regulatory or legislative requirements, most go well beyond what would be necessary for compliance alone. Rather, the emergence of active corporate Aboriginal relations programs in such a broad and diverse set of organizations is a reflection of changes in demographic and political realities.

Demographic trends are compelling many organizations to rethink their relationships with Aboriginal people. Aboriginal people are already a significant part of the population in many parts of Canada. In the Northwest Territories, they account for over 60 percent of the population. In both Manitoba and Saskatchewan about 10 percent of the population is of Aboriginal ancestry. Overall, Aboriginal people now make up almost 4 percent of Canada's population.

This population is growing very rapidly. The Department of Indian Affairs and Northern Development forecasts that the number of Aboriginal people will grow by 50 percent in the 25-year period from 1991 to 2016. Every province and territory will see rapid growth in its Aboriginal population. For corporate Canada, these trends translate into a changing customer base and a new profile for the workforce.

Land-use considerations are important for utilities, pipelines, and companies in the resource sector. Today, Aboriginal people control 20 percent of Canada's land mass; if outstanding land claims are resolved, they could control as much as 30 percent of the land in Canada by the end of the century. In addition, environmental approval processes, which call for community participation, make it essential for many companies that rely on resources and land use for their operations to take into account the concerns of local Aboriginal people.

Governments have also contributed to making corporate Aboriginal relations a more pressing issue. Employment equity legislation, human rights legislation, surface lease agreements, treaty negotiations in British Columbia and land claims together have had a direct or indirect impact on increasing numbers of companies across Canada.

Mutual Benefits

The case studies paint a picture of improving corporate Aboriginal relationships based on shared benefits. The results achieved by the organizations profiled in this book are impressive. As a group, they have had a marked impact on employment and business opportunities for Aboriginal people.

- These organizations have established relationships with hundreds of Aboriginal communities across Canada. The relationships are characterized by improved two-way communication and consultation, cooperative partnerships and collaborative community development initiatives.

- The case organizations have provided education, training and employment opportunities for thousands of Aboriginal people. Increasing numbers of Aboriginal people are entering the workforce, prepared for highly-skilled jobs with good prospects for long-term employment and advancement.

- Contracting opportunities worth hundreds of millions of dollars have been created for Aboriginal businesses and communities. These business opportunities have contributed to the creation of hundreds of new Aboriginal contracting and supply companies as well as some very large and successful joint ventures.

What is notable is that the benefits have flowed both ways. Many of the organizations studied found that, once past the start-up phase, their Aboriginal relations initiatives lead to clear business benefits, demonstrating that improved Aboriginal relations makes good business sense.

- Resource companies benefit from ongoing access to resources and community support for resource development.

- Assistance from Aboriginal communities has helped several companies to implement valuable environmental initiatives.

- Increased exposure to Aboriginal people and communities has improved business understanding of customers and opened new market opportunities.

- Programs for Aboriginal young people are laying the foundation for relationships with the workforce and customers of the future.

- Increasing the number of local Aboriginal employees has helped several companies, particular those operating in remote regions, to develop stable, long-term workforces.

- New Aboriginal suppliers and joint ventures are producing operating economies, cost-savings and improved quality for their corporate customers.

- A solid track record in Aboriginal relations can open opportunities in international markets. Host countries seek foreign investors capable of providing local benefits from their activities.

Organization and Content

The 38 organizations profiled in this book were selected on the basis of their leadership, commitment and expertise in different areas of Aboriginal relations. Each case study documents an organization's experience in a specific area.

The case studies are grouped into five specific themes.

- In *Part One: Building the Commitment*, the case studies illustrate the steps taken by seven organizations to implement effective Aboriginal relations strategies and put in place the organization, resources and skills to carry out the policy.

- *Part Two: Education and Training* shows how twelve organizations have developed and used different approaches to provide Aboriginal people with improved access to education and training opportunities.

- *Part Three: Employment Opportunities* documents measures used by nine organizations to enhance the employment situation of Aboriginal people.

- *Part Four: Business Development* describes the experience of five organizations in opening up contracting opportunities for Aboriginal businesses and communities and working with them to enhance their capacity to become competitive suppliers.

- *Part Five: Community Relations* brings out the processes used by five organizations to establish and sustain effective relationships with Aboriginal communities.

An overview of all of the case studies has been prepared which summarizes the best practices. For those who want to benchmark their activities against a composite list of best practices, we have prepared a checklist that appears at the back of the book.

Who Should Read this Book

The book will be of interest to a wide range of people who want to understand what leading companies are doing to improve employment and business opportunities for Aboriginal people and to develop partnerships with Aboriginal communities.

- Companies working in close proximity to Aboriginal communities can gain insight into how to develop partnership relationships based on shared trust, mutual responsibility and reciprocal cooperation.

- Employers in both the public and private sector will find examples of practical and effective actions to improve Aboriginal employment through outreach, targeted recruitment and pre-employment programs. There are good examples of initiatives to enhance the advancement and retention of Aboriginal people in their workforces.

- Companies with significant procurement requirements will find information on effective policy and program measures that can increase contracting and supplier opportunities for Aboriginal businesses and communities.

- Industry and professional associations can learn about the role that an association can play in providing leadership for an entire industry or coordinating programs that enable industry participants to accomplish more collectively that they could do alone.

- The experience of companies with unionized workforces will be of interest to union leaders. In some case studies, partnership with unions has been essential to ensure the long-term effectiveness of the Aboriginal relations strategy.

- Educators should find many of the case studies useful, not only for help in designing their own educational programs, but also as a teaching tool. The book provides a rich source of material related to business management, Aboriginal studies, and social and economic development.

- Governments will be interested in the insights for both policy development and program design. Many of the case studies demonstrate how federal and provincial governments served as catalysts for partnerships and how government funding has been an important element in the success of some initiatives.

The book should also be valuable to Aboriginal communities, economic development agencies and Aboriginal businesses. Most of the initiatives described have been developed in partnership with Aboriginal people, demonstrating Aboriginal and non-Aboriginal partners working together to solve specific problems or plan specific programs. The case studies offer concrete examples of the types of partnerships that can be forged between Aboriginal and non-Aboriginal organizations and practical ideas about measures that can yield mutual benefit.

Acknowledgements

There are many people who have helped to make this book possible. We would particularly like to express our appreciation to the 38 organizations that agreed to share their experiences for the book. We worked with about 100 people in these organizations who provided information, answered questions and gave feedback on our interpretation of their Aboriginal relations initiatives. Thank you for your time, patience and support.

We would also like to acknowledge the two groups who first asked us to investigate best practices in corporate Aboriginal relations. The federal government's Consultation Group on Employment Equity for Aboriginal Peoples and the Steering Committee for the 1992 Aboriginal Workforce Participation Conference both provided us with valuable insight into the types of practices that are important in building constructive relationships with Aboriginal people.

There are many others who encouraged us professionally and personally to write and publish the case studies. Their interest and advice has helped us throughout the project. We are also grateful to Peter Scaggs for his assistance with production and to Jane Cooney of *Books for Business* for her guidance on business publications.

August 1995   Pamela Sloan
                                                Roger Hill

OVERVIEW OF THE BEST PRACTICES

Positive relationships with Aboriginal people are the result of focused and sustained efforts. The inequitable participation of Aboriginal people in the mainstream economy is well-documented. Labour force participation rates, employment rates and earned income levels of Aboriginal people are well below those of other Canadians. Historically, poor education and inadequate skill development were major causes of inequities. At the same time, corporate employment and purchasing practices have posed barriers to the equitable participation of Aboriginal people.

Specific measures are needed to remove those barriers, solve problems and provide opportunities. The case studies illustrate the types of successful practices that organizations have developed, implemented and refined to build constructive relationships with Aboriginal people.

BUILDING THE COMMITMENT

Making The Strategic Commitment

Any commitment to Aboriginal participation must be anchored in clear corporate policies, reinforced by leadership of the Chief Executive and driven by explicit goals, targets and timetables. All of the organizations profiled here have made significant strategic commitments. Over one-third have formal Aboriginal relations policies.

- SaskEnergy's Aboriginal Policy is based on the recognition that the Indian and Metis communities must be an important part of Canada's economic growth and development. The policy states that the company will encourage and develop relationships in three strategic areas: employment, education and training, and business development. In each area, SaskEnergy pursues parallel and complementary internal and external initiatives.

- Syncrude's Aboriginal Development Program was developed by its first president in 1974. Since then, each of Syncrude's four subsequent presidents has publicly reaffirmed the company's commitment to the program and has ensured that it received the time, resources and visibility to succeed. All have placed particular emphasis on setting goals, monitoring results and communicating achievements. Syncrude is now the largest industrial employer of Aboriginal people in Canada.

- Cameco sets both goals and timetables for Aboriginal employment and business participation. Moreover, it sets steadily increasing targets in order to attain its long-term, strategic goals. In recent years, the company has made dramatic progress in its northern development plans. It is now an industry leader in Canada both for its high employment of Aboriginal people and for the scope of its contracting with northern and Aboriginal businesses.

Building Operational Capability

The strategic commitment must be supported by implementation of the policies. The studies show how Aboriginal relations initiatives can be integrated into core business functions, resources made available to develop and operate specific programs, and employees provided with the skills they need to work effectively with Aboriginal people. A comprehensive set of practical, concrete measures thus becomes the basis for fundamental corporate change.

- B.C. Hydro's Aboriginal Relations Department was created to provide a focal point for action in the company. A staff of 15 full-time employees is organized into four groups dealing with grievance resolution and negotiations, business development and communications, cross-cultural and negotiations training, and special projects. Staff have the mix of expertise and experience to work effectively within Hydro and with Aboriginal peoples.

- After extensive consultations with Aboriginal people, Bank of Montreal developed an integrated set of initiatives which links its Aboriginal banking strategy to increased employment and training opportunities in the bank for Aboriginal people. An Aboriginal Banking Unit was created and the bank's workplace equality policies are fully integrated into the development of the Aboriginal banking strategy.

- The growing number and complexity of Aboriginal issues, such as self-government, Aboriginal rights, land claims, economic development and justice, make it essential for employees of the Department of Indian Affairs and Northern Development to be well-versed in their history and background. The department's Aboriginal Awareness Program is designed both to help employees gain the skills they need to work effectively with communities and to minimize the potential for culturally-based misunderstandings and conflicts.

Sectoral Leadership

Some industry associations have provided sectoral leadership on Aboriginal relations. For example, in 1994 the Council of Forest Industries in British Columbia provided leadership and guidance to its members in the forestry sector by issuing a report containing practical suggestions on how members could take concrete steps to hire more Aboriginal employees, increase contracting opportunities for Aboriginal businesses, provide more internship opportunities, establish cooperative agreements and create joint business ventures.

PROMOTING EDUCATION AND TRAINING

Encouraging Young People to Stay in School

Over 50 percent of the Aboriginal population is below the age of 25. And historically far too many of them drop out of high school. In 1991, while 62 percent of Canadian students completed high school, fewer than 31 percent of on-reserve students achieved the same result. It is imperative that Aboriginal young people are encouraged to stay in school and pursue an education that will prepare them for future job opportunities.

Many organizations have recognized the need to reach out to Aboriginal students while they are still in school, giving them the time and the information needed to make informed choices about their education and career directions. Such organizations provide information, role models, work experience and educational experiences for elementary and high school students.

- Royal Bank has worked with both elementary and secondary schools to encourage Aboriginal students to gain the kind of education needed for career opportunities in business. Junior Achievement programs have been run in urban Aboriginal schools and in on-reserve schools. A national Stay-in-School Program provides grade 11 and 12 students with incentives to continue their education. A work experience program for elementary school students helps them understand the relationship between school subjects and work.

- NOVA Gas Transmission introduced its Native Education Program in 1986 to address the high drop-out rate among Aboriginal students (especially in senior high school) and to boost the pool of qualified Aboriginal workers in Alberta. Each year, NOVA hires two Aboriginal university students to visit junior and senior high schools in the province and conduct motivational workshops to encourage students to stay in school, begin the process of career planning, and continue on to college or university. The presenters are valuable role models for the younger Aboriginal students, an added benefit.

- The Ordre des ingénieurs du Québec and the Faculty of Engineering and Computer Science of Concordia University concluded that achieving increased representation of Aboriginal people in the engineering profession required outreach and motivation. *Engineering Explorations,* a summer engineering camp for Aboriginal students, is one of their joint initiatives designed to stimulate interest in the field.

Providing Educational Opportunities and Support for Aboriginal Students

In recent years, the educational levels of Aboriginal people have been rising rapidly. In 1969, there were 800 Aboriginal people with post-secondary education. By 1991, there were 107,000 Aboriginal people with some post-secondary education. Nonetheless, educational levels, which overall remain below those of other Canadians, constitute a serious barrier to the full participation of Aboriginal people in many organizations.

Educational institutions and employers are responding to the challenge by instituting programs to increase access by Aboriginal people to education and training, helping them to develop the skills and qualifications required to compete in the job market. Scholarships, academic and cultural supports, and relevant summer work experience all provide opportunities for Aboriginal people to participate and succeed in advanced education and training programs.

- The Native Access Program for Engineering offered by the Faculty of Engineering at Lakehead University provides participants with an academic program of pre-engineering instruction which equips students to later enter the regular engineering course at the university.

- The RCMP introduced the Aboriginal Cadet Development Program to assist Aboriginal candidates to upgrade their academic and physical skills so that they could enter the RCMP Training Academy on an equal basis with other participants. All candidates undergo a three-week test of their academic, physical, driving and life-skills abilities. An individual training program is then designed to meet the specific needs of each cadet.

- Petro-Canada's Education Awards Program for Native Students was set up in 1985 to help Aboriginal students to complete post-secondary studies in a discipline applicable to the oil and gas industry. The company now gives about twelve awards annually, each of which can be worth up to $5000. Since the inception of the program in 1985, 138 students have been supported.

- The Law Programme for Indigenous Blacks and Mi'kmaqs at Dalhousie Law School has a number of features that are designed to provide special academic support to participating students. Students have access to Academic Enhancement Sessions. A student tutor is available on request, a Mi'kmaq Student Advisor provides support, and a counsellor helps students experiencing problems in time management skills, study skills and cognitive learning.

Providing Access to Pre-Employment Training

Some corporate initiatives are designed to provide Aboriginal people with training in a specific skill or business area.

- The pre-employment Aboriginal training partnerships used by the Canadian Bankers Association provided disadvantaged job seekers with the skills required for entry-level jobs in the banks. The purpose of the training was to upgrade students to the point where they could handle requirements of an entry-level position as a bank teller or a customer service representative. Usually, a Grade 12 diploma is the academic requirement for these positions.

- BC TEL's Employment Communication Skills Workshop, introduced in 1994, provides participants with the practical knowledge and skills needed for BC TEL job vacancies. The workshop covers several types of skills, including expressing oneself with confidence, using communication equipment, using job search techniques effectively and understanding how to thrive and communicate in different cultures.

- CIBC's Aboriginal Internship Program provides Aboriginal post-secondary students with a structured program of summer work experience. Participants are assigned a "buddy", who acts as a mentor, by the branch. Successful students are then offered scholarships to assist with their continuing studies. The program for returning students provides progressively more challenging tasks, encouraging further growth and development. Students who demonstrate an interest in pursuing a career with CIBC are provided with career counselling.

- The Commission de la construction du Québec has an active program informing Aboriginal people about how they can become qualified in the construction trades and achieve their certificates of competency.

The Commission also helps those who have had experience in construction obtain the necessary proof of relevant experience and apply it towards their qualifications.

- For two decades, Canada Mortgage and Housing Corporation has provided comprehensive training programs designed to give Aboriginal people the knowledge and experience needed to become employed in the delivery, administration and management of Aboriginal housing and to pursue career opportunities with housing agencies in the public, non-profit and private sectors.

ENHANCING EMPLOYMENT OPPORTUNITIES

While there are some exceptions, most employers don't hire Aboriginal staff to the level of their availability in the labour force. In 1993 the representation rate of Aboriginal people in the workforces of employers covered by the federal *Employment Equity Act* was 1.1 percent, significantly less than their census labour market availability of 3.0 percent. Moreover, 25 percent of employers covered by the *Act* reported having **no** Aboriginal people in their workforces.

Implementing Comprehensive Programs

The problem of under-representation has been addressed by some employers through comprehensive programs to increase the recruitment, retention and advancement of Aboriginal people. Often this is done within the framework of a corporate workforce diversity or employment equity program.

- The Department of National Revenue's Aboriginal Employment Program is a multi-year strategy to improve employment opportunities for Aboriginal people. The program is composed of four elements: an outreach component; a series of developmental employment initiatives, including summer employment programs for both Aboriginal high-school and post-secondary students; cross-cultural education and training for departmental employees; and a communications strategy to promote diversity and share successes.

- The Saskatchewan Government's Aboriginal Employment Development Program complements the government's employment equity strategy, but maintains a discrete focus on Aboriginal employment and career development. One component of this program is an inventory of resumes of Indian and Metis people. It was developed, in part, to address the claim that there were no qualified Aboriginal people to fill vacancies. There are now almost 1400 names on the inventory and referrals are made to employers in both the public and private sectors.

- Manitoba Telephone System's initiatives to increase Aboriginal employment are part of its overall employment equity strategy. The *Towards Equality* program seeks to eliminate barriers, both formal and informal, that limit employment opportunities for Aboriginal people and members of other designated groups. Manitoba Telephone System also has used a series of measures, including outreach, educational awards, work experience programs and school partnerships, that are specifically targeted to Aboriginal people.

- Despite massive downsizing and restructuring, CN has been able to increase the rate at which Aboriginal people are represented in its workforce. It has accomplished this by strengthening its outreach to Aboriginal communities and by using the staffing opportunities that do emerge in a strategic fashion. In addition, the company has increased management accountability for achieving a representative workforce, thereby making employment equity an integral part of its business practices.

Using Targeted Measures

Targeted measures can be effective in increasing the representation of Aboriginal peoples in workforces. In some cases, long-standing recruitment practices have been adapted to ensure that Aboriginal people are included in the pool of candidates from which hiring decisions are made. In other cases, specific apprenticeship, training and management development programs have been put in place for Aboriginal employees. These measures both increase the number of Aboriginal people in entry-level positions and promote their advancement to higher-skilled, higher-paid occupations over time.

- The Department of Foreign Affairs uses extensive outreach measures to stimulate the interest of Aboriginal people in working for the department and pursuing careers in the foreign service. Information is sent to Aboriginal organizations and media across Canada. Regional briefings encourage Aboriginal people to apply. These outreach initiatives are designed to complement the Annual Foreign Service campaign.

- Cogema Resources has created many training and apprenticeship opportunities in the skilled trades for Aboriginal people. Recruitment for the company's in-house training programs is done in conjunction with local communities. Apprenticeship programs in six provincially-certified trades (electricians, plumbers, welders, heavy-duty mechanics, millwrights, instrumentation technicians) are reserved exclusively for northern residents, 90 percent of whom are Aboriginal.

- The North West Company introduced its Stores Training Program in 1991, in part to provide opportunities for all employees (70 percent of whom are Aboriginal people) to develop the skills to advance in the company. The training program, which is based on about 120 training modules, incorporates user-friendly and culturally-sensitive learning materials. Module content, materials and support structures encourage Aboriginal staff to progress to management positions. Between 1991 and 1994, there was a 32 percent increase in Aboriginal management staff.

Creating a Positive Environment

One critical issue faced by many organizations is the challenge of creating an environment where Aboriginal people are respected and valued. Informal mentoring and support systems, naturally available to most employees, are often absent for Aboriginal employees, since low representation rates and lack of role models make it difficult for these to develop spontaneously.

Some employers have taken action to create a positive environment for Aboriginal employees. Communication programs raise awareness about Aboriginal people and issues. Mentoring and support groups help Aboriginal people adapt to new working environments. These initiatives aid the recruitment, retention and career advancement of Aboriginal people in the workplace.

- TD Bank's Nakoda Circle of Aboriginal employees identified the importance of building a respectful work environment for Aboriginal employees and the need to increase awareness of the diversity of the Aboriginal population. The Circle itself has emerged as a network that brings together the small, dispersed population of Aboriginal employees in the bank, with members of the Circle making personal commitments to mentor Aboriginal employees. Regional circles have further facilitated the mentoring process.

- The mandate of the Aboriginal Working Group at the Department of Canadian Heritage is to advise managers in the department on how to enhance the employment situation of Aboriginal people, to provide a support group and mentors for Aboriginal employees, and to increase awareness of Aboriginal culture. The group is employee-driven, setting its own objectives and priorities. At the same time, it has the strong and visible support of senior management in the department.

ENHANCING ABORIGINAL BUSINESS PARTICIPATION

Providing Business Opportunities

A growing number of companies are increasing the participation of Aboriginal businesses in their operations. The case studies show how many companies provide opportunities for Aboriginal contractors and suppliers.

In the resource and utilities sectors, some companies have adopted specific procurement policies to increase the volume and value of their purchases from Aboriginal business. Others have used a range of different types of business relationship, including contracting, sub-contracting and cooperative ventures to provide opportunities for Aboriginal suppliers.

- Manitoba Hydro's special procurement provisions directed to northern Aboriginal business include providing information on purchasing policies and upcoming contracts early enough to allow adequate preparation time; breaking contracts into small packages to make them more compatible with the capabilities of northern Aboriginal businesses; and setting aside some contract opportunities exclusively for northern Aboriginal business.

- The key focus of Westcoast Energy's Aboriginal Affairs program is the creation of business opportunities for Aboriginal communities and contractors, both through Westcoast's own operations and those of its subsidiaries. The company has also been a leader in collaborative efforts with other resource developers to create opportunities for Aboriginal people, especially in northeast British Columbia.

Developing Business Capabilities

Many of the organizations that provide opportunities for Aboriginal suppliers also work with them to strengthen their business capabilities and to enable them to compete effectively for contracts.

Some organizations provide training and technical advice, others encourage joint ventures with non-Aboriginal businesses to broaden Aboriginal access to contracts and facilitate skills transfer. An increasing number of organizations enter into cooperative ventures with Aboriginal people, enabling the Aboriginal partner to realize significant direct benefits in the form of employment, skills development, business development, revenues and profits.

- Training is an important element of Canada Post's service partnerships with northern communities. Under the partnership contracts, the bands or hamlets hire their own employees to provide postal service. Canada Post provides a fee for service as well as training for both the employees and the supervisors. Canada Post also has prepared videos on service procedures which are used as refresher training tools.

- Interfor has entered into a number of cooperative ventures with Aboriginal people in British Columbia. These cover a wide range of business relationships. For example, the company has contracting arrangements with the Nisga'a Band to provide helilog rigging crews. A joint business venture with the Toquaht Band included the construction of a sawmill on reserve land. The company has also entered into 16 different cooperative initiatives with the Sechelt Band.

In some regions, companies are working collectively to provide business opportunities and develop Aboriginal business capabilities.

- The Business Development task team of the Northeast B.C. Industry Group was formed to increase the number of Aboriginal businesses and contracting companies in those fields required by the industries operating in the region. This task team has conducted a series of "how to" workshops and courses designed to increase the operating knowledge of business principles among Aboriginal companies. This has included presentations on basic contract operating procedures and courses on book-keeping.

STRENGTHENING RELATIONS WITH ABORIGINAL COMMUNITIES

Comprehensive Agreements

Strengthening relationships with Aboriginal communities as a means of ensuring continuity of operations and corporate growth is a priority for many organizations. Community-based initiatives can include measures to mitigate environmental impact, increase economic development or enhance social development. Overall, community-based measures are usually designed to ensure that the relationships between Aboriginal communities and the enterprises active in their areas are mutually beneficial.

Some companies have entered into comprehensive arrangements with Aboriginal communities that have been formalized in legal agreements.

- Hydro-Québec's negotiated agreements provide the ongoing framework for the relationship between the utility and Aboriginal peoples. Several agreements rely on specially-created, jointly-managed remedial works corporations to carry out the mitigation and enhancement activities needed to circumscribe or offset the negative impacts of Hydro's operations on Aboriginal communities. Today, Hydro-Québec's policy is to try to achieve **integrated** agreements with Aboriginal people that specify remedial measures as well as measures for community, economic and cultural development.

- After a lengthy process of community consultation, Falconbridge has signed an agreement with Makivik Corporation (representing the local Inuit) that gives priority to hiring and training qualified Inuit workers for the Raglan project. This agreement provides contracting opportunities for Inuit enterprises and sets up a trust fund for local Inuit people. The company has also set up a Raglan Committee to consult with local stakeholders on environmental issues as the project proceeds.

Using Collaborative Processes

Community-based initiatives are usually the result of a collaborative process between the Aboriginal and non-Aboriginal partners. The collaborative process ensures that priorities are identified and addressed. Formal structures are often put in place to provide a focal point for action and to facilitate joint decision-making.

- Parks Canada has agreements with some Aboriginal communities to cooperatively manage certain national parks. These agreements provide equal representation for the Aboriginal community on the park's management board which sets the overall site-specific policy and objectives. Some agreements also include provision for cooperative planning and management of park lands, including continuation of traditional resource harvesting by local Aboriginal people in a way that preserves the ecological integrity of the region, and provides ongoing economic opportunities for local communities.

- Ontario Hydro's team-based, problem-solving approach for resolving First Nations' grievances directly involves representatives of both Hydro and the First Nations. This approach relies on developing understanding between the parties as to the physical, environmental, economic and cultural effects of Ontario Hydro's activities on reserves and traditional land-use areas and on the First Nations peoples who occupy or use these areas. The aim is to reach consensus on appropriate action to be taken.

In some regions, industry groups have collaborated both with each other and with local Aboriginal communities to promote opportunities for people in the region.

- The Peace Arch Project in Alberta, begun in 1987, is a formal partnership of community, industry and government members to ensure local Aboriginal people benefit from resource development in the region. Community involvement has been key to the Project's success. Community representatives, elected by the eight northern communities in the region, sit on the Management Committee. This committee is assisted by a full-time project coordinator and a training and employment coordinator, both of whom are selected by the communities. Although industry representatives have provided leadership for the project to date, the long-term objective is for the communities to assume this role.

PART ONE

BUILDING THE COMMITMENT

Developing a Corporate Aboriginal Framework Policy at SaskEnergy

The corporation is targeting three strategic areas to build partnerships with Indian and Metis communities — employment, education and training, and business development.

In 1993, SaskEnergy's Board of Directors approved a formal Aboriginal Policy Framework which states that SaskEnergy will encourage and foster partnerships with Indian and Metis communities in Saskatchewan. The corporation is targeting three strategic areas to build these partnerships, namely employment, education and training, and business development.

The policy was developed after an extensive process of consultation with the Aboriginal community in Saskatchewan. The executive and membership of the Communications, Energy and Paperworkers (CEP) Union Local 649 was also instrumental in putting the policy in place, thereby breaking new ground in establishing relations among unions, employers and Aboriginal people. CEP's Executive Council joined SaskEnergy's Board of Directors in approving the corporation's Aboriginal Policy.

SaskEnergy has introduced a planning and implementation strategy to ensure that its Aboriginal policy objectives are integrated into all the company's planning and management systems and that the company's internal and external Aboriginal initiatives complement each other. Specific strategies and action plans have already been developed.

The initial results from SaskEnergy's Aboriginal Policy Framework have been very positive. A number of partnership agreements are in place with tribal councils to facilitate Aboriginal recruitment. Aboriginal representation rates have increased sharply. Training programs are creating a supportive workplace environment. Progress is being made in creating new opportunities for Aboriginal contractors.

Context for the Policy

SaskEnergy's Aboriginal policy is designed to facilitate Indian and Metis self-determination and to provide the basis for new relationships with Saskatchewan's Indian and Metis communities. The company is committed to a partnership-building process that reflects the Government of Saskatchewan's commitment of enabling Aboriginal people to become "full partners in the processes and benefits of social and economic development in Saskatchewan".

SaskEnergy Incorporated

SaskEnergy is a provincial Crown corporation and natural gas utility that provides natural gas service to residential, farm, commercial and industrial customers in Saskatchewan. SaskEnergy's wholly owned subsidiary, TransGas Limited, is the province's natural gas transmission and storage company.

The corporation has assets of over $900 million and revenues of over $350 million and has a workforce of about 940 full-time and part-time employees, of whom 42 (4.5 percent) have declared themselves to be of Aboriginal ancestry.

Half of all Aboriginal employees work in clerical jobs, 33 percent are in technical or trades positions, and 17 percent are in middle management or professional jobs.

SaskEnergy's Aboriginal Policy was developed through consultation and collaboration with its key partners, including First Nations, the Metis Nation, the company's union and employees, as well as external business partners.

The Communication, Energy and Paperworkers Union's Executive Council joined SaskEnergy's Board of Directors in approving the corporation's Aboriginal Policy.

The Aboriginal Policy Framework is anchored by business considerations. The policy complements the company's vision of being "Canada's leading energy company by anticipating [its] customers' changing needs and providing innovative and responsive solutions". Aboriginal peoples constitute the largest market of expanding consumer demand for SaskEnergy and Transgas services in the province. First Nation Reserves, tribal councils and business development corporations are a growing source of potential joint venture business opportunities.

The new policy also builds on established initiatives with Aboriginal groups such as SaskEnergy's participation in projects that encourage Aboriginal children to explore non-traditional trades, science and technology.

Development and Launch of the Policy

SaskEnergy's Aboriginal Policy was developed as a result of an extensive process of consultation and collaboration with its key partners, including First Nations, the Metis Nation, the company's union and employees, as well as external business partners. Aboriginal communities were consulted in the development of the policy and have continued to be consulted in its implementation.

The Communications, Energy and Paperworkers (CEP) Union, Local 649 also made a critical contribution to the Aboriginal Policy Framework. The union and the company have a well-established relationship based on trust and openness. The cornerstone of this relationship is the "Dialogue Process", a distinctive management approach that makes the union a partner to the business. CEP's President is a member of SaskEnergy's Board of Directors and the union has equal membership in all standing committees. The company and the union have worked together on a wide range of initiatives, including the strategic planning process, business planning, and employment equity.

CEP members participated in the process of designing the Aboriginal policy and brought forward their concerns and issues. Once the policy framework was drafted, it was taken to the CEP's Executive Council for approval. The union's Executive Council joined SaskEnergy's Board of Directors in approving the corporation's Aboriginal Policy, which ensures that job requirements and training standards remain unaffected under the new Framework.

The Aboriginal Policy Framework was formally launched in Saskatoon in January 1994, with SaskEnergy's Board of Directors, Senior Executives and CEP members attending. The launch was co-sponsored by the Saskatoon Tribal Council, which contributed to the credibility and visibility of the policy. The launch was held in conjunction with a Federation of Saskatchewan Indian Nations economic development conference, which served to increase the presence of representatives of the Aboriginal community in a business forum and to demonstrate the company's willingness to work within the Aboriginal community's timeframe and environment.

Key Elements of the Policy

SaskEnergy's Aboriginal Policy is based on the recognition that the Indian and Metis communities of Saskatchewan must be an important part of Canada' economic growth and development. The policy states that the company will encourage and develop relationships and partnerships in three strategic areas: employment, education and training, and business development. In each of these areas, SaskEnergy will pursue parallel and complementary internal and external initiatives.

Increasing the number of Indian and Metis employees within the corporation is a major objective of the policy.

Increasing the number of Indian and Metis employees within the corporation is a major objective of the policy. SaskEnergy is pursuing a number of initiatives in order to accomplish this.

- The company has entered into Partnership Agreements with tribal agencies to increase the number of Aboriginal referrals and hires and provide career planning and promotion opportunities.

- SaskEnergy has taken steps to foster and promote a workplace environment that is culturally sensitive, ideologically supportive and proactive by nature. An in-house, customized, modular education package has been developed to facilitate on-site, in-service delivery of the *Aboriginal Economic Arguments for Change* package.

- The company and its union (CEP) is also undertaking an apprenticeship trades training review. Since both the Tribal Councils and SaskEnergy are active independently in the administration and delivery of apprenticeship programs, the apprenticeship review is examining whether there are opportunities for the company and the Tribal Councils to marry certain aspects of their apprenticeship programs and benefit from potential synergies.

- SaskEnergy is also committed to creating employment opportunities for Aboriginal people working as or for suppliers and contractors to the company and is developing a mechanism for tracking contracts awarded to monitor progress towards Aboriginal employment created.

Education and training is a key dimension of SaskEnergy's Aboriginal Framework Policy.

Education and training is a key dimension of SaskEnergy's Aboriginal Framework Policy. The company is taking steps to encourage, foster and promote higher learning in Saskatchewan's Indian and Metis communities and to ensure that Aboriginal employees have access to education and training opportunities in the company.

- SaskEnergy has drafted a training implementation plan to ensure that Aboriginal education and training is embedded in the overall training schedule of the company and that the Aboriginal training modules are delivered and scheduled cost-effectively in an environment of defined training days per employee.

- SaskEnergy is also creating opportunities to encourage young people to stay in school and complete their education. This involves identifying and fostering locally based stay-in-school partnerships, providing an educational awards program for Aboriginal students, and continuing to partner in Aboriginal education initiatives, such as the Federation of Saskatchewan Indian Nations summer science camp and the Indian and Metis Girls Exploring Science and Technology program.

To promote Aboriginal business development, SaskEnergy will foster and support Indian and Metis businesses and contractors doing business with and for SaskEnergy. This involves developing partnerships that encourage and support the development of Aboriginal community-based entrepreneurial projects and aggressively promoting participation by Aboriginal business in SaskEnergy's Supplier Development Program.

A process is also being established to enable direct dialogue between SaskEnergy's partner Tribal Councils and the Communications, Energy and Paperworkers Union. This process will provide a mechanism for the union to work directly with the Aboriginal community and to discuss issues of mutual concern.

Planning and Implementation

SaskEnergy has integrated its Aboriginal policy into departmental and organizational business plans. This has been done to ensure that all departments participate fully and that the results can be measured. Aboriginally-focused actions and strategies are an integral part of each element of the planning cycle, including the company's strategic plan, the annual business plan, the budget, the human resource plan, departmental plans, summer student planning and recruitment planning.

In February 1994, the company created the Aboriginal Policy Coordinating Group to drive the process of implementation. The role of this committee is two-fold. First, it ensures that each division integrates Aboriginal action plans and strategies into its operational and business plans. Second, it ensures that all of the corporate strategies and actions work together in a coordinated fashion. The Coordinating Group is designed as a short-term measure. However, SaskEnergy has estimated that the total

SaskEnergy has integrated its Aboriginal policy into departmental and organizational business plans. Aboriginally-focused actions and strategies are an integral part of each element of the planning cycle.

transition process may take about 5 years. This time will be needed to set the stage for fundamental change, develop appropriate procedures, build relationships and integrate the Aboriginal policy fully into general operations.

The Coordinating Group consists of a Standing Committee and three Implementation Committees. The Standing Committee is made up of representatives of senior management in the company and the union. It provides strategic guidance to the process. The Implementation Committees consist of three teams, each vested with the responsibility for one of the three core objectives in the Policy, namely education and training, employment, and business development.

The company has set a five-year target for the Aboriginal Policy to be fully integrated within all planning processes and transferred to general operations.

- The mandate of each implementation team is to design a strategic implementation plan for their designated objective; to ensure that these initiatives are conveyed and incorporated into the corporate planning process; and to advance the initiatives so that they are fully integrated into corporate systems.

- The implementation teams are composed of directors and managers from the relevant functional areas and business units in the company. In this way, the implementation process involves all the individuals in a position to anticipate, plan, influence and facilitate the changes and adjustments required by the company. For example the Business Development team is composed of people from Marketing, Supplier Development and Construction. The Employment team has directors and managers from Training, Recruitment and Construction. The Education and Training team consists of representatives from Operations, Land, and Customer Services.

Results will be monitored, assessed and rewarded. The link to individual performance assessment is key to continued long-term momentum and ongoing commitment to the policy. SaskEnergy is also taking steps to ensure that the results of its external initiatives can be measured so that the company and the Indian and Metis communities can assess whether progress is being made. Partnership agreements will be defined in such a way as to provide a tool for joint benchmarking and success measurement.

The company has set a five-year target for the Aboriginal Policy to be fully integrated within all corporate, annual and strategic planning processes and transferred to general operations. At the end of this timeframe, the Aboriginal Policy Coordinating Group should no longer be required on a permanent basis because responsibility for delivery of the policy will have been fully integrated into general operations.

Results

SaskEnergy has already achieved significant results since the Aboriginal Policy was implemented.

The company has signed three partnership agreements with Tribal Councils representing 44 Indian Bands and 50,000 status Indians. These agreements are designed to facilitate referral and access of Aboriginal candidates for direct and indirect job opportunities created at or by SaskEnergy. There are also three Employment Referral and Access agreements in operation and a Protocol agreement with the Federation of Saskatchewan Indian Nations.

The corporate planning process is well advanced. In the company's 1995 Business Plan, all business units have strategies and actions specific to the Aboriginal Policy. These strategies are now being implemented and progress is being monitored.

There has been progress in increasing the representation of Aboriginal people in SaskEnergy's workforce.

- The 1994 Employment Equity Plan stated that 20 percent of all external hires made in 1995 would be people of Aboriginal ancestry. This target was achieved in 1994.

- In 1994, 17 percent of summer students were Aboriginal, up from 4 percent in 1993.

- By the end of 1994, Aboriginal people made up 4.5 percent of the company's total workforce. This was up significantly from 1993, partly as a result of 17 new hires and partly the result of an increase in the number of existing employees self-identifying themselves as Aboriginal.

- SaskEnergy also provided 25 persons years of employment for Aboriginal people working in contractors' workforces in 1994.

Some progress is also being made in increasing business opportunities for Aboriginal suppliers.

- In 1994, a tender list of over 180 Aboriginal businesses was put together in order to have a single source of the services that can be provided by the Aboriginal community. This list is updated and expanded on an ongoing basis.

- An Aboriginal contractor recently was awarded a $1 million contract to provide services to the company.

The company has signed three partnership agreements with Tribal Councils representing 44 Indian Bands and 50,000 status Indians.

- SaskEnergy's asbestos removal project, a highly complex activity requiring high skill levels, has been delivered by an Aboriginal-dominated work team.

One of the most important results to date is that the *Aboriginal Economics Arguments for Change* education program is now in full operation. All of the training materials have been prepared and approved. The Aboriginal community was one of the parties providing approval. The program is delivered in two parts: a Basic Curriculum and an Advanced Series. The program is delivered by Aboriginal educators in Wanausekewin, thereby providing an environment where employees are fully immersed in an Aboriginal cultural setting.

One of the most important results to date is that the Aboriginal Economics Arguments for Change education program is now in full operation.

- By July 1995, over 500 employees, one half of the total workforce, had voluntarily requested training. Over 150 had completed it. A total of fourteen sessions of the basic curriculum and one of the advanced curriculum are scheduled for 1995.

- Testimonials received from participants have been very positive. One participant wrote: "I discovered many interesting facts regarding Aboriginal policies, treaties, the Indian Act and most importantly the discrimination many have experienced.... I have more appreciation for their culture, respect for their history and compassion for their struggle in today's society".

- The Steering Committee of the Aboriginal Government Employees Network audited the course and found that "the content offers insight and provides much-needed education on topical issues of interest to both Aboriginal and non-Aboriginal persons....the goal of promoting Aboriginal peoples' rich historical contributions and cultural diversity will assist in the eventual elimination of racial discrimination".

In 1995, SaskEnergy was awarded a Training for Excellence Award.

In June 1995, SaskEnergy was awarded the 1995 Training for Excellence Award by the Saskatchewan Labour Force Development Board for its Aboriginal education program.

Senior Management Leadership of Syncrude's Aboriginal Development Program

Syncrude's senior managers have ensured that its Aboriginal relations program has received enough time, resources and visibility to succeed.

The leadership and support of Syncrude's senior management have defined and sustained the company's commitment to Aboriginal development for the past 20 years. Senior managers have ensured that the program received enough time, resources and visibility to succeed. They have placed particular emphasis on setting goals, monitoring results and communicating achievements. Syncrude's Aboriginal development commitments are corporate policy and communicated to its employees, suppliers, local residents, First Nations and Metis locals.

The result has been a successful record of encouraging Aboriginal employment in its own workforce and among its contractors. Syncrude has also succeeded in steadily expanding business opportunities for the Aboriginal people of its region. Syncrude's Aboriginal development program has evolved into an integrated set of initiatives that now embrace employment, education, business development, community development and environment.

Syncrude's senior management has also played an active role in communicating Syncrude's approach to Aboriginal relations to external audiences, especially business audiences. Sharing information about its relationships with Aboriginal people is important because these relationships are a key part of the company's success. In addition, in communicating with external audiences, the company is able to provide an example for other Canadian businesses.

Syncrude Canada Ltd.

Syncrude Canada is the world's largest producer of upgraded crude oil from the oil sands. Its product is called Syncrude Sweet Blend. The company's operations are located at Mildred Lake, 40 kilometres north of Fort McMurray, Alberta. In 1994, Syncrude produced about 70 million barrels of crude oil, the equivalent of 12 percent of Canada's annual petroleum requirements.

Syncrude is a joint venture owned by Alberta Energy Company Ltd., AEC Oil Sands Limited Partnership, Canadian Occidental Petroleum Ltd., Gulf Canada Resources Ltd., Imperial Oil Resources, Mocal Energy Limited, Murphy Oil Company Ltd., PanCanadian Gas Products Ltd., Petro-Canada, and the Province of Alberta.

Syncrude has a workforce of about 3800 employees. There are about 320 Aboriginal workers on the company's payroll and an additional 265 Aboriginal people who work for contractors on the Syncrude site. There are 20 active Aboriginal contractors serving Syncrude, representing about one-fifth of all contractors working on the Syncrude site.

Senior Management's Role in the Evolution of the Aboriginal Development Program

The origins of Syncrude's Aboriginal Development Program date back to 1974. Syncrude's Aboriginal Development Program was initiated by its first president, Frank Spraggins.

The program was initiated by Syncrude's first president. Each of the four subsequent presidents has publicly reaffirmed the company's commitment to the program and guided it as it has evolved.

Syncrude's current President has emphasized partnerships with Aboriginal people and working with communities to encourage them to develop their own, long-range community plans.

Since then, each of Syncrude's four subsequent presidents has publicly reaffirmed the company's commitment to the program and guided the program as it has evolved to embrace five key components: employment, education, business development, community development and environment. In each of these areas, Syncrude has tried to respond to the needs of the region and be sensitive to local requirements. The program continues to open new opportunities for Aboriginal communities while providing Syncrude with skilled employees and trusted suppliers.

Employment initiatives were the first component of the Aboriginal Development Program. Syncrude was initially required to have a hiring program for Aboriginal people as a condition of its license to operate. In 1974, the Syncrude Action Plan for Native Training and Counselling was established. The plan set out housing and recruitment policies, educational requirements for job entry and target goals for Aboriginal employment. This program nearly foundered due to high turnover of Aboriginal employees who, being accustomed to a traditional lifestyle of seasonal activities, found the transition to full-time industrial employment difficult.

By 1977, Syncrude's president Brent Scott recognized that, in order the fulfil the hiring requirements, the company would need an Aboriginal development program that focused on recruiting the right people and preparing them for the workplace. In addition, other employees, particularly managers and supervisors, would need cross-cultural training to ensure they had a better understanding of the values of Aboriginal people.

Syncrude's formal commitments to Aboriginal business development date back to 1976. The company signed the Syncrude Indian Opportunities Agreement with the Indian Association of Alberta and the federal government. This agreement provided the underpinning for recruitment initiatives and business opportunities for Aboriginal people with treaty status in the province. In order to promote Aboriginal business development, Syncrude has introduced a policy of sole sourcing with Aboriginal suppliers and, on occasion, restricting bids to Aboriginal entrepreneurs.

Traditional Aboriginal skills form the basis of cooperative environmental initiatives between Syncrude and Aboriginal communities. As far back as 1983, Syncrude's President John Lynn highlighted the work done by the people from Fort Chipewyan in reclaiming bitumen from the tailings pond. In recent years, the Fort McKay First Nation has worked closely with Syncrude on a number of environmental projects.

Syncrude's current President, Eric Newell, has placed strong emphasis on partnerships with Aboriginal people and on the company's work with communities to encourage them to develop their own, long-range community plans. This provides the basis for Syncrude to identify opportunities where it can support the plan. Direct financial assistance has helped build community halls, ice arenas, tourist lodges, and training centres in Aboriginal towns and villages.

Setting Goals and Tracking Progress

Senior management has been instrumental is setting clear objectives and targets for the Aboriginal Development Program and in establishing the plans necessary to achieve them.

Senior management has been instrumental is setting clear objectives and targets for the Aboriginal Development Program and in establishing the plans necessary to achieve them. The company has set specific goals for Aboriginal employment representation and for the value of its procurement contracts with Aboriginal suppliers.

Syncrude's long-standing goal has been to develop a workforce that reflects the population makeup of the local community. To that end, the company established a goal of 10 percent Aboriginal representation in its workforce. Currently about 8 percent of the workforce is Aboriginal. The company is still working toward its overall employment goal. In addition, Syncrude established a goal of reaching $20 million a year of business with Aboriginal-owned companies. This goal was achieved in 1993.

In early 1994, senior management set new targets. Syncrude's President and CEO, along with the four Vice-Presidents, reaffirmed Syncrude's goals to continue to increase employment and business opportunities for Aboriginal people in the region. These goals were published in the company's first Aboriginal Review.

The Aboriginal Development Steering Committee monitors the company's performance and that of its contractors with respect to Aboriginal employment. Its chair reports to Syncrude's Executive Committee annually.

- "Aboriginal employees...represent 10.6 percent of the total workforce (direct payroll and contractors) at Syncrude. Our goal is to increase Syncrude's total Aboriginal workforce, including contractors, to represent 13 percent of the total workforce by 1997". At that time, Aboriginal employees should represent 10 percent of Syncrude's direct workforce.

- "In 1993 alone, Syncrude contracted with Aboriginal entrepreneurs for over $20 million in goods and services. By 1997, that volume is expected to reach $30 million annually". In fact, the $30 million target was reached by the end of 1994.

Department heads set their own realistic Aboriginal recruitment targets annually and performance is tracked by Syncrude's senior executives on quarterly basis.

Syncrude has an Aboriginal Development Steering Committee which monitors its performance and that of its contractors with respect to Aboriginal employment. This committee is made up of key managers from contracting, human resources and emergency response and site services. The chair of the Aboriginal Development Steering Committee reports to

Syncrude's Executive Committee annually and updates the company's Operations Management Committee as needed. The Materials Services Department monitors procurement activities and provides reports to the Aboriginal Steering Committee.

Implementation Strategy

The leadership of senior management has been supported and complemented by the company's Aboriginal Affairs Coordinator.

The leadership of senior management for the Aboriginal Development Program has been supported and complemented by the work of the company's Aboriginal Affairs Coordinator. Syncrude appointed its first Aboriginal Affairs Coordinator in 1978 to sustain the momentum of its employment initiatives. Particular attention was paid to increasing the quality of the company's efforts to recruit Aboriginal people and to improving the retention of Aboriginal employees in its workforce.

A key strategy was working with the Aboriginal leaders at the local community level. Syncrude began to consult with communities when screening potential job candidates. The Aboriginal Affairs Coordinator also worked with new employees, developing trust and understanding, as well as helping with coping strategies. People selected by their communities for employment also served as role models for others in their communities.

The current Aboriginal affairs advisor bases his work on a community development model. He works with the five different First Nation communities and six Metis locals in the Fort McMurray region, each of which is at a different stage of development, to implement, monitor and promote the company's Aboriginal Development Program. An important part of his work involves building bridges between Syncrude and the local communities, especially in the areas of community development and business development.

Senior management actively communicates Syncrude's approach to external audiences because relationships with Aboriginal people are a key part of the company's success.

Syncrude also has an Aboriginal Development Coordinator who, among other responsibilities, works on developing Aboriginal business opportunities. In addition, all managers, employee relations representatives and contract coordinators have responsibilities for Aboriginal business development.

External Leadership

Syncrude's senior management has played an active role in communicating Syncrude's approach to Aboriginal relations to external audiences. Syncrude believes that it is important to share information about its relationships with Aboriginal people because these relationships are a key part of the company's success. The company also feels that its record with Aboriginal peoples provides an example for other Canadian businesses.

Over the past decade, Syncrude's Presidents and Vice Presidents have consistently used major speaking engagements, across Canada as well as in Europe, the United States and Japan, as opportunities to discuss the company's economic partnerships with Aboriginal people.

- In 1983, John Lynn highlighted Syncrude's Aboriginal employment initiatives in a meeting of the Institute of Management Consultants.

- In 1991, one of Syncrude's vice-presidents addressed the Conference Board's conference in Val David, Quebec, on Aboriginal development at Syncrude. In 1993, this forum was used to speak about *Why Partnerships with Aboriginal People Make Sense.*

- In 1992, at the Conference Board of Europe's conference in France, the President spoke on Syncrude's Aboriginal development initiatives.

- A 1993, a vice-president gave a speech entitled *Syncrude and Aboriginals: Partners in Securing Canada's Energy Future* to the Annual General Meeting of Canadian Institute of Mining, Metallurgy and Petroleum in Calgary.

- In 1993, the President addressed the Rotary Club of Edmonton on the role of Aboriginal people in the company's workforce.

- In 1994, Syncrude's President participated, with National Chief Ovide Mercredi and other Aboriginal and corporate leaders, in the CANDO Roundtable.

Ovide Mercredi, National Chief of the Assembly of First Nations, has singled out Syncrude for its excellence in support of Aboriginal people

Syncrude has also recently strengthened its publications about it relationships with Aboriginal peoples. In 1994, Syncrude became the first company in Canada to provide a comprehensive report on its relationships with Aboriginal peoples by publishing its first *Aboriginal Review.* The report was put together because of the long-standing partnership between Syncrude and the Aboriginal people of the Athabasca region and the recognition of the importance of this partnership in Syncrude's success. The report was widely distributed to politicians and officials in the provincial and federal governments, media, First Nations and the general public. Ovide Mercredi, National Chief of the Assembly of First Nations has singled out Syncrude for its excellence in support of Aboriginal people.

Syncrude has also supported organizations and events that promote relationships with Aboriginal people. In 1995, Syncrude was the major sponsor of the RCMP Aboriginal Conference on Youth and became a founding member of the Conference Board of Canada's Council on Corporate Aboriginal Relations. Syncrude also has taken steps to promote positive images of the Aboriginal community. One of the projects that Syncrude sponsored for Canada's 125th birthday was a *Celebration of Contemporary Native Visual Arts* which toured Canada and went to Tokyo. The intent was to highlight the artistic talents of Aboriginal peoples and share their rich and varied culture with other Canadians.

Results

In 1978, Syncrude awarded contracts worth $3 million to Aboriginal enterprises. By 1993, this had increased to $20 million and climbed to $30 million in 1994.

In 1978, Syncrude awarded contracts worth $3 million to Aboriginal enterprises. By 1993, this had increased to $20 million and climbed to $30 million in 1994. There are 20 active Aboriginal contractors servicing Syncrude, representing 20 percent of all contractors working at the contract site. They provide Syncrude with a variety of services.

- The Goodfish Lake Indian Band supplies work clothing and laundry services worth half a million dollars annually. This contract is forming the basis for a cottage textile industry.

- Clearwater Welding and Fabricating provides maintenance and labour services to Syncrude. The company, formed in 1984, with one welding rig has expanded to include a trucking operation, a fabricating shop and a separate machine shop.

- Syncrude has a contract with the Fort McKay Indian Band to provide transportation services. The contract, which was recently renewed, has enabled the Band to finance the purchase of the buses and train Aboriginal people as drivers, mechanics and dispatchers.

- DMJ Enterprises runs the wash bays which clean Syncrude's heavy haulers. The company was founded by a former Syncrude employee. Her firm now employs 13 people from Janvier, her Aboriginal community.

- Project 2000 is an Aboriginal company set up in Fort Chipewyan to supply labour to Syncrude and other companies. Project 2000 has successfully bid on providing general labour to both Syncrude and other contractors on the Syncrude site.

In 1993, Syncrude started a research program to analyze the possibility of sustaining bison on reclaimed grassland. Syncrude currently has 63 bison and the program, although not completed, is promising. The program is directed by a Bison Liaison Committee, with equal membership from Syncrude and the Fort McKay First Nation. The eventual goal of this venture is for the Fort McKay First Nation to run an economically viable ranching operation.

*Syncrude is the largest
industrial employer of
Aboriginal people in
Canada.*

Syncrude's employment strategy also has been successful. Syncrude now has about 319 Aboriginal workers on its payroll and another 265 who work for contractors at the Syncrude site. This makes Syncrude the largest industrial employer of Aboriginal people in Canada. The average length of service for Aboriginal employees is 7.6 years which is on par with the rest of the workforce.

Aboriginal employees are concentrated in mining activities. However, there is increasing representation in other aspects of Syncrude's operations. The percentages of Aboriginal employees in various major areas are as follows: mining (40 percent); extraction (19 percent); upgrading (18 percent); central maintenance services (12 percent); and utilities (3 percent). Growing numbers of Aboriginal people are moving into skilled trades as welders, millwrights, mechanics, electricians and into office-based occupations, as administrators and staff specialists.

A significant effort has been made to recruit Aboriginal people into professional occupations. There are now four Aboriginal engineers on staff (plus several in the summer student program), two computer business graduates working as LAN administrators, two lab technicians, one nurse, one chartered management accountant, two human resource specialists, two public relations tour guides and one community relations representative.

Cameco's Stretch Goals for Aboriginal Employment and Business Participation

A distinctive feature of Cameco's approach is the way that it sets steadily increasing goals for Aboriginal employment and business development.

Cameco has an extensive and integrated set of initiatives to promote Aboriginal employment and training, business development and community relations, primarily in its northern Saskatchewan mining operations. A distinctive feature of Cameco's approach to Aboriginal relations is the way that it sets steadily increasing goals for Aboriginal employment and business development.

The Northern Affairs Office in La Ronge coordinates and implements Cameco's Aboriginal relations initiatives. A key function is establishing and maintaining positive working relationships with northern Aboriginal communities. The office also coordinates the company's northern programs, including recruitment, training, business development and public relations.

Cameco has achieved dramatic progress in recent years, overcoming significant challenges in the process. The company is now an industrial leader in Canada in employing Aboriginal people and in contracting with Aboriginal businesses. These relationships have been of mutual benefit to the company and to the Aboriginal communities and businesses in its region. Cameco has also been able to turn its Aboriginal development experience to competitive advantage in bidding for and winning a major international mining project.

Cameco Corporation

Cameco Corporation is one of the world's largest uranium producers. It has mining operations in Northern Saskatchewan, primarily at Key Lake and Rabbit Lake. The company's processing facilities are in Ontario, where uranium concentrates are converted into fuel products for nuclear power plants.

Cameco is a publicly-traded company, although the Province of Saskatchewan still owns 30 percent of the shares of the company. Cameco's head office is in Saskatoon. Total revenues exceed $300 million annually.

The company has about 1100 employees. Almost three-quarters of the employees work in Saskatchewan, with the rest in Ontario. Cameco has about 550 employees in its northern Saskatchewan mining operations, 45 percent of whom are of Aboriginal ancestry.

Setting Goals

Under the terms of its surface lease, Cameco is required to maximize the employment opportunities for northern people at its mines in Saskatchewan. Cameco is also covered under the federal government's employment equity legislation. Neither of these obligations specify any specific goals or timetable. However, Cameco sets both goals and timetables for Aboriginal employment and business participation. Moreover, it sets steadily increasing annual goals in order to attain its long-term, strategic targets.

In 1990, Cameco announced that it would take steps to ensure that half of the workforce at its minesites in northern Saskatchewan would be northern residents by 1995. This represented a fifty percent increase from the 33 percent northern representation rate in 1990. At the same time, the company required that all of its contractors seek to maximize employment opportunities for northern residents as a condition of contract. With over three-quarters of northern Saskatchewan residents being of Aboriginal ancestry, these commitments meant a significant increase in employment opportunities for Aboriginal people.

In 1990, Cameco announced that it would take steps to ensure that half of the workforce at its minesites in northern Saskatchewan would be northern residents by 1995.

Cameco is also taking steps to provide more opportunities for northern Aboriginal businesses. Since 1991, Cameco has set steadily higher goals for the volume of purchasing it plans to do with northern Saskatchewan businesses. In 1991 the target was $10 million; by 1995, Cameco had raised its target to $30 million.

The responsibility for annual goal-setting is shared between Cameco's Human Resources Department, Northern Affairs Department, and the Purchasing and Transportation Department.

- Cameco's Human Resources Department and its Northern Affairs Office set annual performance objectives related to northern and Aboriginal employment. These include overall targets for Aboriginal employment, targets by job category and targets by impact region.

- The Purchasing and Transportation Department sets employment targets for Cameco contractors and monitors performance relative to contractual obligations.

- The Purchasing and Transportation Department also sets annual targets for northern business participation.

Employment Initiatives

To achieve its long-term targets and short-term goals, Cameco has put in place a comprehensive set of employment and training initiatives.

To achieve its long-term targets and short-term goals, Cameco has put in place a comprehensive set of employment and training initiatives. The plan for reaching its northern employment target is a multi-faceted one that includes specific measures for increasing Aboriginal participation in its operations workforce and its contractor workforce.

When a position in Cameco's operations becomes vacant, the company works actively to recruit northerners first. Recruitment does not occur from anywhere else until it has been determined that there is no qualified northerner available. Realistic qualifications for job vacancies are set in order to eliminate unnecessary barriers to Aboriginal participation.

In implementing this part of the plan, the company has had to address difficulties in recruiting from a small, dispersed population as well as challenges posed by the level of education and training among the northern population.

The plan also includes education and training initiatives designed to increase northern and Aboriginal participation in the workforce over the longer term. The school dropout rate in northern Saskatchewan is double the national average and to address this, Cameco has introduced a number of initiatives exclusively for northerners. Northern education and career incentive programs encourage Aboriginal students to stay in school and achieve higher levels of academic training. Career information services expose Aboriginal students to career opportunities in the mining industry. Work placement and summer employment provide work experience opportunities for Aboriginal students. An annual scholarship program provides financial assistance for post-secondary education.

Cameco sponsors northern institutional training initiatives and participates directly in the development and implementation of mining related northern training programs. These programs include mine and mill operator training, pre-employment mine mill worker, underground mining orientation and training, chemical laboratory technician and apprenticeship trades training. Cameco offers a guarantee of employment to graduates from selected northern training programs, on a job availability basis.

Cameco places Aboriginal employees in technical, trades and management training positions within the company.

Cameco has in-house training and development initiatives for northern Aboriginal employees. It places Aboriginal employees in technical, trades and management training positions within the company and has introduced succession planning for senior experienced Aboriginal employees. In the technical jobs area, for example, the company has created 21 in-house technical training positions that are supernumerary to operational requirements and has made these opportunities available primarily to northern Aboriginal candidates. The same model is being used to improve Aboriginal representation in trades jobs.

The collective agreement between Cameco and its union, the United Steel Workers Local 8914, contains an affirmative action provision that calls for cooperation and joint participation in the formulation of strategies that will maximize Aboriginal employment. The collective agreement contains a provision that allows every second apprenticeship vacancy to be awarded to an employee of Indian ancestry, on the basis of seniority. The article goes further to allow for apprenticeship vacancies to be filled by candidates of Indian ancestry from outside the bargaining unit if no qualified internal candid.ates exist.

Aboriginal Business Development

Cameco has a proactive program to develop northern and Aboriginal business. The company uses its procurement leverage to create opportunities

The company uses its procurement leverage to create opportunities for Aboriginal businesses. Its supplier development initiatives foster the creation of viable enterprises.

for Aboriginal businesses and a range of supplier development initiatives to foster the creation of viable enterprises. Cameco requires that its major contractors seek and develop northern/Aboriginal sources of supply for goods and sub-contract services. Contracts are awarded with planned objectives in mind.

Selective tendering and preferential bidding create opportunities for new Aboriginal and northern suppliers. The company's size and strength as a customer has also been used to facilitate the creation of several Aboriginal enterprises that now provide product and services to northern Saskatchewan, such as Athabasca Caterers (a northern-based business now jointly owned by five First Nations in conjunction with a catering company from Saskatoon) that provides catering services to three of Cameco's major mining operations. In cases where supplying Cameco alone may not be sufficient to create a viable market opportunity, Cameco has also joined with other mining interests to support the development of northern Aboriginal suppliers.

Cameco takes a careful and strategic approach to supplier development. Displacing existing non-Aboriginal suppliers can be difficult and new entrants can undermine the viability of existing Aboriginal supplier relationships. Commercial competitiveness is the most important consideration and the development of a new Aboriginal supplier can take up to two years. The company places considerable emphasis on identifying and communicating additional business opportunities for potential Aboriginal suppliers. It makes numerous community presentations about its specific development plans and, whenever possible, provides translation services in Dene and Cree. The company also provides operational support in a variety of forms, including transportation subsidies, to encourage the creation of independent Aboriginal contractors.

Major Cameco Contractors with Significant Aboriginal Ownership

Contractor	% Aboriginal Ownership
Northern Resource Trucking	71%
Athabasca Catering	83%
Snake Lake Construction	100%
PADC Security	100%
Northern Dene Air	25%
Knudsen Construction	51%
Eagle Air	100%
Kitsaki Meats	100%

Source: Cameco Corporation - 1995

The Northern Resource Trucking Example

One of the strategies that Cameco has used to achieve its goal of increasing the volume of purchasing from Aboriginal suppliers is facilitating the formation of joint ventures between Aboriginal and non-Aboriginal businesses. This is done in the case of its larger supply contracts in order to encourage management expertise to be transferred to the northern Aboriginal partner.

Cameco monitors the joint venture to ensure it contributes to long-term Aboriginal business development. In particular, the company wants to ensure that the joint venture results in the transfer and development of business and management expertise that contribute to increasing the capabilities of northern Aboriginal communities to handle large supply contracts for Cameco and other northern mining interests.

Northern Resources Trucking (NRT) is one example of how this strategy works. NRT was formed in 1986 by the La Ronge Indian Band and Trimac, a large international trucking firm. The Band is the majority owner and gained the benefit of extensive experience from its partner. Cameco awarded an initial contract of about $3 million.

By 1993, it was clear that a new set of arrangements would be needed if this venture was going to achieve significant Aboriginal employment. Although the Kitsaki Development Corporation (which is owned and controlled by Saskatchewan's largest Indian Band, the Lac La Ronge Band) had a 51 percent stake in Northern Resource Trucking, Aboriginal people accounted for only a very small percentage of the company's 52 person workforce. The short duration of contracts (1-3 years), combined with highly competitive pricing, forced NRT to focus on profitability at the expense of longer-term training and development of an Aboriginal workforce.

In the spring of 1994, Cameco signed an agreement in principle under which Cameco would award an exclusive six-year contract to NRT provided that NRT agreed to restructure its equity to provide ownership opportunities for other First Nation and Metis communities in northern Saskatchewan; move an office, warehouse and terminal facilities to La Ronge; train and maximize employment for northerners of Aboriginal ancestry; and provide sub-contracting opportunities to independent northern truck owners. Under NRT's new ownership structure, Kitsaki Development Corporation has a 30 percent interest, Trimac has 29 percent, and other limited partners 41 percent. The other limited partners consist of 8 First Nations and 3 municipalities that represent the northern Dene, Woodlands Cree and Metis People.

The new deal provides significant advantages for NRT and the Lac La Ronge Band. These include a minimum 50 percent increase in annual sales,

Cameco facilitates the formation of joint ventures between Aboriginal and non-Aboriginal businesses to increase its volume of purchasing with Aboriginal suppliers.

a virtual guarantee of long-term growth and profitability, enhanced opportunities to compete for hauling contracts with other major mining interests, and a unique opportunity to build on the alliance with northern First Nations and capture other business development opportunities in areas such as mining, catering, forestry and transportation.

Northern Resources Trucking is now in its ninth year of operation, has almost $13 million of annual business with Cameco and delivers most of the supplies needed at Cameco's northern mine sites.

Results

In recent years, Cameco has made dramatic progress in its northern development initiatives. The company is now an industrial leader in Canada in terms of the employment of Aboriginal people and in the magnitude of its contracting activities with northern and Aboriginal businesses.

The share of Aboriginal people in Cameco's workforce has been increasing steadily. In 1989, Aboriginal employees accounted for 29 percent of Cameco's direct employment in its northern Saskatchewan mining operations; by 1994, Cameco had over 700 employees in its northern mining operations, 39 percent of whom are of Aboriginal ancestry.

Another 151 Aboriginal people worked for Cameco's contractors in 1994. They account for 50 percent of the total employees in the contractors' workforces. In total, Cameco's northern employment policy resulted in employment opportunities for 425 Aboriginal people in 1994, which now makes Cameco one of the largest industrial employers of Aboriginal people in Canada.

Cameco has also been very successful in its Aboriginal business development initiatives.

Overall, Cameco has surpassed its northern purchasing targets in each of the past four years and has doubled the number of northern Aboriginal suppliers from 6 to 12 over the same period.

The company is now an industrial leader in Canada in terms of the employment of Aboriginal people and in the magnitude of its contracting activities with northern and Aboriginal businesses.

Cameco has surpassed its overall northern purchasing targets in each of the past four years.

Cameco's Volume of Northern Business - $ million		
	Targeted $ million	Actual $ million
1991	10.0	10.5
1992	12.5	16.6
1993	20.0	22.8
1994	25.0	27.8
1995	30.0	n/a
Source: Cameco 1995		

Mutual Benefits

Resource extraction, especially uranium mining, comes under intense public scrutiny making it essential to develop and maintain strong relationships with the communities in the region. Cameco's commitment to local Aboriginal employment has been advantageous for both the company and the communities in which it operates. Communities benefit from the employment and business development opportunities that result from Cameco's activities. Cameco partnerships with Aboriginal communities anchor support for its existing operations and facilitate the prospects of expansion and new mine development. Cameco's President and CEO, Bernard Michel, has noted that: "Our relationship with northerners is as valuable to us as the richness of our ore deposits".

Cameco's business development partnerships with Aboriginal suppliers often bring significant mutual benefits to both parties. For example, under the new deal with Northern Resource Trucking, Cameco benefits from guaranteed reasonable rates and cost control over the longer term while at the same time promoting its goal of maximizing opportunities for Aboriginal employment, training and business development. The new ownership structure at NRT creates strategic alliances with many northern Aboriginal groups and enhances the long-term stability of economic development in northern Saskatchewan. NRT benefits by becoming a large, more stable Aboriginal-owned business, capable of competing in markets other than those in northern Saskatchewan.

The success of Cameco's Aboriginal initiatives has been instrumental in winning a major international development opportunity. In 1994, Cameco was chosen by the Krygysz government to develop one of the largest gold deposits in the world. The Krygysz government identified Cameco's experience working with the indigenous peoples of Canada as a key consideration in choosing a development partner. Cameco intends to use the experience gained in northern Saskatchewan working with Aboriginal people as the model for training, recruitment, business development and community relations in the Republic of Krygystan.

"Our relationship with northerners is as valuable to us as the richness of our ore deposits". (Bernard Michel, President and CEO)

The success of Cameco's Aboriginal initiatives has been instrumental in winning a major international development opportunity.

B.C. Hydro's Corporate Framework for Constructive Relationships with Aboriginal Peoples

B.C. Hydro's desire to forge new relationships with Aboriginal people is underpinned by practical business reasons.

Pragmatic business considerations are driving B.C. Hydro's process of forging new and more constructive relationships with Aboriginal people in the province. The corporation needs mutually beneficial relationships with Aboriginal people if it is to achieve its corporate objectives and fulfil its corporate responsibility to support economic development in the province.

Since 1990, B.C. Hydro has systematically strengthened its organizational capability to build constructive relationships with Aboriginal peoples. It has done this by putting a comprehensive corporate Aboriginal relations strategy in place; by creating the Aboriginal Relations Department to provide a focal point for action; and by increasing knowledge and understanding within the corporation about Aboriginal people and Aboriginal issues.

This approach already has achieved significant results. B.C. Hydro has made progress in a number of specific operational areas, such as the resolution of historical grievances. There is a well-established corporate framework to support the process of change, now and in the future. Most importantly, First Nations and other corporate entities in B.C. have recognized that B.C. Hydro is making a sincere effort to address Aboriginal issues and to build mutually beneficial business relationships.

B.C. Hydro

B.C. Hydro is a provincial crown corporation which generates, transmits and distributes electricity. It is the third largest utility in Canada, serving more than 1.3 million customers in a service area containing over 92 percent of B.C.'s population. B.C. Hydro's revenues in 1995 were $2.1 billion.

More than 95 percent of B.C. Hydro's output is produced by hydro-electric generating stations. Electricity is delivered to customers through an inter-connected system of over 69,000 kilometres of transmission and distribution lines.

The corporation has about 6018 regular employees, with the rest being temporary. Aboriginal people account for less than one percent of B.C. Hydro's workforce.

Context for Aboriginal Relations

B.C. Hydro's desire to forge new relationships with Aboriginal people is underpinned by practical business reasons. The company has several thousand kilometres of transmission and distribution lines, worth million of dollars, running over rights-of-way on about 500 reserves belonging to 150 bands. Plans for the expansion of the power grid frequently require additional rights-of-way on reserves. However, more First Nations are taking the position that old grievances must be resolved before moving on to new business.

Many rights-of-way, originally negotiated by the Department of Indian Affairs and Northern Development, are agreements in per-

The first step was to map out a corporate-level, comprehensive Aboriginal relations strategy.

petuity for a small lump-sum payment or no payment at all. As a result, First Nations derive no revenue from rights-of-way and cannot use them for their own purposes. Environmental and socio-economic impacts associated with past B.C. Hydro projects have also resulted in claims for mitigation and compensation.

Emerging political and social realities reinforce this impetus to re-think corporate attitudes and practices toward Aboriginal peoples. Because treaties were never signed with First Nations in British Columbia, the unique situation exist that more than 95 percent of the province's land mass is subject to comprehensive land claims. First Nations people are gaining greater control and jurisdiction over land and resources, including water resources that are essential for power generation. First Nations are also re-establishing their own governments and acquiring the skills to become part of B.C.'s future workforce. In addition, they make up an increasingly significant portion of B.C. Hydro's customer base.

Comprehensive Aboriginal Relations Strategy

The first step in creating B.C. Hydro's capability for building constructive relationships with Aboriginal people was to map out a corporate-level, comprehensive Aboriginal relations strategy. This has been developed in a number of steps. In 1990, the corporation's Native Affairs Steering Committee, which had been inactive, was re-established and a full-time Native Affairs Coordinator was hired to define and develop a strategy.

The Statement of Principles for Relations with Aboriginal People recognizes that the Aboriginal population of B.C. has a distinct legal, historical and cultural status.

In 1992, the Board of Directors of B.C. Hydro approved the comprehensive Aboriginal relations strategy. A key element was the adoption of a *Statement of Principles for Relations with Aboriginal People.* This statement, which anchors the company's Aboriginal relations initiatives, recognizes that the Aboriginal population of British Columbia has a distinct legal, historical and cultural status and commits the company to working with the Aboriginal population according to principles of cooperation and communication. The Statement of Principles also makes specific commitments related to fair compensation, environmental responsibility, resolution of disputes, community and economic development and employment.

Further direction was provided by the Board in the 1993 Corporate Strategic Plan, *The Way Ahead,* where it identified relations with Aboriginal people as a key strategic issue for the company and set out its expectations for future results in this area. The Board has identified initiatives relating to Aboriginal peoples as being necessary to contribute to the corporation's operational responsibility and has set the following direction in this respect:

"B.C. Hydro will establish mutually beneficial business relationships with Aboriginal peoples that will be recognized as models for others to follow."

Aboriginal Relations Department

The Aboriginal Relations Department (ARD) was created to implement the Board's strategy.

The Aboriginal Relations Department (ARD) was created in late 1992 to implement the Board's strategy. This department has overall responsibility for leading B.C. Hydro's initiative on Aboriginal relations and managing the resolution of Aboriginal issues in consultation with First Nations and in collaboration with other B.C. Hydro business units.

In June 1993, a traditional Aboriginal ceremony launched the department. The Coast Salish elders performed the ceremony and blessing at B.C. Hydro headquarters in Vancouver. The audience was made up equally of Aboriginal and corporate witnesses. The ceremony was intended not only to launch ARD, but to send a clear message to the Aboriginal community that the utility is serious about meeting its mandate to "establish mutually beneficial business relationships with Aboriginal peoples that will be recognized as models for others to follow", and that cultural traditions of Aboriginal peoples will be respected in the new relationship.

Core staff for the Aboriginal Relations Department have been drawn from other business units within Hydro as well as through external recruitment. In staffing the Aboriginal Relations Department, the company has ensured that the staff has the mix of expertise and experience to work effectively within Hydro and with Aboriginal peoples. In particular, the company has recognized the importance of putting together a group of people with solid reputations with First Nations in British Columbia. This has helped significantly in bridging the corporate and Aboriginal interests and in overcoming mistrust.

In staffing the department, the company has ensured that the staff has the mix of expertise and experience to work effectively within Hydro and with Aboriginal peoples.

The Aboriginal Relations Department has 15 full-time employees. The Manager, Aboriginal Relations reports to the Senior Vice President, Human Resources, Aboriginal Relations and Environment.

The manager's key areas of responsibility include strategic linkages with First Nation leaders, as well as overall leadership and management of the department. Staff are organized into four groups that reflect key strategic and operational priorities. Each group is headed by a coordinator.

- The Negotiations and Support to Strategic Business Units group is responsible for grievance resolution and negotiation processes as well as for providing support to other business units and operating the Aboriginal Relations Information System database.

- The Business Development and Communications group works on corporate initiatives to increase the number of Aboriginal businesses supplying B.C. Hydro with goods and services and is responsible for internal and external communications, including those with First Nations, about the company's Aboriginal relations initiatives.

- The Training and Development group is responsible for the development and delivery of the cross-cultural and negotiations training programs and other awareness-building initiatives. The group also provides training to external groups on a commercial basis.

- The Special Projects group is responsible for initiatives that deal with the employment of Aboriginal people in the corporation and for policy development and government liaison.

The Aboriginal Relations Department embodies Aboriginal values and is infusing these values into Hydro's business relationships with First Nations, while, at the same time, working within a framework of sound business practices. The Aboriginal values include a great emphasis on listening, discussion, patience and respect for other peoples positions and way of doing things. These values have been melded with basic tenets of good business management: researching customers, understanding their needs and interests, identifying areas of mutual interest and benefit, and developing action plans accordingly.

Building Knowledge and Understanding

One of the most prominent features of B.C. Hydro's Aboriginal relations strategy is its commitment to developing relationships on the basis of knowledge and understanding. As such, B.C. Hydro has made significant investments in developing its knowledge of Aboriginal people and Aboriginal issues. It has also taken steps to increase the knowledge and understanding of Aboriginal people about the company. Developing this shared understanding strengthens the foundation for other initiatives and provides the underpinnings for long-term success and mutual benefit.

Cross-cultural training is one of the ways that B.C. Hydro helps its employees and managers to gain an understanding of Aboriginal cultures and issues. The company's comprehensive cross-cultural training program has been developed with the participation of First Nations in British Columbia. There are three elements to the program.

One of the most prominent features of B.C. Hydro's Aboriginal relations strategy is its commitment to developing relationships on the basis of knowledge and understanding.

The company's comprehensive cross-cultural training program has been developed with the participation of First Nations in British Columbia.

The company's Aboriginal Relations Information System is a computer-based, central information system on each Aboriginal community in the province.

The leadership and direction of the Board of Directors to establish Aboriginal relations as a strategic priority has already translated into important operational results, including the resolution of historical grievances.

- A three-hour introductory training program, which is available to employees and managers. Although this program is not mandatory, demand for this training has been heavy and by December 1994, over 2000 people had attended, representing one-third of the total workforce.

- Customized cross-cultural training, which is activity-based training that is very closely aligned with work-related matters. This training is available to managers who require more in-depth information on a particular area.

- Community-based training, which is developed and delivered by First Nations, thereby providing the opportunity for building direct relationships and better understanding between B.C. Hydro personnel and Aboriginal people. The training program is usually between one and one-half to two days long, takes place in Aboriginal communities and deals with issues from the Aboriginal perspective.

Very recently, the department has responded to external recognition of the quality of the program by providing it, on a contractual basis, to external clients in the private and public sectors.

To further support the development of effective working relationships, B.C. Hydro has created a computer-based Aboriginal Relations Information System (ARIS) which is a central information system on each Aboriginal community in the province. The database is designed to enhance strategic planning, analysis and decision-making and to support grievance resolution, negotiations and economic development activities. ARIS is also available to First Nations as a valuable tool and resource in the ongoing exchange of information and concerns. It is being considered for purchase by a number of third parties.

B.C. Hydro is committed to open, honest dialogue with Aboriginal peoples, which it does on an ongoing basis through direct consultation and business interactions. The company has also undertaken a number of specific communications initiatives designed to promote better awareness and understanding. These include publishing a quarterly newsletter, entitled *Talking Circle,* which covers a number of current issues of interest to Aboriginal people. It is widely distributed to Aboriginal customers, businesses and political organizations.

Results to Date

B.C. Hydro has laid the foundation for establishing mutually beneficial business relationships with Aboriginal peoples. A well-established corporate framework is now in place to support the process of change. The

First Nations have recognized that B.C. Hydro is making a sincere effort to address Aboriginal issues and to build mutually beneficial business relationships.

leadership and direction of the Board of Directors has established Aboriginal relations as a strategic priority and provided legitimacy for all of the Aboriginal relations initiatives, both within the company and with First Nations. The corporation's efforts to create and maintain constructive relationships with Aboriginal people by focusing on business principles, integrating Aboriginal issues throughout the company, and equipping employees with the necessary skills provides a strong foundation for the future.

This has already translated into important operational results, including the resolution of historical grievances. Some long-standing grievances are under negotiation and some issues have been resolved. A particularly important access agreement was concluded with the Alkali Lake Indian Band in September 1993. In November 1993, a negotiating protocol was signed with a major First Nation, which commits both sides to a process of dealing with grievances, economic development and traditional lands issues. In one acquisition matter, the existing relationship enabled B.C. Hydro to reach an agreement with a Band and start actual project construction within a four-month period.

B.C. Hydro's initiatives have resulted in the recognition by First Nations in B.C., that B.C. Hydro is making a sincere effort to address Aboriginal issues and to build mutually beneficial business relationships. The corporation was profoundly honoured in April 1994, when the Coast Salish Elders' Council and the Squamish Nation held a potlatch ceremony in the Squamish Nation's Capilano Longhouse and presented a "talking stick" to B.C. Hydro. It was the first time that a potlatch was held to honour a public corporation. The talking stick is an important symbol in the longhouse, a symbol that obligates its holder to speak with integrity and authority and the audience to listen carefully. Its presentation was a significant recognition by First Nations that B.C. Hydro is making an effort to change.

Bank of Montreal's Initiatives to Integrate Aboriginal Relations into its Core Business

Bank of Montreal has developed a comprehensive, integrated set of initiatives to provide Aboriginal people with improved access to financial services, employment opportunities and training opportunities.

Bank of Montreal's Aboriginal banking strategy is based on the recognition that its ability to attract business from Aboriginal communities is linked to the development of effective relationships with those communities. The bank's strategy for becoming the bank of choice for Aboriginal communities is to develop a better understanding of the banking needs of Aboriginal businesses and communities, to make its services more accessible to Aboriginal communities and to increase the representation of Aboriginal people in its workforce. Building a workforce that better reflects the Aboriginal communities that it serves gives the bank an enhanced understanding of the needs of those communities, builds mutual trust and respect, and enables the bank to provide Aboriginal people with better customer service.

Bank of Montreal has developed a comprehensive, integrated set of initiatives to provide Aboriginal people with improved access to financial services, employment opportunities and training opportunities. These initiatives have been based on an extensive process of consultations with Aboriginal people and organizations. An Aboriginal Banking Unit has been created and the bank's workplace equality initiatives have been fully integrated into the development and implementation of the Bank's Aboriginal banking strategy.

Bank of Montreal is seeing very positive results from its initiatives to integrate its Aboriginal banking objectives with its Aboriginal employment and training commitment. Loans to Aboriginal communities are up, the bank has increased the number of Aboriginal accounts, and employment opportunities for Aboriginal people have increased significantly. The bank also hopes to contribute to the economic self-sufficiency of Aboriginal peoples through its initiatives to provide improved access to financial services.

Task Force on Aboriginal Employment

Bank of Montreal set up a Task Force on the Advancement of Aboriginal Employment in 1991 to identify barriers and establish action plans to support the bank's efforts to employ

---

Bank of Montreal

Bank of Montreal is the third largest chartered bank in Canada, measured by assets. In 1994, total assets were $138 billion. The bank has about 1160 branches in Canada and also operates in the US and 17 other countries. Bank of Montreal owns Harris Bankcorp, based in Chicago, and Nesbitt Burns, a full service investment dealer.

The bank's head office is located in Montreal. In mid-1995, the bank had 26,800 employees, 1.7 percent of whom were of Aboriginal ancestry.

Bank of Montreal set up a Task Force on the Advancement of Aboriginal Employment in 1991 to identify barriers and establish action plans to support the bank's efforts to employ Aboriginal people.

In its dialogue with Aboriginal communities about employment opportunities, it became obvious that they also had a need for improved access to financial services.

Aboriginal people. The task force conducted extensive research across Canada in partnership with Aboriginal people and organizations.

The task force undertook its investigations with the help of 44 individuals organized into five divisional Action Teams. They were selected from all banking groups and included Aboriginal employees. Each team retained its own consultant who was well informed about the region's employment issues from the perspective of Aboriginal people. Every team sought information and advice from Aboriginal colleagues, Aboriginal business contacts and local Aboriginal leaders.

When the results were compiled and analyzed, the task force recommended 31 actions to begin building bridges with Aboriginal communities. The most prominent of the action plans was to develop a national workforce that comprises at least 2 percent Aboriginal employees by 1995 (compared with 0.5 percent in 1992). This goal was set to exceed the Aboriginal component of the communities that the bank served.

Aboriginal Banking Strategy

In its dialogue with Aboriginal communities about employment opportunities, it became obvious that they also had a need for improved access to financial services. The bank established a steering committee headed by a Vice-Chairman, to explore business opportunities within Aboriginal communities, and to develop a strategy to take a leadership role in this new market area. The committee consisted of senior vice-presidents from the bank's front line operations, representatives of the workplace equality team and an external Aboriginal consultant.

After significant consultations with the Aboriginal community and internally with the banking community, the committee made three major recommendations.

- Bank of Montreal should establish an Aboriginal Banking Unit headed by a vice-president, who should be a business leader from the Aboriginal community.

- The bank should create a Circle of Aboriginal Business Leaders to guide the bank's business and employment initiatives within Aboriginal communities.

- The bank should explore opportunities to bring the delivery of financial services closer to the Aboriginal communities.

The Aboriginal Banking Unit

Bank of Montreal set up its Aboriginal Banking Unit in 1992 to develop and implement strategies to provide Aboriginal people with improved access

Bank of Montreal has established a Circle of Aboriginal Business Leaders to act as advisors on Aboriginal banking issues.

to financial services, as well as to facilitate employment and training opportunities for Aboriginal people within the Bank.

The Aboriginal Banking Unit is headed by a Vice President, Aboriginal Banking. Managers of Aboriginal Banking (all of whom are Aboriginal people) are located in each of the bank's eight divisions to help the community banking experts develop linkages with Aboriginal communities. The National Manager, Aboriginal Programs (who is part of the Workplace Equality Unit) acts both as a liaison and as a consultant to the Aboriginal Banking Unit on recruitment and education matters.

Since 1992, the bank's Aboriginal Banking team has spent a great deal of time travelling throughout the country, uncovering the needs of Aboriginal people firsthand. As a result the bank has established several key initiatives, including establishing on-reserve branches and providing Aboriginal business and community leaders with customized financial and business management training.

Circle of Aboriginal Business Leaders

Bank of Montreal has established a Circle of Aboriginal Business Leaders to act as advisors on Aboriginal banking issues. The Circle, which comprises nine members drawn from Indian, Inuit, and Metis communities, advises the bank on the financial needs and concerns of their respective communities. Meetings take place across Canada on a quarterly basis.

The Circle has provided guidance on many topics, ranging from business initiatives to the referral of Aboriginal candidates to the bank. The Circle provided insight on self-identification issues which help improve the effectiveness of the bank's survey of its employees. The Circle also reinforced the importance of the connection between business opportunities and the need to develop employment opportunities.

Branches in Aboriginal Communities

Bank of Montreal is trying to make its banking services more accessible to Aboriginal communities, especially through creative ways of bringing the fullest possible range of banking services to more remote reserves and settlements. For example, in a pilot project currently being conducted on Akwesasne Mohawk Territory, the bank is providing loans to members for renovations or improvements to their homes with security other than guarantees from CMHC or the Department of Indian Affairs. In the Iqaluit Branch, which was opened in June 1995, all of the banking services, key product brochures and banking forms are offered in Inuktitut.

To date, the bank has established six on-reserve branches to serve Aboriginal people directly and plans to open six more on-reserve branches in

To date, the bank has established six on-reserve branches to serve Aboriginal people directly. Wherever possible, the branches are staffed by Aboriginal people.

1995. Wherever possible, the branches are staffed by Aboriginal people. Where pre-employment training is necessary, a partnership is often formed with the community to ensure the success of new Aboriginal employees who may not have had previous experience working in a large organization. The training is usually delivered jointly by the bank and First Nation. The bank is committed to training Aboriginal people to assume all positions in the branch, particularly management positions, within a realistic timeframe. All of the managers of on-reserve branches are Aboriginal people who were specially trained and mentored by the bank.

Wherever possible, the bank uses Aboriginal contractors to build its branches on or near reserves. The branch at the Akwesasne First Nation near Cornwall was built by Aboriginal contractors. The branch on the Siksika Nation in Alberta was designed to reflect the layout of activities in traditional teepee design and to incorporate design motifs that reflect the community's culture. The Bank also contracts with Aboriginal people in other areas, such as coordinating pre-employment training programs, delivering cross-cultural training and providing form design and printing services.

Aboriginal Business Seminars

The bank sponsors Aboriginal Business Seminars which are held in Aboriginal communities across the country.

Bank of Montreal sponsors Aboriginal Business Seminars which are held (at the request of an Aboriginal business association or Council) in Aboriginal communities across the country. These seminars are designed to provide Aboriginal business people, community leaders and community members with customized training in business, management, financial management, investment planning and administration. The seminars are based on the series of *Problem Solver* brochures that the bank developed for business customers and which have been recently adapted to the needs of Aboriginal business. In 1994, the bank sponsored or participated in 150 workshops, seminars and conferences.

Increasing Aboriginal Employment Opportunities across the Bank

In order to increase the representation of Aboriginal people in its workforce, the bank is reaching out to Aboriginal communities through a series of special recruitment initiatives in partnership with Aboriginal educators, counsellors and internship networks. The Bank is also undertaking cooperative community-based initiatives to overcome employment barriers, particularly to improve the job readiness of Aboriginal people. The bank has recently introduced a new stay-in-school program that was developed

Equality in the workplace and diversity in its workforce are clear business goals. Bank of Montreal has now integrated accountability for workplace equality into its business planning process.

Bank of Montreal's holistic approach to Aboriginal banking is starting to yield results.

specifically for Aboriginal people. The program, which is called APPEAL, enables Aboriginal students in post-secondary business-related programs, to obtain work experience and earn income while they are studying.

Achieving equality in the workplace and diversity in its workforce are clear business goals established in the bank's Corporate Strategic plan. Bank of Montreal has now integrated accountability for workplace equality into its business planning process. Executives and senior managers are setting annual hiring, retention and advancement goals, reflecting what they can aggressively but realistically accomplish. Accountability for workplace equality results is now included in each manager's Performance Planning and Review.

The bank is committed to creating a welcoming workplace for Aboriginal people and is working to create an environment that fosters the retention and career advancement of Aboriginal employees. A number of structures have been put in place to coordinate its workplace equality efforts and embed its commitment to equality and diversity into its corporate culture. These include the establishment of a Workplace Equality Unit and a national Advisory Council on the Equitable Workplace to oversee bank-wide implementation of all workplace equality measures.

Results

Bank of Montreal's holistic approach to Aboriginal banking is starting to yield results. Loans to Aboriginal communities have grown and the bank has increased the number of Aboriginal accounts.

- In 1993, the bank made an $88 million loan to the Inuvialuit people of the Western Arctic - the largest loan ever by a financial institution to Aboriginal people.

- Between 1993 and 1994, the bank has increased the number of Aboriginal loans by 200 percent and increased the number of accounts for Aboriginals by 70 percent.

The team-based approach to recruitment has resulted in a significant increase in the hiring of Aboriginal people. In 1993, 122 people, representing over 7 percent of all new employees hired by the bank, were of Aboriginal ancestry. In 1994, 130 Aboriginal people were hired by the bank. Aboriginal employees have also benefitted from promotional opportunities. In 1994, Aboriginal people received 0.9 percent of all promotions, up from 0.5 percent the previous year and greater than the Aboriginal employee representation rate of 0.6 percent at the beginning of 1994. The representation rate for Aboriginal employees has almost tripled since 1994.

By mid-1995, the representation rate was 1.7 percent, putting it on track to meet the bank's "social contract" of 2 percent.

This experience has reinforced the bank's conviction that banking opportunities and employment needs are closely linked within Aboriginal communities and that an integrated approach yielding mutual advantage ensures a continuing relationship with Aboriginal people based on mutual trust and respect.

DIAND's Aboriginal Awareness Program

Aboriginal awareness training develops the skills that employees need in order to work effectively with Aboriginal peoples and to minimize the potential for culturally-based misunderstandings and conflicts.

In 1993, the Department of Indian Affairs and Northern Development (DIAND) introduced its new Aboriginal Awareness Program. The program was the result of an extensive review process which was designed to identify deficiencies in previous cross cultural training programs and to recommend a new approach that would ensure that departmental employees received the training that would assist them to work effectively with Aboriginal peoples.

The growth of many complex issues, such as self-government, Aboriginal rights, land claims, economic development and justice, has made it increasingly important that DIAND's workforce is well-versed in the history and background of these issues. Aboriginal awareness training is also needed to develop the skills that the department's employees need to work effectively with Aboriginal peoples and communities and to minimize the potential for culturally-based misunderstandings and conflicts.

DIAND's Aboriginal Awareness Program now consists of three-day workshops held in Aboriginal communities. The workshops, which cover historical, cultural and regional perspectives, are designed to provide for extensive interaction between workshop participants and members of the community. The addition of nine regional components, one for each major region of Canada, has been one of the key enhancements to the Aboriginal Awareness Program.

The first of the new workshops was offered in 1993. To date, more than 60 workshops have been run in 15 communities across the country.

The Need for Change

DIAND has had a long-standing commitment to providing Aboriginal awareness training to employees. The purpose of this training is to promote an understanding of Aboriginal cultures and to increase awareness of Aboriginal issues that will enable employees to achieve departmental objectives.

Cross cultural training that addressed Aboriginal history, culture and values was first introduced in 1980. Until 1990, the training was provided in 2 1/2 day workshops that

---

Department of Indian Affairs and Northern Development

The Department of Indian Affairs and Northern Development (DIAND) was created in 1966.

The department's responsibilities include fulfilling the obligations of the federal government, arising from treaties, the Indian Act and other legislation; providing for the delivery of base services to status Indians and Inuit communities; assisting Indians and Inuit to acquire employment skills and to develop viable businesses and negotiating the settlement of accepted claims relating to Aboriginal title not dealt with by treaty or to past non-fulfilment of government obligations.

The department employs about 3200 people, of whom 630 or 19 percent are of Aboriginal ancestry.

In 1990, DIAND asked a working group of employees and experts to evaluate its Aboriginal Awareness Program and to recommend an effective strategy in this area.

were held in conference rooms of local hotels. There was no involvement of Aboriginal communities and little interaction with Aboriginal peoples. The workshops did not provide opportunities for spirituality or cultural exposure. The lecture format did not encourage interaction among participants.

In 1990, DIAND asked a working group of employees and experts to evaluate its Aboriginal Awareness Program and to recommend a strategy that would enable the department to effectively fulfil its mandate in this area. The group was led by senior managers. Employees who were interested in being involved in the initiative were invited to do so through a special edition of the department's employee newsletter. A National Review Committee was formed to ensure that all of the regions would be represented. A prominent leader from an Aboriginal community acted as an outside resource to the committee. An external consultant specializing in the field was hired to work with the group.

The working group's review of the existing Aboriginal awareness program identified a number of issues and limitations.

- The workshops provided only introductory Aboriginal awareness training.

- The cultural differences and characteristics of Aboriginal groups that DIAND served were not addressed in-depth.

- The major cultural differences between employees (in all their diversity) and their Aboriginal constituents and the way these differences may lead to conflicts and misunderstandings were dealt with in an elementary fashion.

Based on its findings, the working group recommended a new approach to Aboriginal awareness training in the department.

A New Approach to Aboriginal Awareness Training

DIAND's new Aboriginal Awareness Program is designed to achieve the following objectives:

- to provide employees with a better understanding of the history, values, customs, aspirations, beliefs and diversity of Aboriginal peoples, and the contemporary issues facing Aboriginal peoples;

- to provide employees with information necessary to improve their ability to communicate effectively and work with Aboriginal peoples; and

The program is a three-day immersion course conducted in an Aboriginal community. Community representatives act as resource people.

• to increase DIAND staff's respect for and understanding of Aboriginal cultures and values.

The program is a three-day immersion course conducted in an Aboriginal community. Community representatives act as resource people to the workshop and there are opportunities for community representatives to present their concerns and aspirations. The learning that takes place in the workshops is designed to be as experiential as possible.

• Each day an Elder from the community holds a traditional opening and closing ceremony.

• Participants have the opportunity to meet and speak with members of the host community.

• Each day is different. Activities include a tour of the reserve, band offices, schools and other sites.

• Participants take part in cultural events, such as a feast, drumming and dancing.

Facilitators for the program are selected by the regional DIAND offices. Successful bidders are provided with a facilitator's guide that has been prepared for the program. Since implementing the new program, most sessions are facilitated by the Aboriginal community itself.

Most sessions are facilitated by the Aboriginal community itself.

The guide contains an extensive array of materials, including detailed training modules and sample outlines for each day of the program. In addition, there are many supporting materials, such as hand-outs, audio-visual resources, flip charts and overhead transparencies as well as an annotated bibliography on Aboriginal issues. The facilitator's guide has been designed to provide flexibility for the facilitator and to accommodate different styles, time frames, audiences and resource availability.

Program Content

The first day of the program provides an overview of Aboriginal history and politics. This module is designed to take place in a community centre on the host reserve and is delivered by the facilitator.

• The purpose of this module is to provide participants with the historical background of relations between Europeans and Aboriginal peoples.

• Through a series of activities, participants become aware of the history of Aboriginal peoples in Canada, examine the assimilation policies of the past, gain an understanding of who is an Aboriginal person, and examine the origins of current policies of the federal government towards Aboriginal peoples. By exploring the different areas of Aboriginal history, participants gain a base of knowledge pertaining to the historical background of Aboriginal peoples, their lifestyles, values, belief systems and the effects of ignorance and intolerance toward Aboriginal peoples.

The first day of the program gives participants a base of knowledge about the historical background of Aboriginal peoples, their lifestyles, values, belief systems and the effects of ignorance and intolerance toward them.

The second day of the program deals with cultural perspectives. This module is delivered by members of the host community.

- The purpose of this module is to provide participants with an opportunity to hear Aboriginal people explain their perception of the effects of history, their cultural values, and their aspirations.

- The specific content of this module varies according to each community. Very often, the morning is spent learning from elders about traditional spiritual beliefs, ceremonies and values. The afternoon is usually spent with speakers from the community addressing issues of specific concern to the host community. Speakers for the afternoon session may be people from the band council, education council, or from health and social services. In the evening, the community members generally host a traditional feast or a cultural event, such as dancing, drumming and singing, which enables workshop participants to join in a community activity in an informal way.

The addition of regional components has been one of the key enhancements to the Aboriginal Awareness Program.

The module on regional perspectives is delivered on the third day of the program by both the facilitator and members of the community. The addition of regional components has been one of the key enhancements to the Aboriginal Awareness Program.

- The purpose of this module is to provide participants with an awareness of issues that affect Aboriginal people living in that region.

- The activities suggested in this module enable participants to become familiar with the demographics of the region and to examine specific regional concerns, such as land claims, education, and governance. There is a review of the Aboriginal political structures of the region and a tour of the community, including the Band Office, schools, health centre and other points of interest.

Participants become familiar with the demographics of the region and to examine specific regional concerns, such as land claims, education, and governance.

Regional components have been prepared for Alberta, Atlantic Canada, British Columbia, Manitoba, Northwest Territories, Ontario, Quebec,

Saskatchewan and the Yukon. Each one is tailored to the specific region. The British Columbia component, for example, contains information and deals with issues that are distinctive to B.C..

- A profile and history of Aboriginal people in British Columbia is presented. Information on the major language groups and the diversity of Aboriginal people within B.C. also is provided.

- Background information on land claims and related issues, such as Native fisheries and Aboriginal rights, is included in this regional module.

- A list of tribal councils in British Columbia summarizes information on bands, their linguistic, language and cultural groups.

In early 1995, DIAND piloted three Inuit Awareness workshops in the National Capital Region. These workshops are similar in objectives, content and format to the Aboriginal Awareness workshops but are not held in a northern community setting. The workshops are specifically designed for DIAND employees working directly or indirectly on initiatives in partnership with the Inuit.

The workshops provide a valuable opportunity to learn about Canada's First Peoples and to see, first hand, the reality of life on a reserve.

Results to Date

The new Aboriginal Awareness Program has been offered since 1993. In total, 591 DIAND employees have participated in the program. Employees from all classification levels, including executives, middle and junior managers, and support staff, have participated in the program.

- . In the first year, 20 workshops were held, with an average of 23 participants in each one.

- In the second year, a total of 30 workshops were held across the country. Ten were held in the National Capital region; seven of these were in English and three in French. Twenty workshops were held in different regions across Canada.

Both Aboriginal and non-Aboriginal employees have participated in the new workshops. For non-Aboriginal employees, the workshops have been found to provide a valuable opportunity to learn about the differences between them and Canada's First Peoples and to see, first hand, the reality of life on a reserve. The workshops have also benefitted some of DIAND's

Aboriginal employees. For example, an employee who is a Blood Indian from Alberta participated in a session hosted by the Mohawks of Akwesasne and found that he learned a great deal about the differences between the plains culture and the Mohawk culture.

Initial responses to the program have been very positive. A formal evaluation of the program is being done in 1995.

The B.C. Council of Forest Industries' Aboriginal Forestry Strategy

COFI has provided leadership to encourage more Aboriginal participation in the mainstream of the BC forest economy.

The Council of Forest Industries in British Columbia (COFI) initiated an Aboriginal Forestry Strategy designed to encourage more Aboriginal participation in the mainstream of the provincial forest economy. This reflects a growing belief in the B.C. forest industry that economic integration will be beneficial to Aboriginal people and forest industry companies. COFI recognizes that Aboriginal people are important stakeholders in the forest resource and that greater efforts by the forest industry to offer expanded opportunities to Aboriginal groups can build positive relationships which will serve all parties well, before, during and after treaty negotiations.

One of COFI's key strategic thrusts has been to provide leadership to the forest industry in its relationships with the Aboriginal peoples of British Columbia. The Council has provided leadership for the industry role in three principal areas.

- The first has been developing an industry-wide fact base that demonstrates that Aboriginal people are already active economic partners in the B.C. forestry sector.

- Second, in recognizing that B.C.'s Aboriginal peoples have indicated their desire to engage in more forestry businesses and ventures, the Council has provided industry members with practical guidance on expanding employment opportunities and encouraging, initiating and developing joint business ventures and cooperative working arrangements in forestry with Aboriginal peoples in B.C..

- Third, COFI has been a very active participant in the treaty negotiating process.

To date, COFI's strategy has been successful in building a better base of understanding among its members, members of the Aboriginal community and government officials about the needs and aspirations of First Na-

Council of Forest Industries of B.C.

The Council of Forest Industries (COFI) is a B.C. forest trade association. COFI is an association of associations with six active members. These are the Northern Forest Products Association, Cariboo Lumber Manufacturers Association, Interior Lumber Manufacturers Association, Coast Forest and Lumber Association, B.C. Pulp and Paper Association, and the Canadian Plywood Association.

COFI has established six ongoing committees to address each of its priority issues, namely Aboriginal affairs, competitiveness, environment and energy, forestry, markets and trade, and occupational health and safety. Committee members are drawn from the member associations and their member forest companies. A senior industry member chairs each committee. Staff support to the committees is provided by the COFI Vice-President responsible for the strategic issue.

tions in forestry and the practical steps that can be taken to increase the scope and potential for greater economic involvement by Aboriginal people in the B.C. forest industry.

Documenting Aboriginal Involvement in the B.C. Forest Industry

An important element of the Aboriginal Forest Strategy has been to develop a comprehensive fact base documenting the participation of Aboriginal peoples in the B.C. forestry sector. This work, undertaken for COFI's Committee on Aboriginal Affairs, involved the following steps.

- An initial assessment of the interests and objectives of First Nations and the forest industry was undertaken by reviewing documents and reports.

- An analysis of the economics of forestry in B.C. was undertaken to understand how economic wealth is created and how it is distributed to those participating in the industry.

- Existing Aboriginal forestry businesses, cooperative arrangements and joint business ventures were studied and documented to gain insight into the current level of Aboriginal participation.

A database was developed that documents the various ways in which Aboriginal people participate in the forest industry in British Columbia. Several sources of information were used in compiling the database. Information was drawn from the Report on the Task Force on Native Forestry released in 1991. Another important source was the 1993 Report on the Aboriginal Participation Survey published by the Ministry of Forests, together with background material. Information from direct contacts and interviews with participants in the forestry industry were also incorporated into the database.

In 1994, COFI's Committee on Aboriginal Affairs released its study of Aboriginal participation in the forest industry. The study indicated that the B.C. forest industry was one of the single largest employers of Aboriginal people in the province, demonstrating that Aboriginal people are already active economic partners in the B.C. forestry sector.

- More than 4000 Aboriginal people are employed in the industry, which makes the forestry sector the largest single source of employment for Aboriginal people in the province.

An important element of the Aboriginal Forest Strategy has been to develop a comprehensive fact base documenting the participation of Aboriginal peoples in the B.C. forestry sector.

The study showed that the B.C. forest industry is one of the single largest employers of Aboriginal people in the province, demonstrating that Aboriginal people are already active economic partners in the sector.

The study also showed that there are a large number of Aboriginal contractors working in the B.C. forest industry.

- Aboriginal employment is between 4 percent and 5 percent of the total industry workforce, suggesting that Aboriginal participation is roughly in line with their representation in the B.C. population.

- A significant and growing number of Aboriginal people are employed indirectly by Aboriginal and non-Aboriginal contractors and in joint business ventures, as well as working as direct employees of companies and government.

The study also showed that there are a large number of Aboriginal contractors working in the B.C. forest industry. About 70 percent of all the contracts awarded to Aboriginal firms in B.C. by the forest industry are for silviculture contracts. Harvesting contracts account for most of the rest. Other Aboriginal contractors are involved in log hauling, maintenance activities, and road building.

At least 14 active joint business ventures between Aboriginal groups and forest companies have been identified. There has been considerable interest in these types of arrangements because they result in the employment of Aboriginal people and also provide opportunities for Aboriginal people to gain skills and experience that can lead to independent enterprises in the future. Joint business ventures already exist in timber harvesting, silviculture contracting, saw-milling and remanufacturing operations. Several initiatives are in the proposal or discussion stage.

The forest industry has the capacity to provide significant economic development opportunities to Aboriginal people. To assist members, COFI has offered practical guidance on how to expand these opportunities.

Actions to Increase Aboriginal Participation

The 1994 study by COFI's Committee on Aboriginal Affairs also explicitly acknowledges the desire articulated by B.C.'s Aboriginal peoples to engage in more forestry businesses and ventures. The forest industry has the capacity to provide significant economic development opportunities to Aboriginal people. To assist COFI members, the report set out practical guidance on how to expand employment opportunities and encourage, initiate and develop joint business ventures and cooperative working arrangements in forestry with Aboriginal peoples in B.C.. The suggestions provided in the report were the result of distilling information compiled on Aboriginal forestry business and Aboriginal participation in the forest industry and from visits and interviews with Aboriginal and non-Aboriginal principals involved in these ventures.

The following practical suggestions for action are included in the report.

- Hire more Aboriginal employees, especially in harvesting, trucking and silviculture. Although union contracts, especially hire and re-hire

Practical suggestions include: hire more Aboriginal employees; increase contracting opportunities; provide more internship opportunities; establish cooperative agreements; and create joint business ventures.

provisions may constrain flexibility, some field operations (harvesting, trucking, silviculture) can be undertaken under quite flexible operating conditions.

- Increase contracting opportunities for Aboriginal businesses. Two approaches are suggested: the first is to seek out established Aboriginal contractors with established track records; the second is to help new Aboriginal entrepreneurs to get started. In both cases, if the first contract works out successfully, this can lead to larger contracts and more sophisticated business dealings in the future.

- Provide more internship opportunities. Internship programs for Aboriginal graduates of colleges, technical schools and universities can provide a means of developing business skills in the Aboriginal community. The host company not only benefits from the talent of the intern but also gains an opportunity to acquire a better understanding of Aboriginal culture and values and build recognition in the Aboriginal community.

- Establish cooperative agreements, such as cooperative management or working agreements, between Aboriginal groups and forest companies. These can be structured to specify the conditions under which the parties will work together to pursue common goals and interests. They may cover such topics as the management of forest resources and arrangements for hiring Aboriginal employees. They may specify arrangements for activities from road-building to silviculture to harvesting.

- Create joint business ventures. Some forest companies are joining forces with Aboriginal businesses, contractors and communities in applying for new tenures.

Impact of the Strategy

The study by the Committee on Aboriginal Affairs was released and distributed in early 1994. It was distributed to about 200 COFI member companies and to federal and provincial government officials. In B.C., the report was sent to officials in the Ministry of Forests and the Ministry of Aboriginal Affairs. COFI also distributed the report to Aboriginal communities, forestry businesses and associations.

COFI's activities have already had a significant impact.

- The COFI report made clear that, although there is considerable Aboriginal involvement in the forest sector, there are still significant gaps

The COFI report documented the significant Aboriginal involvement in the forest sector but also drew attention to the fact that there was scope for forest companies to do much more.

in the fact base. This provided the impetus for the Ministry of Forests to commission a consulting project to develop benchmarking information and a monitoring process to track developments. This report has now been released.

- For COFI member companies, the report was important in a number of ways. It documented the significant Aboriginal involvement in the forest sector but also drew attention to the fact that there was scope for forest companies to do much more. In particular, there was a significant gap between those companies that had taken a pro-active role in fostering Aboriginal involvement in the forest sector and those which had taken a more passive or reactive approach.

- The report has been an important input into the Treaty Negotiations Advisory Committee (TNAC) process since it has demonstrated that significant economic opportunities can be achieved in the forest sector by Aboriginal people without waiting for the treaty process.

- The report has also had an impact on Aboriginal groups. It has drawn attention to the fact that well-structured joint business ventures or cooperative ventures can contribute significantly to the long-term economic health of a community. Aboriginal communities are becoming more aggressive in their demands for meaningful partnerships with forest companies.

Given the strong and positive response to the Aboriginal Forestry Strategy by member companies, COFI's Aboriginal Affairs Committee has placed its emphasis on the treaty negotiating process. The Council's objective has been to ensure that decisions are not made that would erode the long-term viability of the forestry industry, undermine the wealth of goodwill between First Nations and the forest industry, or forestall the progress that is being made in expanding economic opportunities for the increasing numbers of Aboriginal people who work in the industry.

PART TWO

EDUCATION
AND TRAINING

Royal Bank's School Partnership Programs

Giving Aboriginal youth exposure to the basics of business and finance increases their awareness of opportunities in business and their understanding of the education and skills that are needed to work in or run a business.

School partnerships are one way that Royal Bank is working to encourage Aboriginal students to gain an education that prepares them for opportunities in business. These partnerships are also part of Royal Bank's long-term strategy for working with Aboriginal people. By giving Aboriginal youth exposure to the basics of business and finance, the bank is increasing their awareness of opportunities in business and their understanding of the education and skills that are needed to work in or run a business. In this way, the bank is building relationships with its workforce and customers of the future.

The bank builds its partnerships with schools through its extensive employment equity networks and ongoing outreach initiatives. School partnerships are a small part of Royal Bank's long-standing commitment to improving employment opportunities for Aboriginal people and strengthening relations with First Nations and Aboriginal communities.

The bank has worked with both elementary and secondary schools and has sponsored programs in urban and on-reserve schools. This includes a series of programs with the Children of the Earth High School, the first urban Aboriginal high school in Canada and Junior Achievement programs with the Peguis Central School. A national Stay-in-School Program provides grade 11 and 12 students incentives to continue their schooling and work experience in the bank. A work experience program provides elementary school students with structured opportunities to help them develop a better understanding of the relationship of their school subjects to work.

Schools as a Focal Point for Action

Royal Bank has extensive experience in developing business-education partnerships. The bank enters into these relationships because it believes that partnerships and collaboration between educational and business communities are essential for the future success of Canada's youth. The quality and effectiveness

---

Royal Bank

Royal Bank is Canada's largest chartered bank. The bank operates across Canada and in 32 other countries, providing a full range of banking services for individuals, businesses and communities through its branch network as well as corporate, investment and treasury banking services.

Royal Bank has about 1500 branches in Canada. It is organized into 11 units and eight geographic areas in Canada: Atlantic, Quebec, Metropolitan Toronto, Ontario, Manitoba, Saskatchewan, Alberta and British Columbia. Headquarters for key businesses and functions are in Montreal and Toronto.

In 1994, Royal Bank had almost 47,000 full-time and part-time employees in Canada. There were 333 Aboriginal people employed by Royal Bank, accounting for 0.7 percent of the total workforce.

Partnerships with schools with high Aboriginal populations are particularly valuable since Aboriginal students often lack practical exposure to the basics of business and finance.

Reaching Aboriginal students while they are still in school gives them the time and information needed to make informed choices about their education and career directions.

of education and training involves a lifelong commitment to learning, which in turn requires cooperative effort from business, education, labour, government and community leaders. Most of the partnerships that the bank has entered into over the past decade have been designed to address barriers or disadvantages experienced by specific communities or groups of people across Canada, with many partnerships complementing the bank's employment equity activities.

While each partnership is different and designed to fill a particular need, the overall objectives of the bank's school partnerships are to:

- help students enhance their employability skills;
- raise community awareness of the importance of developing employability skills to ensure Canada's economic prosperity;
- encourage parents to become actively involved in the education of their children; and
- strengthen the link between schools and workplaces.

Partnerships with schools with high Aboriginal populations are particularly valuable since Aboriginal students often lack practical exposure to the basics of business and finance. They are also often are not aware of the range of career opportunities available in business or of the education and skills needed for these careers.

Royal Bank has recognized that if it is to succeed in building a fully representative workforce it must have access to Aboriginal people with the range of skills that the bank needs to grow and compete. Reaching Aboriginal students while they are still in school gives them the time and information needed to make informed choices about their education and career directions. Demographic trends show that Aboriginal people are becoming an increasingly important component of the population and labour market.

In addition to school partnerships, Royal Bank also supports educational initiatives for post-secondary Aboriginal students. The Native Student Awards program was launched in 1992 to help Aboriginal people attend university or college in Canada. Five students receive awards to cover the cost of tuition, textbooks and supplies and to assist with living expenses during the academic year. The maximum amount of each award is $4,000 per year to a maximum of four years per student. The student must be enroled in a discipline relevant to the banking industry, such as business, economics and computer science. As part of the awards program, recipients interested in a banking career are given consideration for summer and post-graduation employment. Award recipients are selected by an independent committee of Aboriginal academics, who review all applicants. The final selection is based on criteria that include personal and academic achievements as well as individual financial need.

Building the Partnerships

Royal Bank builds its partnerships with schools through its extensive employment equity networks and ongoing outreach initiatives.

Royal Bank builds its partnerships with schools through its extensive employment equity networks and ongoing outreach initiatives. In addition to full-time employment equity staff in corporate headquarters and each of the bank's eight geographic regions, there are employment equity committees in each region. These committees include both designated and non-designated group employees from across the region and across all job levels. Each committee is responsible for its own agenda, which typically includes awareness building and educational programs within the bank. In addition, the employment equity committees participate in local career fairs and the implementation of other outreach activities.

The bank also has developed an internal network of approximately 375 employment equity coordinators who are full-time employees with employment equity responsibilities built into their jobs. The coordinators are responsible for outreach activities, including those with Aboriginal people.

These networks are important in helping Royal Bank to identify and implement community-based initiatives such as school partnerships. Partnerships are also established when community organizations approach the bank directly or when contacts are made on location within communities and at career fairs and conferences. Royal Bank, as the largest corporate donor in Canada, also has extensive experience in working with communities on a variety of initiatives. Branches have supported community initiatives with volunteers, in-kind donations as well as financial support.

The school partnerships are funded through Royal Bank's community relations budget and by participating branches and divisions.

Partnerships with the Children of the Earth High School

Children of the Earth High School is the first urban Aboriginal High School in Canada.

In 1993, Royal Bank began a series of initiatives with the Children of the Earth High School, which is located in Winnipeg, Manitoba. Children of the Earth High School is the first urban Aboriginal High School in Canada.

The first initiative was a Junior Achievement project called *Anishinabe E We Chitwowa*, which means People Working Together. It was designed to provide a learning opportunity where students can acquire a basic business knowledge, plus work experience, as they establish their own businesses. The concept for the Junior Achievement project resulted from a discussion between the bank and the Principal on ways in which students could be given practical exposure to business. The bank was asked to make a short presentation to the school, following which the project was adopted. One of the teachers was particularly interested in the project and played an important role in seeing it to completion.

Most Junior Achievement company programs are normally conducted as an extra-curricular activity one evening each week. The program at the Children of the Earth High School was the first time that such a program had been offered during school hours. Through the program, students learn about all aspects of setting up a business, including general administration, finance, personnel, marketing and production. The success of the company is determined by the students' involvement and decisions. Twelve students worked together to set up a small business that would develop and market T-shirt designs. A Royal Bank staff member represented the bank as a business consultant to the project. Other bank representatives made presentations on advertising, marketing, human resources and independent business.

In 1994 and 1995, the bank and the school worked together on a Youth Leadership Program, a version of the Toastmasters program geared specifically for young people. In this eight-week program, the students learned how to make presentations, conduct meetings and use different speaking styles. In 1995, the bank sponsored another Junior Achievement initiative in the school, called Project Business. This involved a series of lectures on different topics related to economics, business and banking.

In January 1995, a six-week work experience program was initiated. This program was designed to give students practice with job interviews as well as direct on-the-job experience. Students who have participated in the program are in a position to obtain part-time employment while they are in school.

The bank also provides a specific scholarship for students at the Children of the Earth High School for outstanding achievements in mathematics, business or computers.

Stay-in-School Program for Grade 11 and 12 Students

Each year, Royal Bank sponsors a national summer Stay-in-School Program for Grades 11 and 12 students who agree to return to school in the fall. This program was initiated as a result of the outreach work of an Aboriginal employee with more than 20 years experience with the bank, who at that time was Assistant Manager, Employment Equity. In her extensive relationships with Aboriginal communities, she listened to concerns about

Each year, Royal Bank sponsors a national summer Stay-in-School Program for Grades 11 and 12 students who agree to return to school in the fall.

school drop-out rates and the serious consequences for Aboriginal youth and community development.

The first program was held in 1993, when 34 students from across Canada participated. The students spent four weeks working in a Royal Bank facility. In most cases, they received a complete overview of how a bank operates. The primary focus of the project was to have students spend time working, observing and asking questions of staff in the various roles represented in the branches (such as customer service representatives, personal banking representatives, administrative positions, manager customer service, etc.) to expand their knowledge of the banking environment. The students were paid during this period.

The program is now an ongoing part of the bank's Aboriginal education initiatives, with about 50 students from across Canada participating annually. Regional offices and branches play the major role in organizing and promoting it in local areas. In addition, the bank has produced a poster about the program and the *Opening Doors* brochure, which is geared specifically to Aboriginal people, also describes it. Royal Bank has also incorporated the Stay-in-School program into its television advertising.

The reaction to the stay-in-school program has been positive from high school principals because of its career focus, the acceptance of responsibility by the students, and the coaching on careers. Parents and families also have described how the students have benefitted from the program. Some of the students who participated in the program have gone on to work part-time in the bank throughout the school year.

The reaction to the stay-in-school program has been positive from high school principals because of its career focus, the acceptance of responsibility by the students, and the coaching on careers.

Work Experience for Grade 6 Students in Winnipeg's Core Area

In 1992, Royal Bank set up a work experience project with the William Whyte Elementary School in Winnipeg's Core Area. The school has about 300 students.

The objectives of this program were to help school children to develop a better understanding of the relationships between their school subjects and the workplace and an awareness of other job requirements, such as time management and accountability. Under the partnership project, three students from each of the school's two grade 6 classes were given the opportunity to go to Royal Bank branches in Winnipeg and work alongside bank employees. The students who went on the program shared their experiences with the rest of their class and with their parents.

The partnership grew out of an initial meeting in March 1992 between Royal Bank and the Inner City Business Education Steering Committee. This committee was aware of the bank's involvement in and focus on busi-

A program with an elementary school was considered to be valuable because many attitudes and skills that are essential for successful employment need to be developed at an early age.

ness education partnerships and invited Royal Bank to discuss participation in partnership activities with their schools. A program with an elementary school was considered to be valuable because many attitudes and skills that are essential for successful employment need to be developed at an early age.

The program with the William Whyte School, which began in September 1992, was developed jointly by the school, the bank and volunteer coordinators. Branch managers at the bank met with their staff to discuss the project, define the objectives and discuss the branch's involvement in the project. The children's parents were also involved.

The program was designed to take place over four half-day sessions in two of the bank's branches in Winnipeg. The first session would give students a tour of the branch and an explanation of different jobs and department's in the bank. In subsequent sessions, the children would rotate through a number of different bank positions. They were provided with a workbook-type journal to record their observations. In the final session, there would be a wrap-up, where the children would prepare a final report.

The teachers at the William Whyte School developed the selection process and an application form modelled on that of the bank. The application forms, along with job descriptions, were given to students who were given a lesson on how to apply for a job. They were advised to involve their families in helping them to complete the application form. The application form had to be signed by their parents. A deadline was set for submission of applications.

Interviews were held for the students who applied for the jobs. Students were asked to bring a sample of their school work (such as notebooks). Their record of punctuality and good attendance was an important factor in the selection process. The teachers identified the students who would participate in the project. Prior to finalizing the placement of the children, the teachers visited the two branches that would be hosting the students. In preparation for the students, branch management met with their staff to discuss the project, define the objectives, describe the branch involvement in the project and set a schedule of activities.

At the conclusion of the program, the students who participated in the program found it to be a very valuable experience. Some of the comments by students include the following.

> "This was good experience for us, because we have never done anything like this before ... We learned many different things ... We learned about team work and about respecting and helping others ... We saw the employees working hard ... We learned that the people liked their jobs. They even had assignments to do by the end of the

day ... The people at the bank were always smiling and polite. They showed respect for themselves and for others ... We saw that the same things that are important at school are important at work."

The results of this project reinforced to the bank the importance and value of working with students at a very young age and this program is now an ongoing initiative with the William Whyte Elementary School.

Junior Achievement in Peguis Central School

In the spring of 1995, Royal Bank ran three Junior Achievement programs in Peguis Central School. This was the first time that Junior Achievement had ever been offered in an on-reserve school. Feedback from the first offering has been positive.

The programs were delivered during school hours by employees of the bank's branch in Peguis. The employees, who are also residents of Peguis, delivered three different programs. The fact that the people delivering the program were Aboriginal themselves and could serve as role models for the students, contributed to the success.

- The *Business Basics* program was run for Grade 6 students, with a total of 50 students participating.

- The *Economics of Staying in School* program was run for Grade 9 students with about 25 students participating.

- *Project Business* was offered to about 25 Grade 10 students.

In addition to Junior Achievement, the bank participates in the community's career fairs which are held twice a year. Student tours of the branch are available for teachers who request them. The bank also offered a program in personal budgeting for Grade 12 students who were going on to post-secondary education, in order to help develop their skills in managing their living allowances while they were in college or university.

Results

There has been good feedback to the programs from student participants and their families and teachers. The bank has found that the partnerships have proven to be an effective way of building knowledge among Aboriginal youth about banking and business. The programs have helped to demystify banks by providing a positive, welcoming environment. Linking their school experiences to the workplace can also help the students to

Royal Bank ran three Junior Achievement programs in Peguis Central School. This was the first time that Junior Achievement had ever been offered in an on-reserve school.

Linking their school experiences to the workplace can also help the students to examine their future educational options and make more informed decisions about them.

By developing a good working relationship with Aboriginal students, the bank is building relationships with its workforce and customers of the future.

examine their future educational options and make more informed decisions about them.

The school partnerships have also provided opportunities for two-way learning. Royal Bank employees who have participated in these initiatives have given very positive feedback about the school partnerships with Aboriginal people.

The bank continues to develop new partnerships as opportunities occur. Royal Bank views the school partnerships as beneficial to long-term business development. By developing a good working relationship with Aboriginal students, the bank is building relationships with its workforce and customers of the future. Aboriginal education initiatives help build a bridge to the bank's Aboriginal business goals. They sent a message to Royal Bank staff that the bank has a long-term commitment to the recruitment of Aboriginal employees. These initiatives also give Royal Bank employees exposure to Aboriginal students and a better understanding that their skills, goals and aspirations are similar to those of the population at large.

NOVA Gas Transmission's Native Education Program

NOVA's Native Education Program has two primary goals: to inform, encourage and motivate Native students to continue their education, and to introduce them to the concept of career planning.

NOVA Gas Transmission introduced its Native Education Program in 1986. The program was introduced to address the high school drop-out rate among Native people (particularly in senior high school) and to boost the pool of qualified Native workers in Alberta.

The program has two primary goals: to inform, encourage and motivate Native students to continue their education, and to introduce them to the concept of career planning. It has been so well received that NOVA is committed to doing it annually. It is now in its tenth year and has reached almost 7000 students through 300 presentations at 170 schools.

The Native Education Program is one component of NOVA's comprehensive and integrated approach to Aboriginal employment and community relations. Increasing the participation of Aboriginal people in all of NOVA's activities is one of the company's specific corporate goals.

NOVA's Native Policy and Programs

NOVA's commitment to Aboriginal people began in the 1970s when the company was planning and sponsoring major pipeline projects in the North. Although activities with Native communities were firmly established by the late 1970s, the company's commitments in this area were not formally spelled out until July 1982 when the Native Employment and Business Opportunities Policy was adopted. Today, the key program elements in NOVA's Native Policy include the Native business opportunities program, the Native employment program, the Native education program and the educational awards program.

The four core Native programs have specific objectives.

- The Native Education Program was established to help motivate Native students to finish high school, continue with post-secondary studies and plan their careers.

NOVA Gas Transmission Ltd.

NOVA Corporation was incorporated in 1954 to transport Alberta's vast reserves of natural gas.

NOVA Gas Transmission Ltd. (NGTL), a wholly owned subsidiary, owns and operates NOVA's natural gas pipeline system consisting of 12,600 miles of pipeline, 49 compressor stations, and over 1000 receipt and delivery points. NGTL is a large, low-cost, rapidly expanding company with anticipated capital expenditures of $3.1 billion between 1994 and 1998. In 1994, NGTL delivered 4.1 trillion cubic feet of natural gas, representing over 80 percent of the gas produced in Canada and 15 percent of the natural gas produced in North America.

NGTL employs about 2800 permanent full-time and part-time employees, including 100 Aboriginal people, who represent 3.5 percent of the total workforce.

- The Educational Awards Program is designed to encourage Native people to obtain post-secondary education relevant to natural gas services or the petrochemicals industry.

- The Native Employment Program's objective is to increase the number of Native employees at NOVA to reflect the proportion of Native people in the Alberta population.

- The Native Business Opportunities Program is designed to give the growing pool of Native businesses and contractors an opportunity to participate in NOVA activities.

The Native Education Program

In keeping with the belief that education is a key ingredient to a more prosperous future, the purpose of the Native Education Program is to encourage Aboriginal students in junior and senior high schools in Alberta to stay in school all the way through to a post-secondary education or training.

The program consists of two parts. The first part consists of a number of motivational workshops and presentations made to Aboriginal students in high schools throughout Alberta; the second part involves the development and distribution of resource materials (in particular the Native Student Handbook and the Directory of Educational Services for Native Students) which are designed to supplement the presentations.

Motivational Presentations

Every year, NOVA hires two Aboriginal university students to visit schools throughout Alberta during May and June and to conduct motivational workshops for Aboriginal high school students.

Every year, NOVA hires two Aboriginal university students to visit schools throughout Alberta during May and June and to conduct motivational workshops for Aboriginal high school students. The program targets junior and senior high schools with high Native student populations. The purpose of the workshops is to encourage students to stay in school, to begin the process of career planning and to continue on to college or university.

The two presenters take about five weeks to visit all of the targeted schools. Each year, 30-35 schools are visited and between 35-40 presentations given to 700-1000 students.

The presentation are about 80 minutes in length. The first 10-15 minutes are spent setting out the purpose of the presentation and explaining NOVA's business. This is followed by a 30 minute video called *Who We Are: A Celebration of Native Youth,* which includes Native students from across Canada discussing the importance of education and culture. The presenters then provide practical information such as details on the types of post-secondary institutions, application procedures, accommodation, costs of tuition and books, etc.. In the remaining time, the presenters discuss their experiences as university students, thereby putting a face to the message they are expounding. This last component deals with the merits of post-secondary education, career planning, maintaining Native languages and cultural identity as well as providing personal examples of why all of these are important.

The ultimate objective is to have students believe in their ability to reach their dreams and to help them understand that furthering their education is one of the best ways to reach those dreams.

The ultimate objective is to have the students believe in their ability to reach their dreams and to help them understand that furthering their education is one of the best ways to reach those dreams.

The presentation has targeted Aboriginal students in grades 7 to 12. The presentations are also attended by teachers and Aboriginal liaison workers. Although the target group of the program is Aboriginal students, the presentations do not exclude non-Native students, especially in the case of schools that are uncomfortable separating students into ethnic groups. However, in these cases, the presentation is given with the understanding that Aboriginal students are the focus audience.

Resource Materials

The second component of the program consists of revising and updating resource materials related to the program and providing students with follow-up information related to post-secondary education.

NOVA has prepared a number of resource documents as part of its Native Education program.

NOVA has prepared a number of resource documents as part of its Native Education program.

- The *Native Student Handbook* for Grade 12 students provides practical information on post-secondary application procedures, budgeting, accommodation and sources of students awards.

- A role model brochure for all students - *Education, Career Planning and Your Future* - highlights successful Aboriginal individuals and quotes their thoughts on the importance of education.

- The *Directory of Educational Services for Native Students* provides teachers and counsellors with information on Native courses, educational institutions, counselling and career planning services and sources of financial assistance.

These resource materials are included in handout materials provided to the schools and communities that have participated in the workshops and made available to institutions and individual students who request them.

Program Evaluation

Students who have attended the presentation are asked to provide an evaluation of the presentation by filling in a questionnaire. The questionnaire asks attendees about the quality of the presentation. It also asks a number of questions designed to identify how useful they found the presentation, i.e.:

- whether they felt that the material covered in the presentation was important to them;

- whether the workshop helped them understand more about post-secondary education;

- whether the workshop helped them understand more about career planning; and

- whether the presentation helped them think about their future.

Over the past decade, 75 percent of the evaluations completed by people who have attended the presentations have been positive.

Results

NOVA's Native Education Program has been active since 1986. Between 1986 and 1994, motivational presentations have been given to almost 7000 students at about 170 schools.

Between 1986 and 1994, motivational presentations have been given to almost 7000 students at about 170 schools.

Summary of the Native Education Program 1986-94			
Year	# of Schools	# of Presentations	# of Students
1986	20	20	579
1987	22	22	535
1988	39	41	857
1989	36	36	777
1990	35	29	789
1991	36	36	815
1992	36	36	698
1993	30	37	989
1994	31	41	852
Total	285	298	6891

Source: NOVA Gas Transmission, June 1994

NOVA consistently receives positive letters of support from students, teachers and counsellors. The company is invited to return to schools year after year.

Students are often very grateful for the information provided and the time taken to encourage them to think about the importance of education and career planning. This is clear from their evaluations of the program and from the comments that often accompany the evaluations.

NOVA consistently receives positive letters of support from students, teachers and counsellors. The company is invited to return to schools year after year.

- A Grade 9 student from Edmonton wrote: "I really enjoyed the presentation... presentations like this that help me believe that education is not just a dead-end, thank you for the information and inspiration."

- A junior high school student from Calgary wrote: "I felt that the presentation has helped me understand how important school is!"

- Lloydminster students wrote: ".. the presentation helped us to understand more about being yourself and staying in school to achieve your goals."

- A Grade 8 Metis student from Edmonton wrote: "Thank you, you made me think about some of the things that I can change and do for myself. Hi! Hi!" (Thank you in Cree)

Evaluations by students have been consistently positive over the past ten years. Most students (91 percent) have agreed that the presentation has helped them to think about their future; 93 percent felt that the material covered in the presentation was important; 82 percent agreed that the presentation helped them understand more about post-secondary education; and 87 percent stated that the workshop helped them understand more about career planning.

The response from teachers and Aboriginal liaison workers has also been very positive.

A teacher wrote: "It is very important for Native students, and especially more remote and rural Native students to see and hear about positive role models from their Native ancestry".

- A teacher at a Band-controlled school wrote: "Positive, inspirational and articulate speakers of Native ancestry are important sources of input that help our students to make important decisions. Thank you for making this possible."

- A Native liaison worker stated: "The Native Education Program is a definite asset in the promotion of education to Native students."

- A teacher from Buck Lake wrote: "It is very important for Native students, and especially more **remote and rural** Native students to see and hear about positive role models from their Native ancestry. P.S. We would love to be on your list for next year."

NOVA's program is a catalyst for positive change.

One of the most valuable elements of these workshops is the impact of the two Native presenters as role models for the younger students.

NOVA's three resource documents have all been well received by educators, Aboriginal students and Aboriginal communities. The company receives numerous calls every month for copies. NOVA estimates that it has distributed 2,300 Directories and about 10,000 each of the Handbook and role model brochure since the program began. The Native Student Handbook has been copied by the Government of Saskatchewan and by groups in British Columbia for distribution in the northern parts of both provinces.

NOVA's program is a catalyst for positive change. The company hopes that it is helping break the cycle of school dropout among Aboriginal youth. For some students, the NOVA presentation is the first time that they have heard about post-secondary education from first hand experience. For other students, it is the first time that they had been addressed directly about their future career goals, questioned about it and openly encouraged to pursue their dreams with the belief that a post-secondary education is the best path to seek and follow. The presentation also allows those students who have given consideration to their career paths the opportunity to obtain more specific information so they could take the next step.

One of the most valuable elements of these workshops is the impact of the two Native presenters as role models for the younger students. Many Native youth have few role models in their lives. The university students that the company hires share their own stories with the younger students and talk about the hardships that they may have had to overcome (such as dropping out, pregnancy, unsupportive family, discrimination, abuse, leaving their home community) to return to school, upgrade their skills and carry on their post-secondary education. When recruiting university students for the program, NOVA often seeks individuals who have overcome such obstacles. The company believes that these role models often have a more powerful impact on the students than the workshop or the resource materials.

L'Ordre des ingénieurs du Québec and Concordia University's Summer Engineering Camp for Aboriginal Students

In the fall of 1993, the Faculty of Engineering and Computer Science of Concordia University and L'Ordre des ingénieurs du Québec (Quebec Order of Engineers) entered into a formal agreement to explore ways to increase the representation of Aboriginal people within the engineering profession in Quebec. The working group developed a long-term strategy to accomplish this.

To kick-start the long-term strategy, the group developed and ran *Engineering Explorations,* a five day summer camp. The camp is designed to acquaint Aboriginal high school students in grades 9 through 11 with the many facets of the engineering profession through a series of hands-on activities related to engineering, science and technology.

In July 1994 the first camp was held on a pilot basis, with 22 Aboriginal students from Quebec attending. The camp was very successful and will be held on an ongoing basis.

Students who participated expressed increased interest in technology and engineering as a potential career option. The camp also opened new opportunities for Concordia University's Faculty of Engineering and Computer Science and the Ordre des ingénieurs du Québec to work together toward their shared long-term objective of increasing the representation of Aboriginal people within the engineering profession in Quebec.

L'Ordre des ingénieurs du Québec

Concordia University Faculty of Engineering and Computer Science

The Faculty of Engineering and Computer Science at Concordia University in Montreal offers programs in mechanical engineering, building engineering, electrical and computer engineering, computer science and civil engineering. There are about 115 faculty members and a student enrolment of approximately 2500. Overall representation of Aboriginal students in the Faculty's programs is less than 1 percent.

The Ordre des ingénieurs du Québec (Quebec Order of Engineers) is the body which governs the engineering profession in Québec. The mission of the OIQ is to promote and ensure the quality of services rendered to society by engineers, individually and as members of a professional body. The OIQ promotes professional and personal development and contributes to the socio-economic development of society. The Ordre des ingénieurs du Québec has approximately 40,000 members.

Long-Term Strategy to Increase Aboriginal Representation in Engineering

There is very low representation of Aboriginal engineers among the membership of L'Ordre des ingénieurs du Québec and simi-

A Joint Working Group on Native Access to Engineering was formed as a result of the shared interest in promoting engineering in all segments of society.

The working group considered a variety of long-term initiatives and concluded that all of the initiatives needed motivated young Aboriginal people prepared to make the commitment to pursuing an education in engineering.

larly low percentages of Aboriginal students registered in undergraduate engineering programs in Quebec. For example, Aboriginal students represent less than one percent of the total enrolment in Concordia's Faculty of Engineering and Computer Science.

To address this, a Joint Working Group on Native Access to Engineering was established early in 1994. The group was formed as a result of the shared interest of the Ordre des ingénieurs du Québec and Concordia's Faculty of Engineering and Computer Science in promoting engineering in all segments of society. Concordia University has a long track record in providing access to post-secondary education to non-traditional students. The Ordre des ingénieurs du Québec states that contributing to the socio-economic development of society is one element of its mission.

Membership of the working group includes the Dean of the Faculty of Engineering and Computer Science of Concordia University, three engineering professors, three members of the Ordre des ingénieurs du Québec, the Advisor to the Dean on Communications and Equity and a representative of the Canadian Aboriginal Science and Engineering Association.

A series of meetings was held to develop both long and short-term strategies. The working group examined the possible reasons for the low representation of Aboriginal people in engineering. It considered a number of potential factors, including post-secondary educational attainment of Aboriginal youth and the absence, in Quebec, of academic support programs related to engineering. The group also reviewed the importance of preparing young Aboriginal people to participate in the growth of local Aboriginal economies. The development of municipal infrastructure, industry and self-government make it increasingly important for Aboriginal youth to acquire the skills and expertise to function as engineering professionals in the future.

The working group considered a variety of long-term initiatives such as university level academic support programs, pre-university transition programs, cooperative initiatives between the university and feeder organizations. It also considered developing curriculum directly related to the needs of Aboriginal communities and incorporating relevant curriculum content into existing engineering courses. Promoting mentorship and role models were also identified as ways to encourage more young people to pursue post secondary education in engineering.

The working group concluded that all of the initiatives that it had identified were inextricably linked to the availability of motivated young Aboriginal people prepared to make the commitment to pursuing an education in engineering. As a result, the long-term strategy would need to focus on developing a pool of motivated students opting for an engineering education and to provide them with a relevant, high-quality education.

The working group decided to concentrate on specific activities that would contribute to the development of a pool of motivated young people.

The group decided that a series of short-term actions were required to kick-start the long-term strategy and to generate the required level of interest among Aboriginal youth. As a result, the working group concentrated its attention on specific short-term activities that would contribute to the development of a pool of motivated young people.

The working group consulted the Canadian Aboriginal Science and Engineering Association (CASEA) to seek advice on how best to inform young people of the benefits both to themselves and to their communities of pursuing post-secondary programs in engineering. The group reached a number of conclusions as a result of its deliberations and advice from CASEA.

- It decided that a number of different "hands-on" opportunities would be the most effective way to reach out to young people.

- Direct involvement of Aboriginal communities would be essential to the success of the initiatives, since the communities would be major beneficiaries of increased numbers of Aboriginal engineers.

The primary target group would be Aboriginal students between the ages of 12 and 17 since they would be the most likely to be considering their career choices.

- The primary target group would be Aboriginal students between the ages of 12 and 17 since they would be the most likely to be considering their career choices. High school students were identified as the primary target group. Elementary students were identified as the secondary target group. Teachers, guidance counsellors and education officers would form a third target group for the development of short-term strategies.

The working group determined that a summer day camp for Aboriginal high school students, called *Engineering Explorations,* would be a short-term initiative that would support the long-term objective shared by Concordia University's Faculty of Engineering and Computer Science and the Quebec Order of Engineers.

Objectives of the Camp

The working group set five specific objectives for *Engineering Explorations.*

- To develop awareness of the engineering profession among young Aboriginal people.

- To provide exposure to different fields of science and technology through hands-on exploration.

- To promote engineering as a career choice.

- To underline the importance that science and technology will play in the economic development of Aboriginal communities in the future.
- To create opportunities for young Aboriginal people from various communities to interact with one other.

Developing the Program

All of the preparatory work for the program for the five day camp was completed between March and June 1994. A key priority was to put sufficient financing in place to develop and run the camp.

- Initial financial contributions were made by the Faculty of Engineering and Computer Science of Concordia University and L'Ordre des ingénieurs du Québec.
- Additional financing was provided by Indian and Northern Affairs Canada, through the Aboriginal Workforce Participation Initiative, and from Human Resources Development Canada, through the Local Aboriginal Management Board of Montreal.
- This base of funding was used to hire three Aboriginal post-secondary students to act as camp counsellors.

Another important priority was ensuring the participation of the partners necessary to make the camp a success and defining their respective roles.

- The Canadian Aboriginal Science and Engineering Association (CASEA) would provide expertise from its members, as well as access to its network of Aboriginal engineers in the province who would help promote the camp.
- REACH, a summer science and engineering camp organization with a track record of introducing science concepts to young people, would provide the initial model for the camp and help to train the project's student counsellors.
- The Native Friendship Centre of Montreal would provide after-hours activities for the campers. This would enable campers to meet other Aboriginal people in Montreal and ensure that the young Aboriginal people coming to the city would have a comfortable place to turn to for assistance or referral.
- Concordia's Centre for Native Education, which was established in 1992, would show a videotape to students about studies in science and engineering and would provide information on admission requirements to Concordia.

Another important priority was ensuring the participation of the partners necessary to make the camp a success.

The REACH summer science and engineering camp program was adapted to make it appropriate for high school students and to include examples which would make it relevant to Aboriginal students.

- Education officers, guidance counsellors and economic development officers in Aboriginal communities in Quebec were provided information about the camp and approached for assistance in recruiting students.

- A Mohawk elder from Akwesasne, who was consulted for advice, offered to come to the camp and speak to the students.

The REACH organization played a particularly important role in developing the camp program for the students. REACH, which is part of YES (Youth Engineering and Science) Camps, was started in 1988 by students at Concordia and McGill Universities. REACH provided the initial model of how to run a successful science and engineering camp for elementary school students. The REACH program was adapted to make it appropriate for high school students and to include examples which would make it relevant to Aboriginal students. REACH also trained the *Engineering Explorations* counsellors and provided volunteer senior counsellors to assist the program's Aboriginal counsellors.

The Joint Working Group had continuous involvement throughout, holding regular meetings to discuss program goals and content.

The Camp Experience

Twenty-two students, 16 young men and 6 young women, attended the camp which took place from July 25-29, 1994. The students, ranging in age from 14 to 22, were Cree, Micmac and Mohawk from Restigouche, Oujé-bougoumou, Kahnawake and Kanesatake and Montreal. Criteria for selection were determined by each local community. Many students were chosen by their communities for their academic promise and community involvement. The cost of the camp was $125 per student.

The camp ran from 9 am to 4 pm each day, with social activities afterwards. There were no absences during the camp.

- Campers had opportunities to conduct scientific experiments such as chemical experiments, bridge-building, concrete-mixing, analysis of structures, computer-simulated urban planning, making holograms, rocket-building and multimedia design. They also participated in problem-solving using group discussion.

- Tours were conducted of research laboratories, mining and metallurgical laboratories and testing facilities. Campers visited engineering laboratories and research centres at Concordia and McGill and several other programs related to the profession.

Student selection criteria were determined by each local community. Many students were chosen by their communities for their academic promise and community involvement.

- A civil engineer from Kahnawake spoke with campers and outlined his professional activities with sample drawings and details of his work in the development of a residential sub-division on the reserve.

- Social activities included dinner at the Native Friendship Centre of Montreal, a closing barbecue and an afternoon at Concordia's Native Student Centre.

Information was provided to campers on academic requirements for admission to various engineering programs. Each camper received a certificate of participation and was awarded a miniature test-tube trophy in a closing ceremony.

Results and Future Directions

Participating students were asked to evaluate their camp experience. Without exception, the comments and ratings of all aspects of the camp were positive. Campers comments ranged from very good to excellent in their assessment of the value of their experience.

The Joint Working Group on Native Access to Engineering met several times to discuss the results of the pilot project and to plan for other short-term strategies related to the objective of increasing Aboriginal representation of Aboriginal people in the profession.

- The working group decided to hold the camp again in 1995.

- It also organized a workshop on science and engineering education for educators and guidance counsellors. In February 1995, twelve people representing all levels of education from kindergarten to the post-secondary counsellor levels, participated in a two-day session entitled *Weaving Technology and Tradition*. As a result of this session, four Inuit students registered for the 1995 camp.

- Also as a direct result of this workshop, 32 junior high school students from Kahnawake Survival School visited the Faculty of Engineering and Computer Science in April 1994.

- Based on the success of the camp at Concordia, the Université de Québec à Chicoutimi is running its own engineering camp for francophone Aboriginal students, starting in the summer of 1995.

Overall, the partnership of the Faculty of Engineering and Computer Science of Concordia University and L'Ordre des ingénieurs du Québec is beginning to achieve its shared objectives of attracting more young Aboriginal people to the engineering profession and enhancing the potential for Aboriginal economic development through the expansion of a group of skilled Aboriginal engineers.

Based on the success of the camp at Concordia, the Université de Québec à Chicoutimi is running its own engineering camp for francophone Aboriginal students.

Lakehead University's Native Access Program for Engineering

Until NAPE began, Lakehead University, despite having an Aboriginal student population of about 10 percent, had graduated only two engineers of Aboriginal descent in 20 years.

In 1992, the Faculty of Engineering of Lakehead University, with the assistance of many Native organizations throughout Ontario, launched the Native Access Program for Engineering (NAPE). The objective of the program is to provide access to an engineering education for Aboriginal people who have not had the opportunity to obtain the preparation necessary to qualify.

The Native Access Program for Engineering provides Aboriginal peoples from the Province of Ontario with an academic program of pre-engineering instruction which permits students to make the transition into engineering education. An academic, cultural and social support system (tutors, elders, counsellors) is available throughout the students' entire engineering education.

The program is unique in Ontario and is the second of its kind in Canada. Corporate sponsors have provided the financial support necessary for the operation of the program.

In its first three years of operation, a total of 46 students have been accepted into the program and 28 students are presently registered in NAPE or one of the engineering programs.

Development of the Program

Lakehead University

Lakehead University is located in Thunder Bay, Ontario. The University was granted its charter in 1965.

Lakehead is a university with a dual role. As a university in the north, it is responsible for bringing to Northwestern Ontario an understanding of the basic academic disciplines as well as knowledge of the province, nation and world. As a university for the north, it is responsible for gathering knowledge about the regions for use in social, economic and cultural development.

The University has over 260 faculty members and a student population of 6000. About 10 percent of the total student population is of Aboriginal ancestry. There are 600 students in the Faculty of Engineering.

Until NAPE began, Lakehead University had graduated only two engineers of Aboriginal descent in 20 years. The University, which has an Aboriginal student population of about 10 percent (well above the Ontario average) is committed to helping Aboriginal students participate in post-secondary education. In the spring of 1991, the Faculty of Engineering began investigating both the need for engineers by Aboriginal communities and the potential for establishing an engineering access program for Aboriginal students.

The investigation began with a series of personal visits by the Dean of the Faculty to a number of Aboriginal educational authorities and other Aboriginal organizations in the regions served by Lakehead University. As a

*The further development of
self-government will create a
demand for trained Aboriginal
engineers who understand the
Aboriginal community and its
needs.*

result of the positive and encouraging responses to the idea among Aboriginal communities, a two-day workshop was held in September, 1991 in Thunder Bay.

The major purpose of the workshop was "to determine an impression of the need for engineering education for Ontario First Nations People". Representatives of over two dozen different Aboriginal organizations, community groups, tribal authorities and provincial organizations were invited. Elders from the local community were approached in the traditional manner to gain the benefit of their guiding presence and participation at the workshop.

The first day of the workshop dealt with four related topics: the supply and demand for Aboriginal engineers; why more Aboriginal students do not choose engineering; how the field of engineering can be explained to communities; and potential students. Several themes emerged.

- It was generally agreed that the further development of self-government will create a demand for trained Aboriginal engineers who understand the Aboriginal community and its needs.

- The lack of role models make it difficult to recruit and to explain engineering as a profession. This is especially true among young women.

- There appeared to be a lack of quality secondary education programs in some communities and a lack of awareness on the part of school counsellors of both the need for engineers and the importance of mathematics and sciences to students.

- A series of actions was required to educate communities and students about the role and importance of engineering.

The second day of the program dealt with a broad range of detailed topics. Participants developed a number of specific recommendations concerning elements of the access program itself, including recruitment, selection, orientation, counselling, contact with communities, support systems and academic support.

*The Native Access Program
for Engineering was designed
jointly by representatives of
Aboriginal communities and
by the university's Faculty of
Engineering.*

The overall result of the workshop was a unanimous decision to proceed with development of the program in cooperation with the Aboriginal community. Committees were formed to deal with the tasks of program development, finance, and the recruitment and selection of students. This process ensured that the Native Access Program for Engineering was designed jointly by representatives of Aboriginal communities and by the university's Faculty of Engineering.

The development and ongoing operation of the program has been supported by financial contributions from a number of corporations and foundations. These include Ontario Hydro, Ontario Energy Corporation, Suncor, Petro-Canada, TransCanada Pipelines, Canadian National, SNC/Lavalin, The Harold Crabtree Foundation, RBC Dominion Securities, Scotia McLeod, Bank of Montreal, and the GE Foundation.

The Native Access Program for Engineering

The Faculty of Engineering at Lakehead University offers a combination of Engineering Technology and Engineering Degree programs in Chemical, Civil, Electrical and Mechanical Engineering.

The Native Access Program for Engineering prepares students to enter into the study of engineering at the University.

- The Engineering Technology programs are three-year programs that prepare graduates for employment as engineering technologists or, if qualified, to proceed on to study for engineering degrees. Students are awarded a diploma on completion of the Engineering Technology program.

- The Engineering Degree programs are two-year post-diploma programs that enable graduates to meet professional qualifications and become eligible for registration as Professional Engineers in their province or territory.

The Native Access Program for Engineering prepares students to enter into the study of engineering at the University. NAPE helps students who, because of residence in remote areas or a lack of formal education, would not otherwise have access to an engineering education.

There are two parts to the access program.

- A six-week Orientation Program starts in mid-July. During this period, staff and students have an opportunity to get to know each other. Staff assess student academic capability and, in consultation with the student, plan the student's future academic program. Orientation is designed to help students obtain information and skills that will enhance their success in the Access and diploma programs. The program is informal so that students will feel comfortable and gain confidence in their ability to succeed at the university. Orientation includes introductory courses in mathematics, sciences, communication, calculator/computer skills as well as an orientation course that is designed to make the student feel comfortable at the university and in the city.

- A one-year Academic Program in pre-engineering continues the instruction in the fundamentals of mathematics, chemistry, physics and communications skills that began in the orientation program. The program consists of those courses selected at the end of the orientation program. The students' academic programs are designed to suit their needs. Students who are academically prepared may be permitted to register for selected engineering technology diploma courses. Students normally complete NAPE courses within one year.

NAPE staff consists of a coordinator who is directly responsible to the Dean of the Faculty of Engineering, a program assistant, two instructors and a counsellor. The present coordinator is a Civil Engineer, with a demonstrated interest in NAPE and ties to various Aboriginal communities. Instructors serve as teachers, tutors, academic counsellors, and on occasion act as personal counsellors. All staff are dedicated full-time to the program, with no external pressures to do research.

Student Recruitment and Selection

The program is designed to meet the needs of the mature student.

In order to be considered for selection to NAPE, applicants must be residents of Ontario and of Aboriginal ancestry. The program is designed to meet the needs of the mature student, i.e., someone who has been out of school for several years but who has work and life experiences. However, students under the age of 21 who meet the admission requirements of engineering may be accepted into the program.

The program is promoted to potential students through career fairs, conferences, advertising in local media, visits to community colleges and Aboriginal communities throughout Ontario. NAPE staff members have worked closely with educational authorities who have students in the program, to further build a positive image. As a result, educational authorities have been encouraging students who are strong in maths and science to consider the NAPE program. The majority of students who are accepted into the program come from communities where NAPE staff have had an opportunity to visit.

The interviewing committee consists of representatives from Aboriginal organizations, the university, NAPE and the engineering profession.

The selection process is designed to choose students who would have a reasonable chance for success with the available program supports. The process consists of an initial screening to remove applicants who are clearly not yet prepared, followed by interviews by two teams for the remainder of the applicants. The interviewing committee consists of representatives from Aboriginal organizations, the university, NAPE and the engineering profession. The interviewing committee makes its recommendations according to an assessment of need and motivation. The final selection decision rests with the NAPE staff.

Program Supports

The program provides academic, cultural and social support.

The program provides academic, cultural and social support.

- Academic support is provided by program instructors and staff who assist students to adjust to and become successful in their program of study. This involves academic program planning, course selection, registration, tutorial and remedial supports, study skills and an on-going evaluation of the student's progress. NAPE students can receive additional tutoring through the University's Learning Assistance Centre.

- To help meet the personal needs of the students, the program has on staff a full-time counsellor whose responsibility is to assist students and their families with the personal and social adjustments of studying at the university and living in the city. The program counsellor maintains communication with the student's educational counsellor from their community to provide an integrated counselling network.

- The program provides for many special events throughout the year that involve the student and family. Some of these events are a family barbecue, potluck, bowling, baseball, and floor hockey.

In addition, in 1993, NAPE established a chapter at Lakehead University in the American Indian Science and Engineering Society (AISES). AISES is a non-profit, professional and educational organization founded in 1977 whose principal mission is to improve Indian education and to increase the number of American Indian scientists and engineers. Lakehead's chapter is one of four in Canada. There are over 100 chapters in the United States.

Results to Date

Since the program began in 1992, 46 students have been accepted into it.

- In 1992, the first year of operation, 16 students applied for the program, of whom 11 were accepted. Two students withdrew during orientation and one went directly into the first year of engineering. One student was asked to leave after the first year. Six returned the following year and entered first year engineering. Of these, two proceeded to the second year and one plans to repeat the first year.

- In 1993, 51 students applied and 19 were accepted into the program. One student was exempt from NAPE and proceeded directly into the first year. Of the remainder, fourteen did extremely well and subsequently entered the first year of engineering.

• In 1994, 45 students applied, of whom 16 were accepted. In January 1995, 11 of these students remained in the program.

The program has had some success in attracting Aboriginal women to engineering.The number of women who applied and were accepted into the program increased from three in 1993 to four in 1994.

The experience of the past three years has revealed a number of issues that need to be addressed.

The program has had some success in attracting Aboriginal women to engineering.

• There have been limited opportunities for relevant summer employment. It was intended that NAPE students would work in engineering-related jobs during the summer months. Summer work experience adds relevance to the student's academic work and eventually produces graduates with practical engineering experience. The program established files on engineering companies with an interest in the students, but in 1994, only eight out of 19 students acquired engineering related positions. Another eight accepted non-engineering positions.

• Financial assistance has been a barrier for some students. To date, all of the students that have entered the program have been Status Indians, who are eligible for support from the Department of Indian Affairs for their post-secondary education. However, many Aboriginal people in Ontario are not Status Indians, and as a result, the program is missing out on potentially excellent students. Financial support for other Aboriginal students would make the program more accessible to all Aboriginal people in Ontario.

The Native Access Program for Engineering has already had success in enabling about two and half dozen Aboriginal students to work towards an engineering degree.

The Faculty of Engineering points to the success that the Native Access Program for Engineering has already had in enabling about two and half dozen Aboriginal students to work towards an engineering degree. Without NAPE, they would not be doing this in the Province of Ontario. The program is preparing an increasing number of Aboriginal people with the qualifications needed for education in engineering. NAPE attributes this success to pedagogical flexibility, informality and trust between students and staff.

The RCMP's Aboriginal Cadet Development Program

The Aboriginal Cadet Development Program is a key component in the RCMP's efforts to provide effective and responsive service for Aboriginal peoples.

The Royal Canadian Mounted Police introduced its Aboriginal Cadet Development Program in 1994. The program is a study and work-based training program designed to enable Aboriginal applicants meet the entrance requirements of the Cadet Training Program. This Aboriginal Cadet Development program is a revised version of the successful Aboriginal Constable Development Program which was first introduced in 1990 and had resulted in the hiring of 108 Aboriginal people during the three years that it was in place. The new program is expected to enrol between 60 and 80 candidates in its first two years.

The Aboriginal Cadet Development Program is a key component in the RCMP's efforts to provide effective and responsive service for Aboriginal peoples through the increased employment of Aboriginal people in the policing role and to develop a police force that is increasingly representative of the communities it serves. The new First Nations Policing Policy has as one of its cornerstones, the principle of Aboriginal people providing policing services to Aboriginal communities.

The Aboriginal Cadet Development Program is one of a number of initiatives by the RCMP to increase Aboriginal employment in the Force. Other initiatives include divisional (i.e. provincial and territorial) summer student programs, where Aboriginal people are a preferred recruitment group and the RCMP Aboriginal Youth Training Program. The Aboriginal Youth Training Program, which was active in 1993 and 1994, has been deferred until the summer of 1996.

The Aboriginal Constable Development Program

Between 1973 and 1989 the focus of Aboriginal recruitment into the RCMP was through the special constable initiative. However, Special Constables were not required to meet all of the standards for a regular member and when the initiative was terminated in 1989, the

Royal Canadian Mounted Police

The Royal Canadian Mounted Police has a mandate to enforce Canadian laws, prevent crime and maintain peace, order and security.

The RCMP is organized geographically into 13 operational divisions, further divided into 52 sub-divisions and 723 detachments. In addition there is an RCMP training academy in Regina. Corporate support is provided by Headquarters in Ottawa.

The RCMP has approximately 20,000 employees located across the country. The employees fall into different categories (ie regular members, civilian members and public service employees) and operate under distinctly different legislative authorities and established procedures. By the end of 1994, approximately 3.8 percent of regular members had identified themselves as being of Aboriginal ancestry.

Like the Aboriginal Constable Development Program it replaced, the Aboriginal Cadet Program assists Aboriginal candidates to upgrade their qualifications so that they can enter the Training Academy on an equal basis with others.

Although the candidates had the opportunity to remain on the program for two years, many required only a short term before were ready to enter the Cadet Training Program at the Academy.

RCMP realized that many Aboriginal people who sought a career in the Force did not meet the minimum standards.

The Aboriginal Constable Development Program was introduced in 1990 as an initiative to increase the number of Aboriginal individuals joining the RCMP. It focused on assisting Aboriginal candidates who wanted to join the RCMP, but did not meet all the entrance requirements, to upgrade deficient areas prior to joining the Cadet Training Program at the RCMP Training Academy. Every new applicant to the RCMP must complete the Cadet Training Program.

The program was designed to ensure that the Aboriginal participants could begin the Cadet Training Program on an equal basis with other participants. Once accepted into the Cadet Training Program, they were expected to meet all benchmarks established by the Academy for successful completion.

The Aboriginal Constable Development Program was developed as a two year study/work program. It was designed to be flexible, taking into account the rate of individual progress would vary, depending on entry level and abilities. Candidates were appointed as Peace Officers for the duration of the program and received a salary from the RCMP equivalent to a newly engaged constable. The program was fully funded through the RCMP's operating budget.

The RCMP was responsible for the design, implementation and supervision of the work-related aspects of the program. Candidates received on-the-job training with the aim of familiarization with, rather than mastery of, police duties. Each candidate was therefore supervised and monitored at all times by a selected, experienced "trainer" within the detachment, and assisted this officer with his or her activities.

The candidates were upgraded to grade 12 equivalency through existing provincial departments of education or through a personalized program delivered by professional educators. This included initial skills assessments, academic upgrading, life skills training, and counselling services if required.

Candidates progressed at their own rates within the two-year time frame, and attended the RCMP Training Academy in Regina once they were deemed academically and physically ready by their RCMP supervisors and the educators involved. Although the candidates had the opportunity to remain on the program for two years, many of them required only a short term before they were assessed and deemed ready to enter the Cadet Training Program at the Academy. If the goals of the program were not met within the two year period, an application could be made to the Director of Training of the RCMP to request an extension. However, if the candidate was not expected to obtain the basic requirements within the period, he or she could be discharged as unsuitable.

The RCMP was forced to cancel the Aboriginal Constable Development program in 1993 because of budget cutbacks. However, strong efforts were made to resurrect the program and alternate funding sources were explored. The Commissioner's National Aboriginal Advisory Committee played an active role in examining alternative ways of re-establishing the program, particularly from a funding perspective. In December 1994, Human Resources Development Canada agreed to provide funding for a new program (the Aboriginal Cadet Development Program) through its Youth Internship Program.

The Aboriginal Cadet Development Program

The Aboriginal Cadet Development Program was introduced in early 1995. Candidates for the Aboriginal Cadet Development Program are recruited through the staffing and personnel offices in each division. The RCMP attempts to recruit Aboriginal people in accordance with their representation in the overall population, to meet the needs of the communities served by the RCMP and to meet the requirements of government legislation, namely the First Nations Policing Policy.

Although the Aboriginal Cadet Development Program shares the same basic goal as the Aboriginal Constable program and the focus remains the same, there have been significant changes in the way the program is funded and delivered.

The Aboriginal Cadet Development Program shares the same basic goal as the Aboriginal Constable program.

The RCMP no longer has an employer/employee relationship with new recruits until they have successfully completed the Cadet Training Program and been engaged as a regular member of the Force.

- Aboriginal recruits are no longer paid as Peace Officers while they go through the work-based training and study components to qualify for admittance to the Training Academy. Instead they are classified as interns (and paid through funding from HRD Canada's Youth Internship Program). This change reflects the new relationship that the RCMP has instituted between itself and all new recruits. The RCMP no longer has an employer/employee relationship with new recruits until they have successfully completed the Cadet Training Program and been engaged as a regular member of the Force. The changed relationship between trainees and the force applies to all new cadets. The underlying philosophy is that cadets are not members of the RCMP until they have successfully completed the Cadet Training Program.

- All candidates now attend the Training Academy for a three-week assessment in which they are tested for academic, physical, driving, life skill, and other related abilities. At the conclusion of the three weeks, they then return to their province of origin with a training plan and it is then be up to the RCMP in that province to develop a training program designed specifically to meet their needs.

- In addition to the study and work-based training activities, candidates participate in a Ride Along program with the local detachment. Candidates are utilized at the Detachment level in community policing activities.

- Regular assessments of progress are conducted and once the candidate meets all basic entrance requirements, he or she will be scheduled to attend the Academy for cadet training at the first available troop.

Results

The RCMP's experience in hiring Aboriginal People over the past ten years is summarized in the following table:

The Aboriginal Cadet Development Program is expected to enrol between 60 and 80 candidates in its first two years.

RCMP's Hiring of Aboriginal People			
	Special Constable Program	Regular Recruitment	Aboriginal Constable Program
1984-85	37	5	n/a
1985-86	35	22	n/a
1986-87	32	22	n/a
1987-88	38	17	n/a
1988-89	34	5	n/a
1989-90	43	14	n/a
1990-91	11	14	18
1991-92	n/a	21	35
1992-93	n/a	22	44
1993-94	n/a	35	11
Total	231	177	108

Source: RCMP 1995

The effectiveness of the Aboriginal Constable program is demonstrated by the fact that it lead to the hiring of 108 Aboriginal people in the short time that it was in place. The new Aboriginal Cadet Development Program is expected to enrol between 60 and 80 candidates in its first two years.

A distinctive feature of the program is that it not only provides for upgrading but also virtually guarantees employment upon successful completion of the program.

A secondary benefit of the program is that even if candidates do not pursue a career in the RCMP, they will have been exposed to the skills and knowledge that will enhance their opportunities in other areas.

Petro-Canada's Education Awards Program for Native Students

Encouraging training and educational opportunities is one of the key elements in Petro-Canada's policy commitment to Canada's Aboriginal peoples.

Petro-Canada's Education Awards Program for Native Students was set up in 1985 to encourage and help Aboriginal men and women complete advanced studies applicable to the oil and gas industry. The program is aimed at improving the participation of Aboriginal people in the company and the industry generally. Encouraging training and educational opportunities is one of the key elements in Petro-Canada's policy commitment to Canada's Aboriginal peoples.

Petro-Canada's Policy Commitment to Canada's Aboriginal Peoples

Petro-Canada has had a commitment to promote employment of Aboriginal Canadians, both directly and indirectly, since its inception as a corporation in 1976.

In 1980, Petro-Canada adopted a Native Employment Policy which specifically addressed the importance of actively recruiting and advancing Aboriginal people. Petro-Canada's Social and Economic Development Policy, implemented in 1983, defined the company's position on maximizing local social and economic development in its areas of operation. The Native Affairs Policy, which was also implemented in 1983, addressed creating business opportunities for all Aboriginal people through procurement contracts and management and technical assistance.

In 1992, Petro-Canada's Leadership Team re-affirmed the company's commitment to Canada's Aboriginal people by approving the following comprehensive policy:

> "Petro-Canada recognizes the special status of Aboriginal peoples within the Canadian Constitution and will encourage a supportive, open relationship based on mutual trust and respect. The Corporation will strive to: work with Aboriginal people in pursuit of mutual interests; provide business development opportunities; encourage job skills training and education; and ensure equal access to employment within the company."

Petro-Canada

Petro-Canada is the largest Canadian-owned oil and gas company. It was established as a Crown Corporation in 1975. Since 1991, Petro-Canada has been a private sector company with shares traded on every Canadian stock exchange. It is organized into two operating divisions with a corporate support group. The Resources division explores for and produces crude oil and natural gas in Western Canada, off the East Coast and in a few countries internationally. The Products division refines and markets a full range of petroleum products across Canada.

Petro-Canada has about 4800 employees. Aboriginal employees account for 0.7 percent its workforce.

Petro-Canada began its Native Education Awards Program in 1985 to encourage and assist Aboriginal individuals to complete advanced education studies applicable to the oil and gas sector.

Awards of up to $5000 are provided to eligible Aboriginal students.

Students who are accepted for an Award are considered for summer employment at Petro-Canada.

Education Awards for Native Students

Petro-Canada offers a number of education awards each year to post-secondary students of Canadian Indian or Inuit ancestry.

Petro-Canada began its Native Education Awards Program in 1985. The objectives of the award were established by Petro-Canada's Human Resources educational committee. The program was introduced to encourage and assist Aboriginal individuals to complete advanced education studies which could be applied in an industrial setting.

The company initially offered 5 awards each year and made them available through a few colleges, technical institutes and universities across Canada which already had proven records in attracting, providing support services for, and graduating Aboriginal students. These included McGill University, Ryerson College, York University and the University of British Columbia.

Today, Aboriginal recipients of the education awards are free to study at any university or college in Canada as long as it is for a first degree.

Scope of the Awards

Awards of up to $5000 are provided to eligible Aboriginal students. The amount of the award varies in response to other funding sources available to the student. The awards are designed to cover part of tuition, textbooks and the student's living expenses during the course of the academic year at a college, technical school or university recognized for the awards program.

The award is for a maximum of four years or until the student attains a first degree. Students must be enroled on a full-time basis. Students wishing to switch from one educational program to another may continue to be eligible for the award provided they advise the company of their intentions.

The award does not automatically continue for the four academic years. The student must reapply each academic year. If the student fails to maintain passing marks or takes an extended break from studies, the award will be discontinued.

Students who are accepted for an Award are considered for summer employment at Petro-Canada.

Administration and Selection

When the Awards program started, a selection committee at each eligible educational institution evaluated applications for the award at that institution. Each application was considered using standard criteria. Recommendations from each selection committee were forwarded to Petro-Canada for final review and approval.

Today, the program is administered by a Native Employment Specialist contracted by the company. Petro-Canada feels that in order to obtain the best candidates for the program, the Administrator of the program should be Aboriginal and well-connected to Aboriginal communities. This facilitates effective communication with and assessment of candidates and ensures that they receive appropriate counselling on their career choices.

The same Native Employment Specialist has been involved in the program since its beginning. The individual is responsible for promoting the program, fielding all enquiries from applicants, screening applicants for the selection committee, and informing all applicants about the status of their request.

The Native Employment Specialist targets schools with support for Aboriginal students to ensure a higher success rate. Brochures describing the program are sent annually to those educational institutions with support systems for Aboriginal students.

A Petro-Canada selection committee composed of human resources professionals meets each July to evaluate all applications recommended by the Native Employment Specialist. Selection is made using criteria that include financial need, academic performance and potential, the applicability of the course of studies to the oil industry and future aspirations. Applicants are informed of the selection committees decision in August. The committee tries to ensure that recipients represent all regions of Canada.

Results

Petro-Canada's Native Education Awards Program has been well received in the Aboriginal communities. With government funding for Aboriginal education being cut and the number of Aboriginal students going on to post-secondary studies (including many more to industry-related disciplines such as engineering, business and environmental science) increasing, there is a great need for business to become more involved in education.

Since the inception of the program, Petro-Canada has supported 138 students. The number of applicants has increased steadily over the years. When the program started in 1985, there were five awards given. Today the company receives applications from more than 75 students and has given out an average of twelve awards annually. This number fluctuates depending on the size of the budget for the awards.

Petro-Canada feels that the Administrator of the program should be Aboriginal and well-connected to Aboriginal communities in order to obtain the best candidates for the program.

With government funding being cut and the number of Aboriginal students going on to post-secondary studies increasing, there is a great need for business to become more involved in education.

Since the inception of the program, Petro-Canada has supported 138 students.

The importance of the awards program to its recipients can be illustrated by some of the letters of appreciation that Petro-Canada has received from awards holders.

- One recipient wrote: "Thank you for selecting me to receive a Petro-Canada Education award. Your decision will aid me in the continuation of my university studies and lessen the burden of the financial costs of the post-secondary education."

- Another wrote: "Being fully occupied in improving oneself through Lakehead University's engineering curriculum, I find myself with little or no time to seek any part-time source of income. Therefore by being selected as one of the recipients of the Petro-Canada Awards for Native Students, I thought of this as a blessing. It will certainly help me achieve my goal of obtaining a Mechanical Engineering degree a lot easier."

Dalhousie Law School's Programme for Indigenous Blacks and Mi'kmaqs

Prior to the implementation of the program there were no Mi'kmaq lawyers in the province of Nova Scotia.

In 1989, after wide consultation with the communities, Dalhousie Law School established the Law Programme for Indigenous Blacks and Mi'kmaqs (I.B.M. Programme). The goal of the program is to increase the representation of Indigenous Nova Scotian Blacks and Mi'kmaqs in the legal professions by making Dalhousie Law School more accessible to applicants from these two communities. Prior to the implementation of the program there were no Mi'kmaq lawyers in the province of Nova Scotia and less than a dozen practising Black lawyers.

An important component of this initiative is the community Advisory Council, which includes members from the Black and Mi'kmaq communities. The Council was created to ensure that the programs meet the needs of the students in the program as well as the needs of the larger Indigenous Black and Aboriginal communities. The Council has placed its emphasis in recent years on encouraging minority perspectives on the legal system and increasing recruitment of law teachers from the Black and Mi'kmaq communities.

The program has been effective in recruiting more students from the Black and Mi'kmaq communities and providing them with academic and financial support during law school. By 1994, a total of 25 Mi'kmaq students had enroled in the program and 10 had graduated from Dalhousie Law School.

Dalhousie Law School

Dalhousie Law School has been in continuous operation since 1883 and is the oldest Canadian common law school. Dalhousie Law School awards the LL.B., LL.M., and J.S.D. degrees. There are between 35 and 40 full-time faculty and 40-50 part-time faculty.

Each year, 156 first year students are admitted. There are approximately 450 students in the total undergraduate student body. Diversity of background is encouraged in students. Students are admitted with science, engineering, arts and other undergraduate degrees and come from a variety of positions, including industrial or technical jobs, teaching and social work.

The Indigenous Black and Mi'kmaq Programme began in 1989. Between 1989 and 1994, 58 students were enroled in the program, of whom 25 were Mi'kmaq students.

Program Objectives

After wide consultation with the public, the law school recognized the problem of under-representation of indigenous people in the legal profession in the Province of Nova Scotia and decided to take steps to overcome this situation of historical inequality.

The program was developed to "produce more legally trained people drawn from minority communities in Nova Scotia, and to open up legal education at Dalhousie to the input of minority perspectives on the Canadian legal system". The program has five elements:

The program was developed to "produce more legally trained people drawn from minority communities in Nova Scotia, and to open up legal education at Dalhousie to the input of minority perspectives on the Canadian legal system".

A community Advisory Council was created to ensure that the program meets the needs of the students in the program as well as the needs of the larger Indigenous Black and Aboriginal communities.

- recruitment and promotion of legal education in the targeted communities;

- a program of pre-law training for applicants;

- institutional support for participants while attending law school;

- a modification of the present legal education system; and

- recruitment of law teachers from the Black and Mi'kmaq communities.

Community Advisory Council

In the fall of 1989, a community Advisory Council was created to assist the Director, the Dean and Faculty Council of the Law School in operating the program. The Council is composed of members from the Black and Mi'kmaq communities, with representation from the University, the Law School, the Bench and Bar. The Council now has 14 members, three of whom are representatives of Mi'kmaq communities. The Native Council of Nova Scotia, The Confederacy of Mainland Micmacs and The Union of Nova Scotia Indians each appoint one of these representatives. The Council meets quarterly.

The major role of the Council is to ensure that the program meets the needs of the students in the program as well as the needs of the larger Indigenous Black and Aboriginal communities. The Council has a Constitution, which was ratified in January 1994. The mandate and purpose of the Council are to:

- ensure that the needs of the Black and Mi'kmaq communities in the delivery and operation of the program are met;

- advise the Director, the Dean, Faculty Council and other relevant policy makers on matters of policy concerning the program;

- provide a mechanism for communication between the Black and Mi'kmaq communities and the University and Legal Communities;

- support the educational experiences of the students in the program;

- support and enhance the career development of students in the program;

- assist and foster the full participation of Indigenous Blacks and Mi'kmaqs in the Nova Scotia legal profession; and

- preserve and promote cross-cultural understanding between Blacks, Mi'kmaqs and all levels of the legal profession.

The Council has five committees. These are the Constitution Committee, Community Liaison Committee, Curriculum Committee, Fund-Raising Committee and Student Services and Recruitment Committee.

Key Features of the Program

The program has three main components: outreach and recruitment; a pre-law program; and institutional support for students.

The Law Programme for Indigenous Blacks and Mi'kmaqs currently consists of three main components: outreach and recruitment initiatives; a pre-law program which is used as part of the admissions evaluations process; and institutional support for students in the program, in the form of academic enhancement, tutoring and counselling services as well as financial assistance for eligible students. The degree requirements for program participants are no different than for any other students. All participants must complete the same examinations, papers and courses.

The degree requirements for program participants are no different than for any other students.

An active outreach and recruitment program takes place each year. The Director of the program, along with a representative from the Public Legal Education Society of Nova Scotia (and when possible a student from the I.B.M. Programme) travels to Black and Mi'kmaq communities, as well as universities throughout the province to promote both the program and legal education in general. Many of the communities are in rural areas. Urban students are reached through university information sessions that are held province-wide. Members of the Advisory Council's Recruitment Committee make information available within their communities. The outreach sessions, which have been supported in part by the Race Relations Committee of the Nova Scotia Barristers Society, are viewed as crucial to the promotion of the program and to the recruitment of qualified applicants.

The outreach sessions are viewed as crucial to the promotion of the program and to the recruitment of qualified applicants.

An information and recruitment video is being produced to support this facet of the program. The video consists of interviews with students currently in the program, graduates of the program, administrators, University representatives and Community support persons. The video is intended to depict all aspects of the I.B.M. Programme specifically and Law School life generally as well as to answer questions of potential applicants.

Admission to the program is based on a number of criteria.

- Applicants to the Law Programme for Indigenous Blacks and Mi'kmaqs are required to write the Law School Admissions Test, to have an interview with the admissions committee and to submit to the Committee a detailed resume of his/her academic and non-academic experience, along with contributions and achievements.

The Pre-Law Programme is part of the evaluation for admission.

Bursaries are available for students who have financial need. Recent practice has been to fund students who are not otherwise eligible for educational funds.

- Most applicants have completed a degree or two full years of study leading to a recognized degree. However, applicants who demonstrate non-academic experience equivalent to the required formal education, can be considered for admission as mature students.

The Pre-Law Programme is part of the evaluation for admission purposes. The Pre-Law Programme is a four-week mandatory program for incoming first year I.B.M. students. It is usually offered during May each year, The course is an intensive introduction to the Law School curriculum and academic skills emphasized in legal education. Attendance is mandatory as are examinations, papers and oral advocacy exercises. Mi'kmaq applicants to the program can substitute the preparatory course for Aboriginal students offered by the Native Law Centre at the University of Saskatchewan.

The program has a number of features that are designed to provide special academic support to participating students.

- Students have access to Academic Enhancement Sessions which are designed to fill a void in the curriculum at Dalhousie Law School by helping students with the skills that are necessary to learn law and the skills that are necessary to cope with and perform well on law exams. The focus of the sessions is on skill development, utilizing a lesson plan (step-by-step) approach.

- A student tutor is made available upon request to each student in the program. Participants work closely with their individual tutors who assist them with substantive areas of law, course materials and specific assignments.

- The university has a Mi'kmaq Student Advisor who is housed in Henson College and a Black Student Advisor on campus who are available to assist students.

- The University's counselling and psychological services has a counsellor who works with students in the areas of time management skills, study skills and cognitive learning.

Bursaries are available for students in the program who have financial need. Recent practice has been to fund students who are not otherwise eligible for educational funds (i.e. Indian education money through Band Councils or the federal departments of Indian Affairs or Justice). Bursaries may cover most basic educational and living expenses: tuition, books and a modest living allowance.

Administration and Funding

The Director of the Programme is a full-time member of the Law Faculty hired on a permanent basis. The Director is in charge of all aspects of the program, including tutorials, the Pre-Law Programme, student services, budget, fund-raising, recruitment and public relations. The Director is also a professor in the regular Law School curriculum.

The annual cost of the program is about $300,000. The major expenditures are related to administration costs, course development, tuition costs for students, and living allowances for students. The program has been funded by contributions from the Law Society of Nova Scotia, the federal departments of Canadian Heritage and Justice Canada, the provincial Attorney General's department, Dalhousie University, the Walter and Duncan Gordon Foundation, Blake, Cassels & Graydon, John Labatt Ltd., CIBC, Imasco Ltd., Torstar Corp., and various donations from corporations, charitable foundations and private donors.

The program has been funded by contributions from private and public sector donors.

Results

The I.B.M. Programme has been very successful in increasing the number of Mi'kmaq people pursuing education and careers in law.

The I.B.M. Programme has been very successful in increasing the number of Mi'kmaq people pursuing education and careers in law. Ten Mi'kmaq students have already graduated.

- Prior to the implementation of the program there were no Mi'kmaq lawyers in the province of Nova Scotia.

- A total of 25 Mi'kmaq students enroled in Dalhousie Law School between 1989 and 1994. (A total of 58 students were enroled in the I.B.M. Programme during this period.) Seventeen of the Mi'kmaq students were female and 8 were male.

- Of the 25 Mi'kmaq students, 17 have come from reserve communities in Nova Scotia, while 8 have come from off-reserve communities.

- In 1994/95 alone, 13 Mi'kmaq students were enroled in the program.

- Ten Mi'kmaq students have already graduated from the program. Eight of these students secured articling positions.

The Law School is also taking steps to achieving the other program objectives. The Programme for Indigenous Blacks and Mi'kmaqs has undertaken a review of all law school curriculum to develop and adapt course materials to reflect the voices, experiences and perspectives of the Black and Mi'kmaq communities. Research has been completed in all first year courses and it is planned to continue researching and preparing materials in the second and third year curriculum.

Canadian Bankers Association's Pre-Employment Aboriginal Training Partnerships

Pre-employment partnerships are one response by the banking sector to the challenge of finding Aboriginal applicants with the specific skills and qualifications for the positions available.

The Canadian Bankers Association has been involved in a number of pre-employment programs for Aboriginal people, all of them in Western Canada. The programs are partnerships between the CBA, Aboriginal service agencies and government departments.

Pre-employment partnerships are one response by the banking sector to the challenge of finding Aboriginal applicants with the specific skills and qualifications for the positions available. The banks have found that pre-employment initiatives provide a cost-effective solution to providing disadvantaged job seekers with the skills required for entry-level jobs in the banks. The industry has similar partnerships in place for other employment equity designated groups.

The pre-employment partnerships are based on the model established by the banking component of the Winnipeg Core Area Initiative, which the banking industry joined in 1986. Subsequently, drawing on the Winnipeg experience, the CBA has entered into similar partnerships in Edmonton, Regina and Vancouver. The focus on Western Canada reflects the fact that there continued to be entry-level hiring opportunities in the western provinces during the recession. As a result, the pre-employment programs could translate into tangible job opportunities for successful participants. Almost 200 Aboriginal people have received training and over 85 percent of graduates have received jobs. While these are very positive results, retention and advancement of Aboriginal people hired through the programs have proven to be a challenge.

The Canadian banking industry is taking other steps to jointly foster opportunities for Aboriginal people. In 1995, a committee composed of the Manitoba branch of the Canadian Bankers Association and the Assembly of Manitoba Chiefs released a report on *Rebuilding the Manitoba First Nations Economy* that addressed ways to improving financing for small business and other economic activity in the province's 61 First Nations.

Canadian Bankers Association

The Canadian Bankers Association (CBA) is an industry association which provides information, research, advocacy, education and operational support to its members, the chartered banks of Canada. The CBA operates through a committee structure so that member banks can participate in all activities and decisions.

The CBA's Employment Equity Standing Committee addresses the needs and concerns of the banking industry with respect to federal employment equity legislation and related issues. The CBA has a provincial committee in each province. Most of the provincial committees have employment equity subcommittees. The CBA's involvement in pre-employment training partnerships has been primarily through these employment equity subcommittees.

The Partnership Model

The pre-employment partnerships are based on the model established by the success of the banking component of the Winnipeg Core Area Initiative. The Core Area Initiative was launched in the early 1980s. One of its components was a Customer Service/Bank Teller Training Program which was undertaken in 1986 with the participation of five banks - Royal Bank, Toronto-Dominion Bank, Bank of Montreal, Scotiabank and the CIBC. The banking program provided skill training and pre-employment experience resulting in the placement of 25 core area residents in entry level teller or customer service positions with the five banks in the Winnipeg region.

Each partnership is structured with three partners: the banks, Aboriginal service agencies and government.

Each partnership is structured with three partners: the banks, Aboriginal service agencies and government.

- The banks bring potential jobs, knowledge and guidance about the type of skills and qualifications required and provide the on-the-job training component.

- Service agencies and/or educational institutions provide a source of candidates, provide support services to student trainees, the training infrastructure and curriculum design.

- Government is the third partner and has provided the necessary funding, usually through the Canadian Jobs Strategy program in Employment and Immigration Canada (now called Human Resources Development Canada).

Typically, a program is developed by an advisory committee composed of representatives of the three partners. The banks are represented by the local CBA employment equity committee. This advisory committee provides overall management of the project, contributes to the design of the program, makes decisions on the selection process, assures the appropriate content and balance in the curriculum and plans the graduation ceremony. In some programs, committee members also act as instructors and teach the classes on banking subjects.

The participating service agency or educational institution does the initial recruitment for the program. Because the programs have usually been funded by governments, the potential candidates have had to meet the eligibility criteria established by the funding program, such as the Canadian Jobs Strategy or Pathways (the Aboriginal Employment and Training Strategy). Generally, candidates must have passed Grade 10 and, on the basis of their qualifications, show the motivation and potential for handling the program and for, ultimately, working with customers in a branch setting. The banks screen the candidates, through an application and interviewing process.

The purpose of the training programs is to upgrade the students to the point where they can handle requirements of an entry-level position as a bank teller or a customer service representative.

Four pre-employment partnerships have been established in Edmonton, Regina, Vancouver and Winnipeg.

The purpose of the training programs is to upgrade the students to the point where they can handle requirements of an entry-level position as a bank teller or a customer service representative. Usually a Grade 12 diploma is the academic requirement for these positions. The training programs all incorporate the following elements: classroom training, work experience and a graduation ceremony.

- Classroom training develops the trainees' basic business knowledge and business skills and enhances their communications, interpersonal and problem-solving skills. Banking courses are included in the classroom component. Participating bankers contribute to and may also teach elements such as banking equipment and keyboarding, terminology, functions and procedures, roles of banks, roles of bank staff, customer relations, bank accounts and bank security.

- On-the-job, in-branch work experience is provided by the individual participating banks. There are usually three or four practicums in a four month program. The first may consist entirely of job shadowing, while the remaining ones may have the trainee performing steadily increasing responsibilities, so that by the last practicum the trainee should be handling tasks at the level of a Grade 12 recruit to the job.

- A graduation ceremony takes place at the end of the program. It is attended by relatives, community leaders and bank representatives. Graduation ceremonies allow wide recognition for the successful students. Frequently the ceremony will be reported in the local media, which is encouraging for the students and provides the banks with an opportunity to gain recognition for their employment equity commitments.

The program length is about 4 months although it can vary, depending on the skills and training needs of the trainees.

The Partnership Experience

Four pre-employment partnerships have been established in Edmonton, Regina, Vancouver and Winnipeg. All of these are based on the basic partnership model. However, each one has been initiated and has evolved in different ways.

The Financial Institutions Skills Training Program in Edmonton was first offered in 1990. This program is the result of a partnership between the CBA, Goodwill Rehabilitation Services and the Canadian Jobs Strategy.

The idea for the initiative came from Goodwill Rehabilitation Services. This four-month program was designed to provide Aboriginal students with entry-level skills and knowledge for teller or customer service representatives jobs in banks. Between August 1990 and November 1993, 9 sessions of the program were offered, with a total enrolment of 123 participants, of whom 94 graduated and 85 were hired by the participating banks.

The Regina Aboriginal Training Program was first offered in 1990-91. The idea for the program came as a result of a brainstorming session of the local employment equity practitioners association. The program was developed as a partnership between the CBA, Saskatchewan Indian and Metis Affairs Secretariat, the Canadian Jobs Strategy and Reliance College of Business. Subsequently Gronnerud & Associates became the provider of classroom instruction. The banks shared the cost of developing the program and, in the first few years of operation, contributed funds towards the actual delivery. Candidates were selected from referrals received from outside agencies, schools and the Canada Employment Centre.

The Regina Aboriginal Training Program was offered three times, with about 15 students graduating each time.

The program was offered three times, with about 15 students graduating each time. However, retention of Aboriginal employees hired through the programs has become an issue for the participating banks. One of the factors causing Aboriginal staff to leave the banks is the lack of role models in more senior positions. The CBA is now pursuing an joint educational program, called "First Nations Banking Program", with the Saskatchewan Indian Federated College at the University of Regina. The objective of this program is to target the growing number of Aboriginal university graduates for entry level management positions, thereby providing role models for other Aboriginal employees and students. To address the retention issue, a mentoring component between students and bankers will be built into the program. Full details of the program are under development.

The Aboriginal Financial Institutions Skills Training Program in Vancouver added a cross-cultural workshop for all partners and participants, which was found to be effective.

The Aboriginal Financial Institutions Skills Training Program in Vancouver was first offered in 1991-92. The program was provided through the Native Education Centre of Vancouver with funding from the Canadian Jobs Strategy. This program added a cross-cultural workshop for all partners and participants and an on-the-job training component, which was found to be effective. The student selection process, which was initially done on a first-come, first-served basis, was modified after the inaugural year to include pre-screening of candidates. In addition, the banks modified their communications and training rating systems to respond to trainee concerns that there was not enough direction and feedback in the on-the-job training component.

Three sessions of this program were offered between 1991 and 1994. A total of 47 people graduated from the Vancouver program. Forty-four of the graduates were hired by the participating banks. The CBA is currently reviewing this initiative due to poor retention.

A Customer Service/Bank Teller Program in Winnipeg provided part-time (guaranteed 20 hours per week) employment opportunities for graduates.

A Customer Service/Bank Teller Program was run in Winnipeg in 1994. The program was sponsored by Native Employment Services of Winnipeg Inc. (now called Aboriginal Training and Employment Services of Manitoba Inc.) in partnership with the Canadian Bankers Association. Funding was provided by the Canadian Jobs Strategy. The objectives of the program were to:

- provide part-time (guaranteed 20 hours per week) employment opportunities for graduates of the program. This employment commitment not only guaranteed jobs for successful participants but, as part-time bank employees, the trainees would become eligible for company benefits and could apply for more hours;

- deliver training that will provide the participants with job-specific skills to secure employment and opportunity for advancement in the banking field; and

- prepare participants academically and socially in a manner that enhances employment opportunities and the ability to maintain employment.

Thirteen of the fifteen participants successfully completed the program and were hired by the five participating banks.

Results

Since 1990, almost 200 Aboriginal people have graduated from CBA partnership programs. Well over 85 percent of all graduates were hired by participating banks.

Each program is formally evaluated to determine its effectiveness and to identify any particular areas which need to be addressed. Evaluations are generally done by the program coordinator. The evaluations have established that the programs have worked well and yielded positive results. The completion rate among students has been good, as has been the hiring rate of successful graduates. Since 1990, almost 200 Aboriginal people have graduated from CBA partnership programs. Well over 85 percent of all graduates were hired by participating banks.

The banking sector has found that a structured joint industry approach to pre-employment training is a cost-effective way of increasing the representation of Aboriginal people in the sector. It ensures that Aboriginal participants receive relevant skills upgrading for entry level jobs. Participation by a number of banks increases the likelihood that successful candidates will be offered job opportunities.

However, retention and advancement of Aboriginal people hired through these partnerships has been an issue. Some of the banks have established informal support groups for Aboriginal staff to share

The banking sector has found that a structured joint industry approach to pre-employment training is a cost-effective way of increasing the representation of Aboriginal people in the sector.

experiences, frustrations and success stories. Some banks have formal buddy systems (or informal mentorships), where Aboriginal and non-Aboriginal staff are paired. The non-Aboriginal staff member will offer advice and answer questions on a variety of issues, such as how the organization works or how to establish a network within the organization. Cultural awareness training for supervisors, designed to increase awareness of discrimination within the workplace, has also been undertaken by many banks. In light of the challenge of retention and advancement of graduates from the pre-employment partnerships, the CBA is evaluating how it should proceed with the program in the future.

The experience that the CBA has built up from its participation in pre-employment partnerships, not only for Aboriginal people but also for other designated groups, can be brought to bear when new training initiatives are proposed. For example, through evaluations and the feedback from students, the CBA tries to ensure that the partnership is well structured, with roles and responsibilities clearly defined; that the training and work experience programs are structured so that participants gain the skills that they need to become successful employees; and that participants bring to the partnerships the flexibility, compromise and adaptability that are critical to satisfying the needs of diverse organizations and a range of trainees.

BC TEL's Employment Communication Skills Workshop

The program assists First Nations people to develop the skills to compete more effectively for positions within the company.

In 1993, BC TEL developed a job-readiness training program targeted at members of the Aboriginal community in British Columbia. The Employment Communications Skills Workshop was introduced on a pilot basis in October 1994. The first workshop was successful and has led to employment opportunities in the company for some of the Aboriginal participants. The program is being repeated in 1995.

The program was developed to serve BC TEL's employment equity goals for Aboriginal people. Specifically, it was designed to assist First Nations people develop the skills to compete more effectively for positions within the company. The program complements other existing initiatives designed to bring more Aboriginal people into the company's workforce.

Other initiatives that BC TEL has undertaken to increase Aboriginal representation include participating in employer panels for the Helping Spirit Lodge Society and the Native Internship Program; being on the Board of Directors of the Canadian Council for Aboriginal Business; providing work experience practicums for the Native Education Centre; co-sponsoring the Native Education Centre Career Fair for the past three years; and placing candidates referred by the United Native Nations in the company's Telesales Centre.

Objectives of the Workshop

The program was targeted at Aboriginal people to help BC TEL increase the representation of Aboriginal people in its workforce. Although BC TEL's other employment equity initiatives, such as employer panels and targeted outreach programs, have yielded some results, it was becoming clear by 1992 that additional proactive measures would be needed if the company was to achieve its employment equity goals for Aboriginal people.

The company decided to use a workshop approach because it would provide the types of practical knowledge and skills that would help Aboriginal candidates to meet the criteria for BC TEL job vacancies. The program was developed to address three specific objectives.

BC TEL

BC Telecom is a holding company. It comprises BC TEL, Canada's second largest telecommunications company and BC TEL Services, a group of subsidiaries that includes BC TEL Mobility Cellular. GTE Corporation owns 50.5 percent of the holding company.

BC TEL has about 11,900 permanent full-time and part-time employees. The company has about 80 permanent employees of Aboriginal ancestry. The company's goal is to have a workforce where Aboriginal people are represented to reflect the labour market availability of Aboriginal people in British Columbia.

- It was designed to help Aboriginal people acquire skills to compete more effectively for BC TEL positions. Ultimately, the company would like to hire as many successful participants as possible thereby increasing its representation of Aboriginal people.

- It was designed to contribute to the general job readiness of Aboriginal participants. During the initial planning stages of the program, BC TEL was in a hiring freeze.

- It was conceived as a way of building mutual understanding by introducing members of the First Nations community to BC TEL and introducing BC TEL to the Aboriginal community.

BC TEL introduced the program (which it called an Employment Communication Skills Workshop) on a pilot basis in October 1994. The program was funded through the corporate employment equity budget. There was no cost for participants.

Course Development

The course, which was developed under the auspices of BC TEL's Employment Equity Department, was designed to cover several types of communication skills that are important in an industrial workplace:

The workshop was developed by BC TEL employees, with input from Aboriginal people.

- expressing oneself with confidence in an interview and on the job;

- using communication equipment;

- using job search techniques effectively, including resume writing and career planning; and

- understanding how to thrive and communicate in different cultures.

The workshop was developed by BC TEL employees, with input from Aboriginal people. All of the facilitators, who were also BC TEL employees, designed their own course material. The course was designed to be delivered in an informal setting, which would be more conducive to learning.

In designing the workshop, a number of factors were taken into consideration. First, the course content needed to focus on areas that would prepare participants for entry level positions, most of which were in clerical and customer service. Second, the course was scheduled for two days a week, after normal business hours, to enable students who were going to school or working elsewhere to attend. Finally, the initial offering of the course was held in the fall so that students would finish in time for BC TEL to consider them for summer employment.

A communication outreach strategy was developed to solicit participation in the program.

Outreach and Awareness

A communication outreach strategy was developed to solicit participation in the program. This took the form of letters to a number of Aboriginal organizations and a bulletin that could be posted to advertise the workshop.

BC TEL has ongoing contact with a large number of Aboriginal organizations, employment agencies and educational institutions as part of its outreach activities. Many of these organizations were approached to participate in recruiting Aboriginal individuals for the first workshop. These included the Native Education Centre, Eslha7an Learning Centre, Burrard Band, Squamish Band, Aboriginal Personnel Services, AIMS Job Development, Department of Indian Affairs and Northern Development, First Nations Focus, Kw'aza'n'Tsut Job Finding Club, Louis Riel Metis Council, Native Employment Outreach Services, Native Youth Job Corp, Public Service Commission, Tsawwassen First Nations, Upper Squamish Village, Homalco Klahoose Bands, Mount Currie Band, Musqueam Band, Sechelt Band, Sliammon Indian Band, Nicola Valley Institute of Technology, First Nations House of Learning (UBC), Capilano College, Cariboo College, Kwantlen College, Simon Fraser University, and Vancouver Community College.

In addition, BC TEL's employment equity group followed up with phone calls to the individual organizations to discuss the course outline and address any other questions.

Employment counsellors and coordinators were asked to help in a number of ways. First, they were asked to help communicate this opportunity to Aboriginal people who might be interested in it. They were also asked to screen and recommend potential applicants, and field questions from interested parties. These employment counsellors were free to use their discretion and forward those applicants who they felt could benefit from attending the workshop.

The course consisted of seven 3-hour sessions of in-class training and practical exercises.

Course Description

The course consisted of seven 3-hour sessions of in-class training and practical exercises. They were held every Tuesday and Thursday evening between 5:00 pm and 8:30 pm at BC TEL locations. Some workshops were given in the Headquarters Building and others in the company's Education Centre.

Workshops were given on each of the following topics.

- Organizational expectations, which discussed what employers can expect from their employees and what employees can expect from their employer.

- Customer service, which gave students the skills to provide good customer service.

- Technical communication training, which gave students hands-on experience with basic office equipment.

- Voice inflection, which helped to enhance tone of service.

- Job search and retention skills, which provided guidance on interviewing skills, resume writing and job search skills. This also provided the students with an overview of the hiring process.

- Employment assessment and interviews, which provided participants with the opportunity to go through the hiring process.

The workshops were presented by BC TEL employees, who were chosen for their area of expertise, skill and work experience.

A graduation ceremony was held at BC TEL Headquarters during the last session. The ceremony included a dinner and a formal presentation by the Vice President of Human Resource Development. The Vice President presented each student with a certificate of completion. Upon acceptance of their certificate, each student gave a short speech about the workshop. In addition, photos were taken of each student as they received their graduation certificate. Copies of these photos were sent to the participants at a later date. Other speeches were given by the Employment Equity Manager and the Employment Centre Manager.

Evaluation and Results

Overall, participants and facilitators concluded that the workshop was valuable and that it would be beneficial to continue it.

A total of 14 Aboriginal people participated in the first workshop. Seven were successful in meeting BC TEL's standards. Three were accommodated for work experience practicums through the Native Education Centre and another three (one of whom was also a Native Education Centre work experience student) were hired into temporary BC TEL positions (one in customer service and two in clerical positions). This is significant because BC TEL does most of its staffing for permanent positions from the eligible pool of temporary workers.

The program was evaluated by participants and facilitators. The overall conclusion was that the workshop was valuable and that it would be beneficial to continue it.

- The instructors felt that the workshops provided Aboriginal participants with a useful introduction to BC TEL, its people, the different departments and potential job opportunities. Instructors also felt that the workshop helped participants examine their own skills and understand better what they had to offer BC TEL.

- The students made it clear that the workshop was both beneficial and enjoyable. They noted that it provided a good insight into the company and the employment opportunities for Aboriginal people. Students felt that the workshop built their confidence and self-esteem, helped them acquire new skills (especially with respect to communications and resume writing) and made them more employable.

Instructors and students made a number of small suggestions for change. Instructors felt that more time could have been allowed for student participation and role playing. In addition, it would have been useful if more information had been provided on the existing skill level of participants so that instructors could have tailored the workshop to their skill level. Students found that the course covered a great deal in a short time and should be somewhat less intensive in the future.

As a result of the evaluation, several changes are being introduced into future workshops. For example, there will be more hands-on experience and more role playing opportunities. In addition, BC TEL is taking steps to tailor the workshop to better match the skill level of the participants.

The program is being repeated in the Fall of 1995. BC TEL is hoping to partner with other organizations that share the same employment equity goals, such as B.C. Hydro and B.C. Gas.

CIBC's Summer Intern Program for Aboriginal Students

Each summer since 1991, CIBC has operated an Aboriginal Internship Program for students enroled in a post-secondary institution. Participation has grown each year. In 1994 summer work experience was provided to 37 Aboriginal students in a number of CIBC branches across Ontario and in the Atlantic provinces. The program was developed and is offered in collaboration with Aboriginal communities.

The Summer Intern Program is one element of the bank's long-term strategy to encourage and foster interest among Aboriginal people about career choices at CIBC.

As a federally-regulated employer under the *Employment Equity Act*, CIBC has put in place an aggressive outreach program to determine and develop resources for the recruitment, training and retention of Aboriginal candidates. The bank is also seeking to develop and strengthen linkages with Aboriginal communities for the purpose of offering Aboriginal people career opportunities at CIBC. The bank's long-term strategy is to encourage and foster interest among Aboriginal people about career choices at CIBC as a means of increasing their representation in the bank's workforce.

Objectives of the Program

The bank has defined a number of specific objectives that it hopes to achieve as a result of its Aboriginal Internship Program.

For Aboriginal students, the program is designed to:

- provide summer work experience at the bank;

- provide an opportunity to gain personal experience of and appreciation for a careers with the financial services industry; and

- assist students to evaluate personal suitability for career options within CIBC.

For the bank, the program is designed to:

- enable the bank to work directly with Aboriginal representatives at university or community agencies to increase the bank's effectiveness in working with Aboriginal students;

CIBC

CIBC was founded in 1867. With assets of more than $121 billion, CIBC is one of Canada's largest financial networks and is among North America's ten largest banks. The bank has over 1600 branches in Canada and around the world.

CIBC has about 35,200 full-time and part-time employees working in such diverse areas as branch banking, national and international investment, management information systems and technical support.

In 1994, the bank had 385 full-time and part-time Aboriginal employees, representing 1.1 percent of its total workforce.

- develop an awareness within the Aboriginal communities of CIBC's objective of developing a resource pool for the entrance of Aboriginal people into the bank's workforce;

- strengthen and develop relationships with Aboriginal communities throughout Canada for the purpose of encouraging long-term business and employment opportunities for Aboriginal people; and

- increase Aboriginal representation in CIBC's workforce at all levels.

Development of the Program

The bank's consultations resulted in the development of a training/scholarship program for Aboriginal students.

In 1991, the CIBC's individual (i.e. retail) banking group in the Ontario East and North region proposed exploring the feasibility of establishing a scholarship program for Aboriginal students attending Lakehead College in Thunder Bay. The initial idea for the program was to provide a scholarship to Aboriginal students attending Lakehead and other northern community educational institutions to assist with their annual tuition costs.

In responding to this request, the bank's Employment and Pay Equity group conducted extensive consultations with representatives of the Aboriginal community, Trent University and the federal department of Employment and Immigration (now Human Resources Development Canada). The result of these consultations was the development of a strategy which would offer both immediate and long-term opportunities for the involvement of Aboriginal students through a training/scholarship program. This program would be designed to provide an opportunity for Aboriginal students to develop a personal relationship with the bank and insight into future career opportunities in banking.

The Aboriginal Internship/Job Link Scholarship Program was recommended to CIBC senior management for implementation as a pilot project during the summer of 1991. The program has been offered annually since then and has grown steadily in its scope.

Student Selection

Candidates are recruited by ads at Friendship Centres, university placement centres and Aboriginal Associations.

To be eligible for the program, candidates must be in a post-secondary program in a community college or university.

Candidates are recruited by ads at Friendship Centres, university placement centres and/or Aboriginal associations. Over the past four years, the bank has built up an extensive network of relationships with administrators of Native and indigenous studies programs at colleges and universities. The bank has also strengthened its contacts with First Nation community organizations, such as career centres, education councils,

learning centres, student centres, student associations, educational counselling centres and school boards. There have been some challenges in
finding qualified, motivated Aboriginal students who wish to participate
in the program. The bank is addressing this through advertising and networking.

Candidates are selected on the basis of their academic performance, general interest and aptitude for success within the banking industry. The
bank uses behaviourial interviewing in the selection process.

Work Experience Component

The work period for the internship is from May to September. Candidates
to the program are given the option of working within their home community, if possible. First year interns generally work as Customer Service
Representatives. The students are provided with a written outline of the required job functions.

*The program for returning
students is structured to
provide progressively more
challenging tasks and different
responsibilities. This assures
further growth and
development by the student.*

The program for returning students is structured to provide progressively more challenging tasks and different responsibilities in order to
assure further growth and development by the student. For example,
where possible, second and third year students are given the following
types of opportunities:

- to work in a job function where they have indicated an interest and
  aptitude during their previous work experience;

- to take on progressively more responsible work assignments in keeping with their interests and aptitudes;

- to broaden their understanding and appreciation of branch operations and their relationship to the banking process; and

- to work in another location of CIBC, such as human resources, administration, investment banking and corporate banking, if they
  express such an interest.

The student's performance is evaluated throughout the work experience
period. Mid-way through the summer, a scheduled supervisory session is
held to advise the student of work performance. The primary purpose of
this session is to provide feedback to students which can be helpful to the
student in the remaining work period. At the end of the work term, a formal written evaluation is conducted and provided to the student.

Candidates who demonstrate an interest in pursuing a career within
CIBC are given additional information and career counselling. Efforts are
made to maintain contact with students during the academic year in or-

der to encourage and foster continued interest in the bank as a possible career option.

Buddy System

A buddy system is one of the key features of the Internship Program. The purpose of the buddy system is to ensure the smooth integration of the Aboriginal intern into the workplace.

A buddy system is one of the key features of the Internship Program.

The buddy is assigned by the branch where the intern is working to act as a mentor for the student. The buddy can be anyone in the branch. On occasion, a returning Aboriginal student has fulfilled the role of a buddy.

The buddy is provided with the written outline of the student's job functions. The buddy is responsible for assisting the student to understand and appreciate the cultural values of the bank, as well as other basic requirements of CIBC staff. The buddy also plays a role in the evaluation of the student's performance.

Orientation and Cross-Cultural Sessions

Cross-cultural sessions are arranged for the interns, buddies and employees of the branch.

Cross-cultural sessions are arranged for the interns, buddies and employees of the branch.

Students are invited, ideally at least one month prior to the commencement of the work term, to attend an orientation/cross-cultural session. The agenda for this session covers the cultural values of CIBC. The intern has the opportunity to learn about corporate values plus information about the bank's business policies and practices, as well as some of the "soft values" of the bank, including work schedule, punctuality, dress code, etc.. The session also provides the interns with the opportunity to discuss impressions, attitudes and how they feel in general about going to work at the bank.

The 1994 cross-cultural session was held at the bank's Leadership Centre at King City, Ontario. Participants included the students, senior vice-presidents of the bank, branch managers, student buddies and staff from the bank's human resources area. One of the senior vice-presidents spoke to the group for about one-half hour about the bank and its values. After that, there was a panel discussion, led by a branch manager and students who had previously been interns. Small groups were formed where expectations were discussed and participants were able to get to know one another. Following lunch, there was a presentation on Aboriginal culture.

An orientation session also is held for students, representatives of management and buddies from the participating branch. This session covers the value and purpose of on-the-job supervision as a tool for enhancing

Scholarship awards are extended to those students who complete the full work term and achieve an acceptable performance review.

performance and the evaluation process and its use in determining the performance rating, as well as opportunities for discussing any other issues that may arise.

Special efforts have sometimes been needed to foster a sense of ownership and understanding of the program among branch employees. Given restructuring, staff meeting and internal communications have been used to let employees know that students are not replacing full-time employees.

Scholarships

Scholarship awards are extended to those students who complete the full work term, achieve an acceptable performance review and have complied with the general requirements of the program. The scholarships are based on the student's ability to learn and do the job; the ability to work with staff; and the service orientation shown to customers. The determination of the scholarship award for each student is done in consultation with the student's manager, supervisor and/or buddy, as well as with one of the region's human resources staff. The value of the scholarship depends on the student's rating.

An awards luncheon is held to present the scholarships to students. This is done as soon as possible following completion of the work term and the evaluation of students.

Results

The number of both internships and participating branches has increased steadily since the program was piloted in 1991.

The number of both internships and participating branches has increased steadily since the program was piloted in 1991. In addition, returning students have been able to increase their responsibilities over time.

- In 1991, 6 Aboriginal students were hired for entry-level jobs in branches in Peterborough, Ontario. Of these, 5 completed their internships.

- In 1992, 11 students in Ontario and Atlantic Canada worked as interns. Of these, three were returning students from the 1991 program.

- In 1993, 15 students worked in 6 cities in Ontario, as well as in Nova Scotia and New Brunswick. All 15 completed their internships.

- In 1994, 37 students (33 in Ontario and 4 in the Atlantic region) participated. This was the first year that branches in Toronto and Hamilton, and in the bank's commercial banking area, participated. One of the interns was hired on a full-time basis.

Student feedback about the program has been positive.

Student feedback about the program has been positive.

- One student wrote that "My very first month on the job I learned more about banking than I would have in a lifetime had I not been with CIBC. My eyes were opened to a much broader picture of finance … I am now looking forward to a career in banking that I would not have otherwise had if I had not answered the knock of opportunity."

- Another noted that the best part of the program was "the opportunity … I had never thought about working in a bank before. I found the experience to be challenging. I know that many of the customers liked that there were Aboriginal people working there — many commented on it."

- The most important thing that one intern learned was "how a financial institution works, since I had no previous experience in this area … I also learned that customer service and team work are essential to a successful organization."

Over the longer term, the bank expects that the internship program will continue to provide a focal point for creating lasting positive relationships between the bank and Aboriginal communities in Canada.

In 1995, the bank expanded the internship program again. The program was run in Vancouver for the first time, with six interns. Over the longer term, the bank expects that the internship program will continue to provide a focal point for creating lasting positive relationships between the bank and Aboriginal communities in Canada.

Outreach by the Commission de la construction du Québec to Aboriginal Communities

There are about 2,000 Aboriginal people in construction trades in Quebec.

The Commission de la construction du Québec (Quebec Construction Commission) has developed an active program to increase Aboriginal representation in the construction trades. It is doing this by making Aboriginal people aware of the opportunities in construction trades, providing information on how to become qualified as construction workers, and assisting Aboriginal people to attain their qualifications. These initiatives are spearheaded by a Counsellor in the Office of the President, who develops and maintains relations with Aboriginal communities across Quebec.

The CCQ has had some success in increasing the number of qualified Aboriginal construction workers. In particular, its work with the Mohawks of Akwesasne and the Montagnais in Sept-Îles have made tangible contributions to increasing Aboriginal training, employment and business development in the construction industry. One of the key priorities for the future is to increase the involvement of Aboriginal people in their own construction enterprises.

Representation of Aboriginal People in the Construction Trades

Commission de la construction du Québec

The construction industry in Quebec is regulated under the *Loi sur les relations du travail, la formation professionnelle et la gestion de la main-d'oeuvre dans l'industrie de la construction.* The Commission de la construction du Québec (CCQ) is responsible for the administration of this law.

The mandate of CCQ is to maintain coherent labour relations across Quebec; to manage the industry's workforce; to put a system of training and professional qualifications in place; and to administer a system of social benefits.

There are about 80,000 construction workers in Quebec, of whom about 2,000 are of Aboriginal ancestry.

There are about 2,000 Aboriginal people in construction trades in Quebec. Historically, Aboriginal construction workers were primarily steel erectors, working on high-rise construction projects in urban centres. In recent years, there has been a diversification in the types of trades where Aboriginal people are working. In particular, there are increasing numbers of Aboriginal heavy equipment operators and carpenters. In the James Bay area, some Aboriginal women work as signalers in road construction projects.

The increase of Aboriginal construction workers and the diversification of their trades can be attributed in part to number of on-reserve construction projects that have provided

While many Aboriginal construction workers have experience in construction, fulfilling the requirements needed to obtain a certificate of competency within the industry has proven to be an issue.

The responsibility for working with Aboriginal communities rests with a Counsellor in the Office of the President of the Commission.

employment opportunities. In addition, schools are raising awareness among Aboriginal youth about construction trades as a career choice, as well as about the education, vocational training and work experience needed to become qualified.

While many Aboriginal construction workers have experience in construction, fulfilling the requirements needed to obtain a certificate of competency within the industry has proven to be an issue. Aboriginal construction workers tend to have experience in several trades (such as carpentry, electrician, etc.), but do not necessarily have the qualifications to become a journey person in one specific trade area.

The Commission's Overall Approach to Increasing Aboriginal Representation

The Commission de la construction du Québec first began to work with Aboriginal communities in the mid-1970s, when major hydro-electric developments began in the north. At that time, the Commission went to northern Cree communities to make local people aware of how to become qualified in the construction trades. The Commission also encouraged people who might be interested in pursuing employment opportunities to begin the training process by taking the construction safety course. This course, which is required by all construction workers, provides a good introduction to the industry and gives participants skills which are valuable in many different situations.

Since then, the Commission has increased its outreach efforts to Aboriginal communities across Quebec. The responsibility for working with Aboriginal communities rests with a Counsellor in the Office of the President of the Commission. The Counsellor is a full-time employee whose responsibilities include developing and maintaining relationships with Aboriginal communities, developing training programs, external relations and government liaison. One of the committees that the CCQ has worked with includes the Department of Indian Affairs and Northern Development's Quebec Aboriginal Workforce Participation Initiative committee.

The Commission's approach is to respond to invitations by First Nations to come to their communities and discuss employment in the construction industry. The Counsellor's participation on external and government committees has raised the visibility of the Commission among Aboriginal communities. As a result, First Nations are aware of the CCQ's interests in increasing Aboriginal representation in the construction trades and of the willingness of the Commission to work with Aboriginal communities, if invited, to achieve this.

Many First Nations in Quebec have invited the Commission to their communities.

Many First Nations in Quebec have invited the Commission to their communities. For example, the CCQ has met with Montagnais communities in Sept-Îles, Mohawk communities in Kahnawake, Kanesetake and Akwesasne, Algonquin communities near Temiskaming and Black Lake, as well as Cree communities in Oujé-Bougoumou.

When meeting with First Nation communities, the Commission describes the industry and opportunities for training and employment. The CCQ representative talks about the different trades as well as the differences between residential, commercial and industrial construction. Some of the issues associated with being in the construction industry, such as the need for job mobility, also are addressed.

An important part of the discussion centres around how Aboriginal people can become fully qualified and achieve the certificates of competency.

An important part of the discussion centres around how Aboriginal people can become fully qualified and achieve their certificates of competency. The CCQ uses a competency-based system of apprenticeship, which requires proof of relevant work experience plus acceptable performance on an examination. For example, 6000 hours of practice and vocational training are needed before an individual is able to write the exam in carpentry. The Commission sets out how Aboriginal people who may have experience working in construction, can obtain the necessary proof of relevant experience and apply it toward their qualifications. The Commission also describes how it can help to identify people who may have relevant experience in construction.

Initiatives with the Mohawks of Akwesasne

The Commission de la construction du Québec has worked with the Mohawks of Akwesasne on several initiatives designed to increase the representation of local people in the construction trades. These initiatives have grown out of relationships that were established between the CCQ and the community over time.

As a result of a pre-apprenticeship training course, a number of students were able to obtain employment in the reserve's infrastructure program. Two of the students started their own electrical contracting businesses.

One of these initiatives involves a pre-apprenticeship training course in electrician and carpentry skills. In 1993, as a result of a meeting in Akwesasne, the community asked the CCQ for assistance in organizing the course. It was held in Akwesasne, with a teacher from the Chateauguay Valley school board acting as instructor. About 30 students participated, with 15 in each of the two trade areas. As a result of this training, a number of students were able to obtain employment in the reserve's infrastructure program. Others have obtained employment outside the reserve.

Two of the students who had participated in this course started their own electrical contracting businesses and have entered into a joint venture with a non-Aboriginal contractor in Quebec. The former students, and now owners of Ratinonwaraherah and Delta Tech, are now working as

The Commission is working with a Mohawk contractor in Akwesasne to qualify Aboriginal people as structural steel erectors.

apprentices toward their certificate of competency. Their businesses are now taking jobs both on and off the reserve.

The CCQ is also working with a Mohawk contractor in Akwesasne to qualify Aboriginal people as structural steel erectors. A number of people from Akwesasne have extensive experience as steelworkers, but do not hold the CCQ's *certificat de compétence,* which is the required working permit.

Oka Erectors has been seeking to hire qualified Mohawk construction workers and has been working with the Commission to develop an up-to-date list of people with experience that fulfils the requirements needed to sit the examination. The CCQ is helping Aboriginal people collect the necessary evidence of the work experience. It is doing this by using the workers' social insurance numbers and matching them to records filed with the CCQ from both employers and unions. This is helping to provide the proof of these workers' relevant past experience.

To date, Oka Erectors has been able to qualify half of the workers that it wishes to hire. An additional five or six workers are also in a position to write the qualifying examination.

Initiatives with the Montagnais of Sept-Îles

The Commission has been part of an innovative project undertaken by the Montagnais of Sept-Îles to facilitate training and employment initiatives for community members.

The Commission has also worked in partnership with Aboriginal communities, and other organizations, to increase the representation of Aboriginal people in the construction trades over the long term.

In addition to its outreach work describing the industry and opportunities for training and employment, the Commission has been part of an innovative project being undertaken by the Montagnais of Sept-Îles designed to facilitate training and employment initiatives for community members.

The Conseil des Attikamekw and des Montagnais, in partnership with the Quebec regional office of the Department of Indian Affairs and Northern Development, the local Pathways board, the Aboriginal Affairs Secretariat of Quebec and the Commission de la construction du Québec, has developed Aboriginal labour market software.

The role of the CCQ in this initiative was to help develop the census questionnaire for the construction trades. The Commission provided the basic list of census questions, which was then tailored to the specific needs of the community. In particular, the census included questions about skills developed in traditional occupations within the community, such as hunting and trapping. As such, the Aboriginal labour market software helps to document the skills of community members across a range of occupations and trades, and lays the groundwork for training and employment initiatives.

CMHC's Aboriginal Training Programs in the Housing Sector

For two decades, CMHC has been actively involved in providing Aboriginal people with comprehensive training programs in the housing sector.

Over the past two decades, Canada Mortgage and Housing Corporation (CMHC) has been actively involved in providing Aboriginal people with comprehensive training programs designed to give them the opportunity to gain the experience and the knowledge to prepare for employment in the delivery, administration and management of Aboriginal housing and to pursue career opportunities with housing agencies in the public, non-profit and private sectors.

CMHC has administered Aboriginal training programs since 1974. Through its Rural and Native Housing (RNH) training budget, CMHC hires and trains individuals under the Native Cadre Program; sponsors training workshops for Aboriginal housing groups under the Client Training Program; and seconds housing specialists to assist Aboriginal housing organizations through the Secondment Program. In 1993, CMHC participated in the development of the Metis Housing Administration Program, which was a pilot training initiative to address the shortage of qualified Metis people involved in the delivery and administration of housing programs in Saskatchewan.

Program Rationale

Through its annual budget for existing social housing portfolios, Canada Mortgage and Housing Corporation provides financial assistance to various Aboriginal non-profit groups and organizations to enable affordable and adequate housing to be made available to Aboriginal people. CMHC has also traditionally played a major role in addressing the training needs of its external clients.

Four key factors underlie CMHC's ongoing support for its specific Aboriginal training initiatives. The first is that the Aboriginal population is experiencing substantial growth within Canada with significant new household formation and increasing migration to urban areas. These factors are creating immediate and future demand for Aboriginal housing.

Canada Mortgage and Housing Corporation

Canada Mortgage and Housing Corporation is a federal Crown corporation, created in 1946, whose mandate is to help house Canadians. CMHC provides mortgage loan insurance, acts as agent for social housing programs and is a prime source of housing expertise (including research and development, demonstration activities and information exchange).

CMHC has about 2600 employees. The national office is based in Ottawa. CMHC has regional offices in Saint John, Montreal, Toronto, Saskatoon and Vancouver. It also operates another 51 branch or local offices across Canada. Aboriginal employees account for 1.5 percent of CMHC's workforce.

In addition, a large portion of the social housing units in a number of provinces are inhabited by Aboriginal people. Aboriginal organizations feel that there should be more management and control of these units by Aboriginal agencies.

A third factor is that self-sufficiency in housing has been identified as an important component of Aboriginal self-government. The current lack of skilled Aboriginal people constrains the ability to achieve this goal.

Finally other programs and courses are usually inaccessible to Aboriginal people due to their costs, experience requirements and/or educational requirements.

The substantial growth of the Aboriginal population is creating immediate and future demand for housing.

Native Cadre Program

CMHC's Native Cadre Program has been in operation since 1974. Its objectives are:

- to provide special training and orientation in housing programs to a cadre of Aboriginal people to enable them the gain the necessary knowledge and skills to assist their communities and organizations develop their own housing programs and achieve their own housing goals;

- to provide employment and other career opportunities within CMHC, provincial housing agencies, non-profit organizations and the private sector; and

- to increase the number of trained Aboriginal personnel in the Canadian workforce.

The Native Cadre Program provides specialized on-the-job training in housing development and management.

The Native Cadre Program provides specialized on-the-job training in housing development and management. Participants gain valuable work experience within CMHC, provincial housing agencies, non-profit organizations or the private sector. Under the program, trainees sign an employment contract with CMHC for a term of from six months to two years. They are trained in the delivery and management of National Housing Act programs to help the Aboriginal community to achieve their own housing goals. The program is also designed to provide the potential for employment and career opportunities within the public and private sectors of the Canadian housing industry through the provision of transferable skills.

The Native Cadre Program is open to people of Inuit, Metis, Status Indian and Non-Status Indian origin. Nominations to the program are made by Aboriginal housing delivery groups or Bands in response to a specific training requirement. Recruitment may also be undertaken by CMHC in cooperation with delivery groups or, in the absence of a group, with local Aboriginal people involved in housing development.

The selection of trainees is made by a committee, with representatives of CMHC, the Aboriginal delivery group, and since the signing of the 1986 Cost-Sharing Agreements, with a representative of the provincial/territorial housing agency.

Trainees are given work experience in a CMHC, provincial or Aboriginal group's office. A training plan is written for each trainee which serves as the terms of reference for the work. Types of work experience may include construction, repair and maintenance, property management, client counselling, housing inspections, program and project administration and land acquisition.

The work performance of Cadre trainees is evaluated. Once they have completed their contract they receive feedback and in turn provide comments on their training experience.

After their work assignments, Cadres are expected to return to work with the Aboriginal group or local community that nominated them. If the trainee was unemployed before participating in the program, he or she will be helped to find employment in housing-related jobs.

CMHC hires about 20 Aboriginal people each year under the Native Cadre Program. Since 1974, more than $10 million has been spent on the Native Cadre Program. The number of Aboriginal people who have received training under the program now exceeds 300.

The Metis Housing Administration Program

The Metis Housing Administration Program (MHAP) is a pilot training initiative, funded by CMHC, Saskatchewan Municipal Government Housing Division (MGHD) and the Metis Nation of Saskatchewan (MNS) in 1993, to address the shortage of qualified Metis people involved in the delivery and administration of housing programs and, at the same time, assisting Metis people to participate in the labour market.

The Metis Housing Administration Program was designed to build on the strengths of the existing Native Cadre Program and avoid its shortcomings. Strengths of the Native Cadre Program involve active participation and constructive feedback. The main improvement in the MHAP program was the inclusion of a formal classroom training portion to provide students with a theoretical background on housing issues. The practical training aspects of the program were expanded to include work assignments in as many as three different housing agencies. The MHAP was also a more structured program, with training plans developed for each student at each participating agency. Training guides were also provided to all trainers, outlining expectations

The number of Aboriginal people who have received training under the Native Cadre Program now exceeds 300.

The Metis Housing Administration Program is a pilot training initiative to address the shortage of qualified Metis people involved in the delivery and administration of housing programs.

The classroom training program had four components.

- Academic Preparation was designed to upgrade the student's academic skills. It consisted of 300 hours of classwork in communications, mathematics, computers and Metis studies.

- Business Administration training involved a number of classes selected from the Saskatchewan Institute of Applied Science and Technology's Business Administration Certificate Program. This involved 320 hours of classwork. Instruction was provided by SIAST staff in financial management, business report writing, presentation skills, counselling skills, etc..

- The largest part of classroom training (500 hours) was the Housing Administration curriculum taught by CMHC and Gabriel Dumont Institute staff. Key elements included property management, portfolio management, federal-provincial relations and social housing programs.

- Instruction for the Rehabilitation Skills course (75 hours) was provided by the Northern Alberta Institute of Technology and included inspecting dwellings, specification writing and cost estimating.

The Work Placement component accounted for approximately one-half of the training provided, consisting of three 10 week on-the-job training placements for each student. The training agencies taking part were CMHC, MGHD, the Provincial Metis Housing Corporation, Gabriel Housing Corporation, Prince Albert Community Housing Corporation and Sasknative Rentals.

Ten students participated in the MHAP pilot. The success of the MHAP program is demonstrated by the fact that 8 of the 10 graduates are currently employed. Six of the 8 are working in the housing field.

The success of the MHAP program is demonstrated by the fact that 8 of the 10 graduates are currently employed. Six of the 8 are working in the housing field.

Future Developments

The formal evaluation of Metis Housing Administration Program noted that there is a definite need for this type of training specifically for Aboriginal people. This reflects both the lack of training alternatives and the growing Aboriginal emphasis on self-sufficiency. The evaluation suggested that the program should be extended to all Aboriginal groups. The program's success was due in large part to its contributing partners. Joint partnership was vital in getting the program off the ground. It was recommended that any future program include the continued involvement of

Aboriginal organizations. An Aboriginal training program must have Aboriginal input in order to remain culturally sensitive.

The evaluation also pointed to areas for improvement.

Joint partnership was vital in getting the program off the ground. An Aboriginal training program must have Aboriginal input in order to remain culturally sensitive.

- Specific improvements to classroom training should include the adoption of a more culturally sensitive approach to subject matter and training procedures. This will be aided by the involvement of Aboriginal organizations.

- Practical training should be enhanced by giving students tasks or specific projects which they could take from start to finish, thus allowing a more beneficial training experience.

- Accreditation would offer a number of benefits. It would provide greater credibility for the program among employers and ensure recognition across the country.

CMHC will assess the recent evaluations of the Native Cadre Program, the Metis Housing Administration Program, as well as other external training approaches, in developing improvements for future Aboriginal training and capacity-building initiatives.

PART THREE

EMPLOYMENT OPPORTUNITIES

National Revenue's Aboriginal Employment Program

The Aboriginal Employment Program is a multi-year strategy to improve employment opportunities for Aboriginal peoples.

Making diversity work is one of the many challenges facing the Department of National Revenue in its efforts to provide a wide range of services to a multiplicity of clients. In 1990, Revenue Canada Taxation launched an initiative to make the department's workforce more representative of, and more responsive to its clients.

The Aboriginal Employment Program is a multi-year strategy to improve employment opportunities for Aboriginal peoples. The specific goals of the program are:

- to increase the representation, promotion and retention of Aboriginal peoples within National Revenue's workforce; and

- to enhance the ability of National Revenue managers to work with a diverse workforce and respond to the needs of a diverse client population.

The program is composed of four elements: an outreach component, a series of developmental employment initiatives, cross-cultural education and training, and a supporting communications strategy. Significant attention is also paid to identifying Aboriginal spokespeople and stakeholders with whom the department must consult and build strategic partnerships.

The Aboriginal Employment Program was designed in consultation with representatives of the Aboriginal community and has proved to be an innovative and successful initiative to improve employment opportunities in the department for Aboriginal peoples across Canada.

Background

The Aboriginal Employment Program was created and is now managed by a career public servant who is an Aboriginal Canadian.

In February 1990, National Revenue recruited an Aboriginal program advisor. In June 1990, the advisor presented a program frame-

---

Department of National Revenue

The Department of National Revenue is responsible for administering Canadian tax, border and trade policies. National Revenue is one of the largest service delivery organizations in the federal government. In each year, it serves over 100 million travellers, 20 million individual tax filers, 2 million GST registrants, 1 million business tax filers and over 150,000 members of the import/export business community. In 1993/94, the Department collected net revenue of approximately $145.0 billion, of which $108.6 billion was federal revenue.

In 1994, the department had a total workforce of about 41,000 employees. The department had 404 Aboriginal employees, who account for almost 1 percent of the department's total workforce.

Following extensive consultation with the Aboriginal community and in the department, it became apparent that a successful program would have to operate on a number of levels.

work and action plan to the department's Senior Management Committee. During 1990, a number of preliminary initiatives were introduced. In the summer cross-cultural workshops were launched. The program advisor also began work with Aboriginal training centres so that trained recruits would be ready for seasonal work in the winter of 1990.

During 1990-91, the program advisor consulted extensively within the Aboriginal community and in the department. It became apparent that, to be successful, a program would have to operate on a number of levels.

- It should encourage Aboriginal youth to stay in school, pursue a broad range of studies and pursue meaningful careers.

- It should help members of the Aboriginal community bridge the transition from life and work on the reserve, to life in a public service office.

- It should enable a responsive, non-Aboriginal community to understand and relate to Aboriginal culture and society.

In December 1991, the program advisor presented a complete program description, delivery strategy and budget to senior management for approval. The Aboriginal Employment Program was introduced in Revenue Canada Taxation in 1991. In 1993, following the merger of Revenue Canada Taxation and Revenue Canada Customs and Excise, the Aboriginal Employment Program was extended to the Customs and Excise functions in the Department of National Revenue.

National Revenue has now committed itself to a full range of corporate change activities needed to bring about permanent change.

Outreach to Aboriginal Communities

An important part of the program advisor's responsibilities is networking with Aboriginal education and employment counsellors.

National Revenue has taken a teamwork approach in its outreach to Aboriginal communities. An important part of the program advisor's responsibilities is networking with Aboriginal education and employment counsellors. The program advisor makes visits (in the company of a representative from a local National Revenue office) to Aboriginal communities, organizations or training institutions to introduce the department and make local contacts.

Specific initiatives include:

- discussing local action plans with Aboriginal education counsellors;

- encouraging Aboriginal counsellors to visit National Revenue offices to familiarize themselves with the workplace;

- working with Aboriginal communities when recruitment is being done;

- having Aboriginal counsellors participate on selection boards;

- participating in special events in Aboriginal communities; and

- increasing the use of Aboriginal community facilities during the selection process.

Cross-Cultural Education and Training

National Revenue identified the need to provide its employees with an understanding of Canadian and Aboriginal history. This was necessary in order to have employee support for efforts to create an atmosphere of acceptance of Aboriginal peoples in the workplace.

Cross-cultural training is available on an as-requested basis. Whenever possible, this training is delivered in the nearest Aboriginal community. The sessions are low-key and focus on providing an understanding of Canadian history and of Aboriginal peoples and their history and status within Canadian society. Topics that are covered include an overview of Canadian history and the relationships with the original inhabitants; the Royal Proclamation of 1863; the treaties signed with Indian nations; the rationale and application of employment equity; Aboriginal culture; differentiating between prejudice and discrimination; and the merit principle and its interpretation and application in the federal public service.

During the workshops, employees interact with the training presenter, the department's Aboriginal advisor and local Aboriginal spokespeople. The objective of the cross-cultural training sessions is to recognize and address misconceptions and cultural stereotypes and to build understanding between the people who will need to work as a team and make a diverse workforce happen.

Some National Revenue offices have established local Aboriginal employees support groups. Expansion to other offices will depend on the interest by Aboriginal employees.

Employment Initiatives

National Revenue has established a series of developmental employment initiatives which can culminate with employment in the Department or with other organizations. The emphasis is placed on offering experience in mathematics and science-related jobs. These are disciplines that Aboriginal youth has traditionally not been encouraged to pursue, but which

The objective of cross-cultural training is to recognize and address misconceptions and cultural stereotypes and to build understanding between the people who will need to work as a team.

National Revenue has a series of developmental initiatives for Aboriginal youth.

form the majority of employment opportunities in National Revenue. A range of different initiatives are in place.

- National Revenue sponsors junior high school students to attend the Federation of Saskatchewan Indian Nations (FSIN) Summer Science Camps.

- The department administers its Aboriginal High School Student Summer Employment Program to expose these students to careers in mathematics and science-related professions. Students are re-hired every summer for as long as they remain in school.

- National Revenue also participates in the federal government's Aboriginal Career Oriented Summer Employment Program (ACOSEP). Students become candidates for ACOSEP after they have completed one-year of post secondary studies. The program provides Aboriginal university students with employment complementary to their fields of study within departmental business lines.

National Revenue also works extensively with Aboriginal training organizations such as Aboriginal Training and Employment Services of Manitoba, the Native Skills Centre in Toronto and the Micmac Indian Learning Centre in Halifax. These organizations recruit, test and train (on site) Aboriginal employees for seasonal employment in the department. The employees receive yearly call-backs.

The department works extensively with Aboriginal training organizations to recruit, test and train Aboriginal employees for seasonal employment.

Communication

Within the department, National Revenue uses internal media (newsletters, employment equity events, etc.) to promote diversity and publicize its successes. Through formal mechanisms, such as the annual Employment Equity Action Plan and the National Advisory Committee of Aboriginal Employees, the department stresses its commitment to making diversity work.

Within the Aboriginal communities, National Revenue encourages its Aboriginal partners and employees to be its ambassadors. The program advisor is always available to make small-group presentations.

Results

As a result of its Aboriginal Employment Program, National Revenue has increased the number of Aboriginal employees in its workforce. In 1991, there were 295 Aboriginal employees; by 1994 there were 404 Aboriginal employees, representing almost one percent of the total workforce.

As a result of its Aboriginal Employment Program, National Revenue has increased the number of Aboriginal employees in its workforce.

The increase is significant because the period was characterized by continuing restraint in the federal public service which constrained the department's ability to hire full-time or part-time employees.

There are also other measures of the program's achievements.

- The department has offered over 100 cross-cultural workshops to approximately 3000 employees since 1990.

- 18 Aboriginal junior high school students have been sponsored to attend the FSIN summer science camp.

- 120 Aboriginal high school students each year participate in the summer employment program.

- 24 Aboriginal university students have participated in the ACOSEP program.

- 30 seasonal employees have been hired, many of whom are now permanent employees.

- A number of Aboriginal graduates have been hired and developed as auditors.

Much of the success of the program is related to the fact that it takes an integrated and focused approach to the issues of Aboriginal employment.

In fiscal 1995-96, National Revenue will double the number of openings for Aboriginal university students so that approximately 40 students will be able to participate in the program.

Much of the success of the program is related to the fact that it takes an integrated and focused approach to the issues of Aboriginal employment. From an Aboriginal perspective, the use of the four program elements in National Revenue's Aboriginal Employment Program symbolizes the department's understanding of the need to work within the framework of Aboriginal culture since four is an important symbolic and spiritual number representing the harmonious cycles in the natural and spiritual world.

Saskatchewan Government's Aboriginal Employment Development Program

The program mobilizes the energies and capacities of employers, Indian and Metis communities and Aboriginal post-secondary institutions as a means of achieving substantive change.

The Saskatchewan Government's Aboriginal Employment Development Program takes a proactive, focused and integrated approach to Indian and Metis employment and economic renewal. The program is designed to build on the strengths of Aboriginal communities and institutions. It is coordinated by the Saskatchewan Government's Indian and Metis Affairs Secretariat (SIMAS) and includes initiatives involving government departments, crown corporations, post-secondary institutions, the private sector and Indian and Metis communities.

The program mobilizes the energies and capacities of employers, Indian and Metis communities and Aboriginal post-secondary institutions as a means of achieving substantive changes in Aboriginal employability, employer commitments and increased Aboriginal employment in the province. Setting up a comprehensive inventory of resumes of Indian and Metis persons in order to improve access to Aboriginal job candidates was one of the program's first projects.

The Aboriginal Employment Development Program complements the Government of Saskatchewan's employment equity strategy which, through a series of special measures has succeeded in increasing the representation of Aboriginal people in the Saskatchewan public service from 3 percent in 1990 to 5.5 percent in 1994.

Objectives

The province established an Aboriginal Employment Development Program in 1992 to link employers with suitable Aboriginal candidates through development of an Aboriginal inventory, support services and cross-cultural awareness.

The program's goal is to increase Aboriginal employability and employment across the public and private sectors in Saskatchewan. The program was put in place to address the fact that the Aboriginal population in

---

Saskatchewan Indian and Metis Affairs Secretariat

The Indian and Metis Affairs Secretariat was established in 1983. It is responsible for Aboriginal affairs in the Saskatchewan government. Its mission is to work in partnership with Indian and Metis people in the province to achieve common goals and aspirations. To this end, it acts as the lead provincial agency in implementing Saskatchewan's Treaty land entitlement agreements, provides funding support to Indian and Metis organizations and administers employment training and business development programs to complement federal initiatives in these areas. It also serves as the window into government for Indian and Metis people.

The Secretariat has a complement of 23 people, an annual administrative budget of approximately $1.7 million, and provides grants and payments of about $15 million annually.

A proactive approach was needed not only to improve the employment situation of Aboriginal people from its current levels, but to ensure that it did not deteriorate with the rapid growth of the labour force.

Saskatchewan is growing very rapidly, with the number of new Aboriginal entrants to the labour market forecast to triple in the next eight years. A proactive approach was needed not only to improve the employment situation of Aboriginal people from its current levels, but to ensure that it did not deteriorate with the rapid growth of the labour force.

The program has adopted the following strategy.

- It maintains a discrete focus on Aboriginal employment and career development.

- It links employers with the Aboriginal workforce by developing and maintaining an inventory of Aboriginal candidates for use by public and private sector employers.

- It relates Aboriginal training to real job opportunities.

- It develops partnership agreements with employers to increase Aboriginal employment.

- It develops partnerships between employers and Indian/Metis institutions of higher learning through "Affiliation Agreements".

The Aboriginal Inventory Project

In 1992, a special project was initiated by the Saskatchewan government to develop a comprehensive inventory of resumes of Indian and Metis persons to improve employer access to Aboriginal candidates and thereby increase the representation of Aboriginal people in the Saskatchewan public service.

A comprehensive inventory of resumes of Indian and Metis persons was developed to improve employer access to Aboriginal candidates.

The project was undertaken as part of a partnership between Saskatchewan's Indian and Metis Affairs Secretariat and the Federation of Saskatchewan Indian Nations. As part of the agreement, the Federation of Saskatchewan Indian Nations (FSIN) seconded an Aboriginal employee to work with SIMAS on the design and development of an Aboriginal human resources inventory. Other organizations, such as the Department of Indian Affairs and Northern Development (through its Aboriginal Workforce Participation Initiative) were also included in the project.

The project was initiated to address two key barriers to increased Aboriginal employment in the Saskatchewan public service.

- The first barrier was the claim made by Saskatchewan government departments and crown corporations that "there were no qualified Aboriginal people" to fill vacancies.

Equivalencies that enable the skill categorization of past experience of Aboriginal people, gained for example by working in Aboriginal governments, are being developed.

- The second barrier was that Aboriginal people did not view the Saskatchewan government as an employer of first choice.

Resumes were collected for the inventory using community networks. Forms used to collect information were modified to include a question asking job candidates to self-identify as being Aboriginal. A legal opinion on this matter took the position this questions could be asked if the information was being used for positive reasons. Information about applicants has been categorized into nine families of skills that are used by the Saskatchewan government. Equivalencies that enable the categorization of past experience of Aboriginal people (gained, for example, by working in Aboriginal governments) are being developed.

The inventory is now operated by the Saskatchewan Public Service Commission. It can be accessed on-line by Saskatchewan government departments. External employers with positions to fill, such as Crown corporations and private sector companies, can telephone the Public Service Commission with their request and receive hard copy back. There is no charge for this service.

There are now almost 1400 resumes on the inventory that can be accessed for competitions at entry levels, middle and senior management and non-traditional positions. Resumes are kept on file for six months. At the end of six months, the Public Service Commission requests updated information. If this is not received, the name is removed.

The Aboriginal Inventory Project is being reviewed in order to implement changes that would improve its effectiveness. These improvements will address ways in which the inventory can be marketed better so that more managers in both the public and private sector in Saskatchewan turn to it to fill vacancies. Changes in organization and information flows will ensure that there is better monitoring and feedback of results.

Aboriginal Employment Development Initiatives

The Aboriginal Employment Development Program also facilitates a variety of different initiatives to develop and enhance employment opportunities for Aboriginal people.

For example, employers receive assistance in designing workplans for Aboriginal employment development. These plans are intended to address barriers and constraints in recruitment, placement, supervision, career pathing and performance assessments. Employers can also receive help in designing "cross-cultural management plans" for new personnel, senior and middle management, supervisors, and colleagues at the worksite. Employers are encouraged to ensure that cross-cultural education and awareness initiatives are delivered by Indian or Metis institutions of higher learning (such as the Saskatchewan Indian Cultural Centre and the Gabriel Dumont Institute).

Employers are encouraged to ensure that cross-cultural education and awareness initiatives are delivered by Indian or Metis institutions of higher learning.

The program facilitates the establishment of employer and employee support services, both of which are designed to promote retention and career enhancement for Aboriginal employees. One example is the Saskatchewan Government's Aboriginal Employees Network. The network was set up to identify issues and promote change within departments in the Saskatchewan government. There are already several hundred Aboriginal members of the network. Members are expected to uphold three principles.

- They must help break down barriers to Aboriginal employment.
- They must be good role models.
- They must help support their communities.

The annual conference is one of the most important activities of the Aboriginal Government Employees Network. Each year the conference, attended by over 500 people, addresses key issues affecting Aboriginal employment. In 1995, the representatives at the conference are designing a workforce strategy which will be presented to human rights organizations in Saskatchewan as well as to Aboriginal political organizations.

Partnership and Affiliation Agreements

SIMAS is developing formal partnership agreements with public and private sector employers throughout the province.

The Saskatchewan Indian and Metis Affairs Secretariat is developing formal partnership agreements with public and private sector employers throughout the province. These agreements commit SIMAS and the employer to work together, in conjunction with the Aboriginal community, unions and employees, to develop Aboriginal employment. The partnerships focus on three areas.

- Programs to facilitate constructive race and cultural relations.
- Aboriginal employment and career development initiatives.
- Business development initiatives of mutual benefit to generate opportunities for Aboriginal employment.

The partners agree to develop an action plan indicating both short and long-term strategies. This also involves co-monitoring progress of the agreement and co-evaluating its results.

The partnership agreements in the health care sector are the first of their kind in Canada.

SIMAS has already signed or obtained commitments for a number of partnership agreements. For example, it has signed two agreements with the Saskatoon District Health Board and the Sherbrooke Community Society to increase Aboriginal employment in the health care sector. The partners are working together to meet Aboriginal health needs in the community while at the same time creating opportunities for Aboriginal employment and business development. The four unions in the health care sector are becoming involved in the partnership, further strengthening the prospects of achieving significant gains for Aboriginal people.

Additional partnership agreements in health care are underway. The Regional Health Board has agreed to form a partnership and the Prince Albert Health Board has given agreement-in-principle.

Affiliation Agreements with Aboriginal educational institutions are another strategy that the Saskatchewan Government is pursuing as part of its Aboriginal Employment Development Program. Affiliation Agreements are intended to encourage Aboriginal educational institutions to forge new relationships with employers across the province. The employment prospects of Aboriginal students will be enhanced to the extent that educational institutions are able to tailor or provide programs to meet the needs of employers. These Agreements are just getting underway.

Results

The Aboriginal Employment Development Program is beginning to yield positive results.

The Aboriginal Inventory Project has been effective in building a large data base of potential Aboriginal candidates and helping them gain employment in government and industry in the province. It has been instrumental in placing Indian and Metis candidates in various positions in the public and private sector. For example, since 1993, 1381 resumes have been coded and entered into the Inventory. A total of 511 job orders from government departments, crown corporations and private sector organizations have been posted through the Inventory, which has resulted in 951 referrals given to government departments, 210 referrals to crown corporations and 186 referrals to private companies. This activity has resulted in at least 73 Aboriginal people hired since 1993. In fact, the number is probably much larger since employers do not necessarily inform the inventory once they have made a hire.

The representation of Aboriginal employees in the Saskatchewan Public Service has increased significantly.

The representation of Aboriginal employees in the Saskatchewan Public Service has also increased significantly. In 1990, Aboriginal people represented 3.0 percent of the Public Service. By 1994, this had increased to 5.5 percent.

The partnership agreements to increase Aboriginal employment in the health care sector are the first of their kind in Canada. They will improve the ability of the health district to meet the health needs of Indian and Metis people since they relate not only to the conventional aspects of healing and health but also to culture, business and other aspects of individual and community health. SIMAS intends to use this model and extend its efforts to work in partnership with employers in other sectors, including education and insurance.

Increasing Aboriginal Employment through the Multi-Year Corporate Equity Program of the Manitoba Telephone System

MTS has found that its employment equity process has contributed to improvements in the overall quality of the work environment and streamlined outmoded procedures, bringing them in line with business priorities.

Since its *Towards Equality* employment equity program was introduced in 1989, Manitoba Telephone System (MTS) has doubled the representation of Aboriginal people in its workforce from 1 percent to 2 percent. There have also been improvements in the occupational representation of Aboriginal people.

These results have been achieved by identifying and removing employment barriers, setting multi-year goals and by continuously monitoring the company's progress. This process has provided the basis for targeting special pre-employment and recruitment measures and for ensuring that other barriers to employment and advancement of Aboriginal people are addressed in an ongoing fashion.

MTS carried out its first thorough examination of its employment systems in 1988 in conjunction with its three unions. Since then, the company has taken steps to remove employment barriers by adapting its recruitment and selection practices and introducing new training and development initiatives. Ongoing auditing of employment practices and monitoring of performance has led to new initiatives designed to promote equal employment opportunities for Aboriginal people.

In addition to increasing the representativeness of its workforce, MTS has found that its employment equity process has contributed to improvements in the overall quality of the work environment and, in many cases, streamlined old, outmoded procedures and brought them back into line with business priorities.

Manitoba Telephone System

Manitoba Telephone System (MTS) is a provincial Crown Corporation providing telecommunications service to the citizens of Manitoba. MTS is part of the Stentor Alliance.

MTS employs nearly 5000 people in a wide range of occupations such as engineering, accounting, occupational health, education and training, electronic technologies, sales and service, and marketing. Aboriginal people make up 2 percent of the corporation's workforce.

MTS's Employment Equity Strategy

In January 1989, Manitoba Telephone System adopted an employment equity program entitled *Towards Equality*. The program is designed to develop a representative workforce in the company by removing employment barriers to the four designated groups (women,

The program is designed to develop a representative workforce by removing employment barriers and taking special measures to provide equal opportunities.

Recruitment and selection barriers that affected Aboriginal candidates included lack of awareness of opportunities and lack of career information available to Aboriginal students.

Measures targeted to Aboriginal people included a scholarship program for Aboriginal students, an operator services job readiness program and a pre-apprenticeship program for women.

Aboriginal people, visible minorities and persons with disabilities) and taking special measures to provide them with equal opportunities. It was motivated in large part by the belief that a more representative workforce is good for the corporation and good for the communities that it serves.

The long-term strategy for employment equity was the result of a joint labour/management advisory committee that was created in 1988. The company's three unions were members of the Advisory Committee that oversaw the process of barrier identification and approved the *Towards Equality* plan prior to corporate approval. Eleven working committees from throughout the province were formed, with about 100 staff members working on the plan. The advisory committee's first task was to analyze MTS operations and to identify past discriminatory practices and employment barriers (both formal and informal) particularly as applied to Aboriginal people, women, visible minorities and people with disabilities. Over 60 barriers were identified. These fell into three categories, namely recruitment and selection, training and development, and benefits or conditions of work.

- Recruitment and selection barriers that affected Aboriginal candidates included lack of awareness of opportunities, access to the application process, equivalency standards, lack of training of managers involved in selection committees, and lack of career information available to Aboriginal students and organizations representing Aboriginal people.

- Training and development barriers that were identified included inadequate information about training opportunities and career options, lack of career pathing guidelines, ad hoc training approval and monitoring processes, access to apprenticeship positions, and the lack of systematic processes with respect to the company's training and development activities.

- In terms of benefits and conditions of work, the company found that the criteria used for evaluating positions were not always valid or consistently applied. Also, MTS had no consistent policy framework on flexible working arrangements.

Following the analysis, committee members identified special measures and initiatives to remove barriers, halt discriminatory practices and to generally improve the equality of the workplace for all employees. Sixty four initiatives were developed. The bulk of the action items, while designed to remove potential barriers for members of the designated groups, would also generally improve the quality of the workplace for everyone. Some of the measures developed in the strategic plan were targeted specifically to Aboriginal people and included a scholarship program for Aboriginal students entering post-secondary education, a job readiness program designed to prepare Aboriginal people for operator services, and a pre-apprentice-ship program for women which included Aboriginal women.

Setting Priorities for Aboriginal Employment

The need for targeted action to increase Aboriginal employment became more apparent in 1989, when the company analyzed its workforce against the external labour market availability. The assessment was done to determine the extent to which the company's workforce was representative of the availability of Aboriginal people in the Manitoba labour market. The comparison revealed that Aboriginal people were under-represented in all eleven job categories in MTS. Goals and timetables for each of the under-represented occupational categories were established for 1990, 1993 1995 and 2000. The objective was to achieve a representative workforce by the year 2000.

Taking Action

Initial emphasis was placed on outreach and recruitment activities.

Since 1989, Manitoba Telephone System has developed, adopted and refined a wide range of initiatives aimed at achieving its goal of having a representative workforce. Initially, emphasis was placed on outreach and recruitment activities to increase the awareness of Aboriginal people about job opportunities in MTS and to encourage them to apply for them.

- In 1989, MTS's western region participated in school symposiums and held an open house for towns and reserves in the region. Recruitment efforts were made in the Community College, Dakota Ojibway Tribal Council, Path Finder and Bridging Gap, with the result that several Aboriginal people were placed in jobs.

- In 1990, MTS recruitment initiatives included a number of community outreach activities. For example, Winnipeg departments were represented in the annual Winnipeg Career symposium and at a career symposium at the University of Manitoba Faculty of Commerce and Economics. Northern, Eastern and Western Regions took their recruitment initiatives on the road, presenting MTS career information at schools in urban and rural communities, as well as at Aboriginal reserve schools.

- MTS has also undertaken on-reserve recruitment activities to overcome the barrier posed by the fact that some Aboriginal people were reluctant to go, on spec, to the nearest urban community to seek job opportunities. MTS contacted the Band Offices on reserves near Thompson and made arrangements for them to receive application forms for their members. MTS employees have made career presentations on reserves and employees from Employment and Immigration Canada (now HRD Canada) would occasionally take applications to the reserves when they went there. In one instance, MTS employees went to a reserve to recruit for an apprentice. Testing and informal interviews were conducted on the reserve.

Several initiatives encourage Aboriginal people to gain education and training that will be needed to prepare them for future job opportunities.

Although MTS continues to be active in attending career symposiums, working on advisory committees and maintaining contact with Aboriginal advisory groups, the company has ceased accepting applications for employment from individuals outside the organization since 1993.

MTS has also introduced several initiatives that are designed to encourage Aboriginal people to gain education and training that will be needed to prepare them for future job opportunities, either in the company or in the economy.

- In 1989, educational awards were established specifically for Aboriginal students as part of the company's comprehensive awards program. The award can be used at any Manitoba accredited post-secondary academic institutions. Preference is given to students pursuing fields of study applicable to MTS, such as computer science, electronic or electrical technology, engineering and telecommunications technology. A total of 20 Aboriginal students have received scholarships. None have been hired on a permanent basis because of the freeze on external hiring. However, where opportunities existed, scholarship recipients were hired for summer employment.

- Since 1991, MTS has provided work experience opportunities for at least 12 Aboriginal people. Work placements (of between one to three weeks) are designed to expose participants to jobs in the telecommunications industry and to provide information on the types of training and education that they will need to become qualified for them. MTS has worked with a variety of Aboriginal organizations as part of this program.

- In 1993, MTS set up a mentoring program with Argyle Alternative High School which is located in the core area of Winnipeg. The students are predominantly Aboriginal. The purpose of the program is to ease the transition of students into the next phase of life through relationships built on mutual support, trust, respect and shared optimism. MTS employees act as mentors. Their responsibilities are to act as a coach on both life and academic issues, and be an advocate, friend, motivator and role model for the students. Of the 12 students who have participated in this initiative, 10 are still in school.

MTS has also put training and development programs in place as a means of increasing the representation of Aboriginal people in specific occupations in the company. For example, in 1990, an Operator Services program was established as a one-time cooperative venture between the MTS and the Winnipeg Core Area initiative. The program offered pre-employment training through courses in language development, typing, communication and personal development. Its purpose was to give persons of Aboriginal ancestry and visible minorities equal opportunity for employment in the Operator Services field. Of the 18 people who took the course, 10 were Aboriginal. All participants were provided employment as Operators with MTS.

Fostering Enhanced Relationships

MTS has been increasing its efforts to create attitudinal change among its employees as a means of creating an environment where diversity is respected and valued. A number of these initiatives have been specifically designed to foster enhanced relationships with Aboriginal people.

- In 1992, a Cross Cultural Exchange project between Sagkeeng First Nation and MTS took place. Leaders from Sagkeeng hosted an interactive seminar and tour for seniors managers from MTS. The initiative was intended to provide a basis for understanding and appreciating cultural differences in structure, administration and management styles of the two organizations.

- MTS Northern Region and the Thompson Multicultural Centre co-sponsored the delivery of a cross cultural awareness course, designed for MTS employees and other organizations. Course content focused on working with a diversified workforce and overcoming cultural barriers.

- In 1994, two half-day workshops entitled "Walk a Mile in my Moccasins" were held for MTS managers. The purpose of the workshops was to learn how to communicate and interact more effectively with Aboriginal people.

- Also in 1994, MTS managers participated in a four-day workshop at the Red Willow Lodge, which specializes in the delivery of Aboriginal cultural awareness education. Employees who participated in the

MTS has been increasing its efforts to create attitudinal change among its employees as a means of creating an environment where diversity is respected and valued.

MTS managers participated in a four-day workshop at the Red Willow Lodge. Employees gained an awareness that would benefit both co-workers and customers.

workshop left with an awareness that would benefit both co-workers and customers.

Results

Between 1989 and 1993, MTS increased the representation of Aboriginal people in its workforce. Key results with respect to Aboriginal employment include the following.

Setting realistic goals, systematically removing barriers and targeting initiatives to specific problem areas has been valuable for the corporation.

- The total Aboriginal representation rate doubled between 1988 and 1993. Aboriginal people now represent 2 percent of MTS total workforce.

- Aboriginal employment increased in 6 of the 11 occupational groups including middle and other managers, professionals, supervisors, clerical workers, sales workers and other manual workers.

- MTS has achieved most of the goals that it set in 1988 for Aboriginal representation in different occupations. By the end of 1992, MTS had met or exceeded its goals in 8 of the eleven occupation groups.

It is important to note that the company reduced its workforce in 1991, which caused a slowing in the movement toward a representative workforce. The decision to freeze all external recruitment in 1993 and fill all opportunities from within (either by competition or re-deployment) means that overall representation rates for Aboriginal people in MTS's workforce are not anticipated to change in 1995.

Manitoba Telephone System has found that its approach of setting realistic goals, systematically removing barriers and targeting initiatives to specific problem areas has been valuable for the corporation. Removing the barriers has improved the overall quality of the work environment and has streamlined outmoded procedures and brought them back into line with business priorities.

CN's Strategy for Maintaining Aboriginal Employment During Corporate Downsizing

Despite massive downsizing, CN has been able to increase the representation of Aboriginal people in its workforce.

Canadian National has had a long-standing commitment to achieving equitable representation of Aboriginal people in its workforce. Since the mid-1980s, the company has adopted employment equity practices to increase the representation of Aboriginal people, and other designated group members, in its workforce. The continuing goal has been to create and maintain an environment which fosters the hiring and promotion of qualified members of the four designated groups.

However, since the early commitments to employment equity were made, CN has been forced by economic factors to streamline its overall workforce. The company's total workforce has declined by close to 40 percent, from almost 44,000 employees in 1986 to just about 25,000 employees by the end of 1994.

Despite massive downsizing, CN has been able to increase the representation of Aboriginal people in its workforce. It has accomplished this by strengthening its outreach to Aboriginal communities and by using staffing opportunities that do emerge in a strategic fashion. In addition, the company has taken steps to increase management accountability for achieving a representative workforce, thereby making employment equity an integral part of its business practices.

The Challenges

Economic conditions in the past decade have forced CN to reduce its costs and improve service in order to survive as a viable, competitive business. In the past decade, the company has gone through the difficult task of streamlining and restructuring its operations. Massive downsizing of the workforce has been one of the most visible aspects of streamlining and restructuring.

In this environment, there have been significant challenges to achieving a workforce that is representative of the Canadian workforce as a whole.

Canadian National

Canadian National operates Canada's largest railway system, supplying customers with freight rail transportation and related services. Canadian National is composed of CN North America (rail operations) and CN Enterprises. CN Enterprises includes: CN Real Estate, CN Tower, CANAC International and AMF Technotransport. Together they employ about 25,000 people (excluding AMF Technotransport), the majority of whom work for CN North America.

CN North America, the company's railway operation, represents 90 percent of CN's total revenues. CN North America supplies carload and intermodal distribution systems in Canada and the United States.

The Corporation was established by an Act of Parliament in 1919 and has been wholly owned by the federal government. Plans to privatize the company were announced in 1995.

In 1994, there were 402 Aboriginal employees in CN, representing 1.6 percent of the total workforce.

- Hiring opportunities diminished steadily over the decade, for a total of only 555 new hires in 1994.

- Promotion opportunities declined as the company became smaller and more streamlined.

- Collective agreements required that people who had been laid off and who had recall rights be offered employment before hiring externally.

- The company's obligation to non-unionized employees declared surplus meant that they had to be re-integrated before hiring externally.

In the climate of downsizing, the need to pay particular attention to equity in the workplace increased significantly.

In this climate, the company recognized that the need to pay particular attention to equity in the workplace had increased significantly. Backing off from employment equity would mean that gains that took years to achieve could easily be wiped out and that the prospects of achieving a representative workforce would be delayed well into the future.

This was of particular concern because the necessity of corporate renewal pointed to the increased value of a representative workforce. The company required highly motivated, qualified employees if it was to compete and survive. CN recognized that it would have to draw on the broadest pool of talent, energy and creativity to achieve this. As such, employment equity, which the company had found to be effective in creating a diversely-talented workforce, took on new importance.

CN also recognized that it was important to maintain the momentum towards increasing the representation of Aboriginal people in its workforce. In 1986, the company had 436 Aboriginal employees, representing only 1 percent of its workforce, well below the labour market availability of Aboriginal people.

Strengthened Outreach to Aboriginal Communities

The most important strategy that CN has pursued in order to maintain Aboriginal employment has been to increase its outreach initiatives.

The most important strategy that CN has pursued to maintain Aboriginal employment has been to increase its outreach initiatives. This has built awareness among Aboriginal people of CN as a corporation and of the employment opportunities that may emerge in both the short and long-term. As a result, when hiring opportunities do emerge, the company is often able to find and attract qualified employees.

The company uses a number of different approaches, including providing educational awards for Aboriginal students, maintaining regular contact with community organizations, using a telecommunications link to publicize job openings, and arranging short-term work-placements and *stages* for Aboriginal youth.

In 1988, CN established its Native Educational Award Program to assist and encourage Aboriginal people to follow university studies that would lead to a career related in some way to transportation. The program is promoted through advertising and the distribution of CN's Native Educational Awards Program brochure to over 500 band councils, Native Friendship Centres, colleges, universities and other organizations. The company requests the assistance from the contact person in each organization in reaching as many Aboriginal students as possible and distributing brochures to Aboriginal students who may be interested in an award. The program is also advertised in Aboriginal publications.

Since the program's inception, 30 scholarship of $1500 have been awarded. Award recipients have pursued studies in industrial relations, management studies, engineering, medicine, law, geology, journalism, and translation. Aboriginal students from across the country have received awards. About 37 percent of recipients have been Status Indians, 20 percent non-status Indians, 37 percent of Metis ancestry and 7 percent have been Inuit. Women have received 60 percent of all awards. CN makes every effort to provide award winners with employment during the summer break.

Much of CN's outreach effort involves working with Aboriginal community groups and associations. CN maintains regular contact with these groups to ensure that their members are aware of CN as a potential employer. Some of these organizations include band councils, Friendship Centres, Aboriginal employment centres as well as Aboriginal training and education organizations. Direct visits by CN staff to First Nations have resulted in hiring of Aboriginal employees.

The company attends conferences, workshops and career fairs. For example, in 1994, CN collaborated in the preparation of a workshop on the recruitment and retention of Aboriginal employees. Company representatives also attended this workshop.

Equi-Link is one of the most valuable tools that the company has developed to enhance its capacity to reach organizations representing members of all designated groups. Equi-Link was launched in 1991 and there are now over 140 partners on the network, 49 of which represent Aboriginal people. Some of the Aboriginal partners are Algonquin Lake First Nation, Anigawcigig Institute for Native Training, Can-Am Indian Friendship Centre, Matawa Tribal Council, Mohawk Council at Akwesasne and the Native Canadian Centre of Toronto.

Equi-Link takes advantage of the speed and efficiency of facsimile machines to publicize special company initiatives, such as scholarships and tours for special groups. It has also been very effective in disseminating information on job openings at CN. The system has helped to ensure that designated group people quickly receive information they need to assess whether they possess the minimal qualifications for a specific job opening

Much of CN's outreach effort involves working with Aboriginal community groups and associations, especially through its Equi-Link fax network. Forty nine of the 140 partners on the network represent Aboriginal people.

and to submit a timely application. The widespread dissemination of CN's needs through this network means that the positions are filled by the best possible candidates.

CN has developed several other outreach initiatives.

- In 1994, a short-term work-placement (or *stage*) was organized for an Aboriginal woman at the Transcona Shop in Winnipeg.

- A donation was made to the Native Student Services at the University of Alberta in support of Aboriginal people seeking university degrees.

- Direct contact has been increased between CN representatives and members of Aboriginal communities residing near CN's operations.

Using Staffing Opportunities Strategically

To achieve sustained increases in the representation of Aboriginal people in the workforce, during the company's massive downsizing and restructuring, has meant paying particular attention to hiring, promotion and retention of Aboriginal employees.

CN managed to increase the level of representation of Aboriginal people in recruitment, even though difficult economic conditions resulted in few hirings.

Achieving sustained increases in the representation of Aboriginal people has meant paying particular attention to hiring, promotion and retention of Aboriginal employees.

CN's Hiring of Aboriginal People 1986-94 (selected years)		
	Representation of Aboriginal People	
	% of New Hires	% of Total Workforce
1986	0.5	1.0
1990	6.3	1.3
1994	6.3	1.6

Source: CN Employment Equity Reports

The company's strengthened outreach initiatives made it possible to find and hire qualified Aboriginal candidates for the available job openings.

The company's strengthened outreach initiatives made it possible to find and hire qualified Aboriginal candidates for the available job openings. In each year between 1987 and 1994, the representation rate of Aboriginal people in the total number of new hires by the company exceeded their representation rate in the workforce as a whole. For example, in 1994, the 6.3 percent share of Aboriginal people in CN's new hires is well above their census labour market availability of 3 percent. This contributed to the overall increase in representation over time.

CN has taken steps to ensure that Aboriginal people are represented in its University Recruitment Program. In 1994, of the nine people recruited overall, one person was of Aboriginal ancestry. This program also has a formal mentoring component, which is designed to facilitate the integration of new employees into the company and to increase the retention rate of new, high-potential employees.

CN has also been successful in recruiting Aboriginal people for seasonal track work. In 1994, 9 percent of new hires were Aboriginal people. This success is the result of all outreach activities, notably Equi-Link and direct contact with Aboriginal peoples. The long-term effects on permanent employment for Aboriginal people as a result of this is positive. Despite downsizing, the representation of Aboriginal employees has increased and retention is good.

Increased Management Accountability

The integration of employment equity into management practices will continue to facilitate Aboriginal employment during a sustained period of corporate restructuring.

Part of CN's corporate renewal strategy has involved integrating employment equity into management practices and accountability. This was necessary to maintain progress in increasing the representation of all the designated groups in CN's workforce, not only of Aboriginal people. The integration of employment equity into management practices will continue to facilitate Aboriginal employment during a sustained period of corporate restructuring.

In 1992, the employment equity action planning process was revised so that every level of CN's management is involved. The President and CEO sets corporate objectives and requests qualitative and numerical action plans from all management.

All departments have integrated employment equity goals and action plans into their decision process. Managers at every level and function of the company have specified equity goals and ways to achieve them. Every work unit has outlined its current employment situation, expected results and an action plan that specifies a time frame and person responsible for implementing each proposed solution. Actions and results are reported at year-end.

By involving every region, division, district and department, CN expects to maintain or slightly improve the statistical representation of Aboriginal people, despite limited hiring opportunities and downsizing.

Results

Between 1986 and 1994, the representation of Aboriginal people in the CN workforce increased.

The representation of Aboriginal people in the CN workforce increased from 1.0 percent in 1986 to 1.6 percent in 1994. This increase was achieved while CN's workforce was reduced by almost 40 percent.

Aboriginal people accounted for 1.6 percent of CN's permanent full-time labour force in 1994. This is up from 1.0 percent in 1986. This increase was achieved while CN's workforce was reduced by almost 40 percent.

Despite downsizing, CN remains committed to increasing the representation of Aboriginal people and retaining them in its workforce. This objective constitutes one of CN's employment equity objectives, which are an integral part of the company's business plan.

Foreign Affair's Aboriginal Internship Program

The Department of Foreign Affairs and International Trade is striving to encourage and promote the full participation of Aboriginal peoples within its ranks.

The Department of Foreign Affairs and International Trade is striving to encourage and promote the full participation of Aboriginal peoples within its ranks. The department created the Aboriginal Internship Program in 1991 specifically to improve the representation of Aboriginal people in the Foreign Service Officer group.

The Aboriginal Internship Program is designed to stimulate the interest of Aboriginal people in the department through extensive outreach recruitment measures. It complements the department's Annual Foreign Service Recruitment campaign.

The program has been successful in increasing the number of Aboriginal Foreign Service Officers in the department. Between 1991 and 1993, seven participants were recruited and two completed their training.

The Department's Aboriginal Employment Strategies

The Aboriginal Internship Program is one of a number of initiatives that the department is undertaking to improve the representation of Aboriginal people in its workforce and achieve the full participation of Aboriginal peoples within its ranks. In the context of its 5-year employment equity strategy, which it developed in 1991, the department has implemented a range of initiatives aimed at improving the representation of and career opportunities for Aboriginal people in its workforce.

Other initiatives include targeted recruitment, increased outreach, improved communication with Aboriginal employees, promotion of a supportive work environment, and fostering awareness and appreciation of Aboriginal values and culture. Aboriginal employees have also been provided with training and career development opportunities through the department's Developmental Assignment Program and the Career Assignment Program. The department has also set a minimum target of seven Aboriginal students to participate in the summer employment program.

Foreign Affairs and International Trade

The role of the Department of Foreign Affairs and International Trade is to advise the government on foreign policy matters and represent Canada's interests abroad. The department operates diplomatic offices in more than 80 countries around the world.

The department currently employs approximately 3800 Canadian employees, excluding locally engaged staff. Of that total, about two-third are rotational employees (who must be prepared to serve anywhere in the world) and one-third are non-rotational employees, who serve only at headquarters. Aboriginal employees represent 1.3 percent of the department's workforce.

Goals of the Aboriginal Internship Program

The department created the Aboriginal Internship Program in 1991 specifically to address the significant under-representation of Aboriginal people in the Foreign Service Officer occupational group.

The Aboriginal Internship Program was created to address the under-representation of Aboriginal people in the Foreign Service Officer group.

Foreign Service officers are rotational employees who are required to serve at any location in Canada or the world as determined by the department. Recruitment into the Foreign Service is done at the entry level from outside the Public Service. Recruitment activities for the Foreign Service Officer Group are centred on the annual national recruitment campaigns which are conducted through the Public Service Commission's Post Secondary Recruitment Campaign. This involves advertising in the media and on-campus recruitment. The Public Service Commission has responsibility for channelling applicants and administering the various entry tests.

The department was concerned by the fact that the Foreign Service group has had a lower rate of Aboriginal representation than could have been expected given the corresponding workforce availability figures. This situation was unlikely to improve quickly in the absence of special measures. In particular, the department was concerned that Aboriginal students were not sufficiently aware of the opportunities within the Foreign Service and were not giving consideration to the Department of Foreign Affairs as an employer of first choice.

Aboriginal students were not sufficiently aware of the opportunities within the Foreign Service.

The department set a target that 7 percent of Foreign Service recruits (averaged over a two year period) should be Aboriginal candidates. To help achieve that goal, the department has received approval from the Public Service Commission to recruit three or four Aboriginal persons to entry-level Foreign Service Officer positions each year over the coming years.

Elements of the Program

The key elements of the Aboriginal Internship Program are active outreach to Aboriginal organizations and the use of a selection process specifically designed for this group. Once hired, the individual undergoes the department's extensive Foreign Service Officer training.

Outreach is a key element of the Program. To date, it has been promoted to over 500 Aboriginal associations.

Outreach is a key element of the program. The department actively promotes the program to Aboriginal organizations and Aboriginal media. To date, the Program has been promoted to over 500 Aboriginal associations. Organizations have already been contacted in Quebec, Manitoba, British Columbia and the Atlantic Provinces. Outreach activities also involve providing regional briefings to encourage Aboriginal candidates to apply to the program.

Targeted recruitment is done with the assistance of the Public Service Commission's regional offices and includes promotion of the Program to

The interview panel is made up of managers in the department. Wherever possible, there is Aboriginal representation on the panel.

The Aboriginal Internship Program has proven to be a success. It has been instrumental in increasing the department's overall representation rate of Aboriginal people.

various Aboriginal organizations, and provision of in-depth information on the department and the Foreign Service. Targeted recruitment materials have been developed. For example, a brochure on the program, that includes common questions and answers about the Foreign Service, has been prepared.

Candidates for the program are selected using a process specifically designed for this group. All Aboriginal recruits must take the entry-level selection test that is administered by the Public Service Commission for all entry-level positions within the federal government. In addition to this test of their written communication skills, candidates participate in interviews. The interview panel is made up of managers in the department. Wherever possible, there is Aboriginal representation on the interview panel.

Once hired, all new recruits to the department are based in Ottawa, where they undergo formal classroom and on-the-job training. This leads to a career in one of the following areas: Management and Consular Affairs; the Trade Commissioner Service; and Political and Economic Affairs.

Training programs differ for each career specialty and last from one to four years, including training in one of Canada's official languages (if required), several months of common training at the Canadian Foreign Service Institute and possible pre-posting foreign language training. First international assignments last from two to four years, after which officers typically return to Ottawa or are assigned to another post abroad. The general training program is designed to meet the needs of every Foreign Service recruit.

Results

Given the department's past difficulties in attracting Aboriginal people to the Foreign Service, the Aboriginal Internship Program has proven to be a success.

Since the Program's inception in 1991, more than 50 candidates have been interviewed. Seven Aboriginal candidates have been accepted into the program for training as Foreign Service Officers and two recruits have finished their training.

A number of important employment equity objectives have been achieved through the program including increased awareness among departmental managers of the employability of Aboriginal people, increased interest in the department by Aboriginal people, and increased representation of Aboriginal people. This Program has been instrumental in increasing the department's overall representation rate of Aboriginal people from 0.7 percent in 1989 to 1.3 percent in 1994.

Cogema Resources' Training and Apprenticeship Initiatives

Cogema has been very active in creating training and apprenticeship opportunities for northern residents.

Cogema Resources Inc. owns and operates the Cluff Lake Mine in northern Saskatchewan. For the past 15 years, Cogema has been successful in enhancing employment, training and business opportunities for Aboriginal people and other residents of Northern Saskatchewan.

The company has been very active in creating training and apprenticeship opportunities for northern residents, especially the residents of the communities in its impact area, such as Beauval, Jans Bay, Patunak, Ile-a-la-Crosse, La Loche and Buffalo Narrows. Company training programs have allowed northerners to develop new skills and advance in the company.

Cogema has also been a strong supporter of the establishment of a Northern Apprenticeship Committee and is working closely with it to develop a coordinated and responsive apprenticeship training system in northern Saskatchewan.

Cogema Resources Inc.

Cogema Resources Inc. is wholly owned by Cogema S.A. of France. It holds a 100 percent interest in the Cluff Lake uranium mine and mill in northern Saskatchewan and, through its subsidiary MINATCO Ltd., a 70 percent interest in the McLean Lake uranium project that is currently under construction. Cogema Resources is also a joint venture partner in a number of other uranium mines in Saskatchewan, including Cigar Lake and McArthur River.

Cogema Resources is headquartered in Saskatoon. It has 300 employees. About 200 of these work in the Cluff Lake mine. The majority of its workforce (55 percent) is comprised of northern Saskatchewan residents, of whom most are Aboriginal people. The mines are unionized at both Cluff Lake and McLean Lake. Unionized workers are represented by the Communications, Energy and Paperworkers Union (CEP).

The mines use a fly-in commuter system in which employees are flown to work for seven 11-hour days followed by seven days off. There are no permanent town sites. Instead, residences and recreational facilities are provided at the mine-sites.

Cogema's Commitment

Cogema Resources' policy commitment is to maximize the employment, training and business opportunities for northern Saskatchewan residents. In part, this reflects its obligations under the provincial surface lease to maximize the recruitment, hiring, training and advancement of northern people at all skill levels in the operation. However, Cogema's commitment to the people of northern Saskatchewan goes beyond employment and training. It also encompasses outreach, scholarships, business development and community liaison.

Cogema employs a full-time northern affairs coordinator to implement its northern recruitment strategy and to work with northern communities, organizations and employment agencies to ensure employment and training opportunities.

The company participates in high school career days and attends community college classes on invitation. Cogema also operates a scholarship program under which six university scholarships and three institute scholarships are awarded to northerners each year.

In-House Training Programs

Cogema has developed most of its own training programs. The training programs incorporate principles of adult learning, with courses structured to enable people to learn at their own pace. There are four categories of training programs: mining, mill operations, administration, and camp maintenance. Cogema has set up and offers two in-house training programs in the area of heavy equipment and mill operators training.

All training is done on-site. Training programs consist of a series of training modules which are taught by experienced on-site trainers. The training is progressive and, as the employees master higher level skills, they earn higher wages.

All recruitment for the company's training programs is done by in-house company recruiters who tap into community resources and referring agencies. In addition, jobs are posted on-site and current employees are able to apply for positions as they become open or vacant. In all instances, the best and most qualified candidate is selected for the position. The selection process may involve community or field screening and interviews conducted by the general foreperson or journeyperson, together with a member of the human resources department. While some of the entrants into these programs are recently out of high school, most of the heavy equipment operators are mature workers.

The mill operator training program illustrates the approach taken by Cogema in its in-house training. There are eight core training modules in the mill operator training program. Each module relates to one of the major parts of the mill process:

- Module A: Crushing
- Module B: Grinding
- Module C: Acid Leaching
- Module D: Counter Current Decantation
- Module E: Solvent Extraction Plant
- Module F: Precipitation
- Module G: Reagents and Packaging
- Module H: Mill General Services

There is also training in areas other than mill areas, including forklift operation and pump classes.

Much of the mill training is done by senior operators or the shift foreperson. Most of the training is based on textbooks, with some video training as

Cogema's training programs incorporate principles of adult learning, with courses structured to enable people to learn at their own pace.

The selection process may involve community or field screening and interviews. In all instances, the best and most qualified candidate is selected for the position.

well. Performance objectives are set for each module and there is an exam for each area.

The trainee spends approximately six months in each training area. The training program is broken into a number of on-the-job and classroom training segments.

- The area introduction segment takes about one week. The employee is first shown around by the trainer. The employee is given time to read the manual as well as to learn how to take readings, safety hazards, safety equipment, startup and shutdown procedures, cleanup, etc..

- Following this, trainees receive one week of on-the-job training during which they run the area on their own, with either the trainer or another operator on hand to help in the case of difficulties.

- The next segment is a half day of classroom training. The trainer will go over the training manual with the new operator and explain it in more detail and answer questions.

- New operators receive a further three months of on-the job training during which they run the area on their own. If needed, they spend more time with the trainer or senior operator. When the shift foreman feels the operator is ready, the trainer is advised that it is time for the new operator to write the area exam.

- After the employee has passed the area exam and has spent six months in a certain area, he/she is evaluated by the supervisor. A satisfactory evaluation means that the new operator receives a wage raise and moves on to another area.

The procedure is repeated in the new area. In total, it takes 66 months to become a 1A senior mill operator.

Apprenticeship Initiatives

Cogema's apprenticeship programs are reserved exclusively for northern residents. This commitment is an integral part of the collective agreement with the Communications, Energy and Paperworkers Union (CEP). Apprentices can be registered in six provincially certified trades, namely as electricians, plumbers, welders, heavy duty mechanics, millwrights, and instrumentation technicians.

Under the collective agreement, all apprenticeship positions are first posted in-house. If there are no suitable internal candidates, Cogema will recruit from the communities in its impact area.

Cogema's apprenticeship programs are reserved exclusively for northern residents. This commitment is an integral part of the collective agreement with the Communications, Energy and Paperworkers Union.

The Northern Affairs Coordinator is actively involved in initiatives to identify northerners for entry-level, skilled and semi-skilled jobs and for on-site training programs.

The Northern Affairs Coordinator is actively involved in initiatives to identify northerners for entry-level, skilled and semi-skilled jobs and for on-site training programs. This involves contacting the Band Office, economic development office or employment counsellor in local communities, as well as school principals and contacts in relevant agencies. The company has also found that in-home meetings can be very effective in getting an insight into individuals in the community who are both interested and suited to a career in a mine.

Prior to indentureship into a trade as an apprentice, the applicant is normally required to work for six months in the trade as a tradeshelper. However, recognition is also given to individuals who have previous training or experience in any of the trades.

Upon successful completion and assessment, the tradeshelper is offered the apprenticeship position. The apprentice is registered with the Saskatchewan apprenticeship program.

An in-house counsellor is assigned to the apprentice. The counsellor has the following roles and responsibilities:

- to provide assistance to the apprentice in making the transition from northern communities to urban centres;

- to familiarize the trainee to the institution;

- to act as a liaison between the institute and the apprentice;

- to assist with personal problems (related to home life, school, etc.) while in training;

- to arrange for tutors, if required by the student; and

- to assist in finding appropriate accommodations.

Cogema has been actively involved in the establishment of the Northern Apprenticeship Committee.

Since the apprenticeship program is based on progression, a student will only attend institute training once in each calender year. If a student requires educational upgrading, the company will provide tutors in the communities or will provide tutors through the training institutes.

Upon successful completion of the apprenticeship program the apprentice moves to journeyman status.

Northern Apprenticeship Committee

Cogema has been actively involved in the establishment of the Northern Apprenticeship Committee (NAC). This was proposed in 1993 by the Saskatchewan Provincial Apprenticeship Board to promote and coordinate an apprenticeship training system that is flexible enough to meet the unique challenges of the northern Saskatchewan labour market while maintaining the industry-set standards of the apprenticeship training system.

This initiative is a response to the fact that apprenticeship opportunities are very limited in northern Saskatchewan (with the notable exception of the mining sector). It is also designed to shift the emphasis away from pre-employment training to training initiatives that will result in higher level, portable skills for northern residents and long-term job opportunities. The committee is particularly interested in promoting apprenticeship opportunities in the forestry and small business services sectors, such as autobody repair, cosmetology, etc..

The Committee is in the process of developing a registry of northerners with trades experience or qualifications.

The Northern Apprenticeship Committee became operational in early 1995. The Committee is in the process of developing a registry of northerners with trades experience or qualifications as well as identifying those individuals in northern Saskatchewan who would be interested in pursuing a career as a tradesperson.

The Northern Apprenticeship Committee is also in the process of signing Memoranda of Agreement with the major stakeholders in the region. Cogema has signed a Memorandum of Agreement with the Committee which makes it clear that the company supports the efforts of the NAC and, consistent with its surface lease agreements and collective agreements, will cooperate closely with the Committee in encouraging the training and advancement of Northern apprentices and tradespeople. Examples of specific commitments are as follows.

- Cogema will encourage existing northern tradespeople to register with the Committee and will accept referrals from the NAC for trade vacancies in its northern operations.

- Where appropriate, Cogema will encourage its contractors to establish a working relationship with the Committee.

- Cogema will cooperate with and support the NAC's efforts to develop and implement post-journey updating training in the north.

Results

Well over half of employees trained over the past few years in all of Cogema's training programs have been Aboriginal people. Most of the workforce has had the opportunity to learn new skills and move up in the company.

Well over half of employees trained over the past few years in all of Cogema's training programs have been Aboriginal people.

- To date, Cogema has indentured 28 people of Indian ancestry in Saskatchewan's apprenticeship trades training program. Over 11 employees have graduated with their ticket from Cogema's apprenticeship programs.

- Training and related job experience have ensured that northerners employed at the Cluff Lake Mine with Cogema have increased their chances for job promotions to more senior positions.

- Northern employees now hold a wide variety of jobs, including mine shift boss, mill operator, heavy duty mechanic, warehouse foreman, trainer, radiation/ventilation technician.

- Both the President and Vice-President positions in the union local have been held by northern Aboriginal people.

As a result of its training initiatives, Cogema has benefitted from a stable, long-term workforce, as well as strong ongoing community support for its operations.

As a result of its training initiatives, Cogema has benefitted from a stable, long-term workforce, as well as strong ongoing community support for its operations. Over 50 percent of the Cluff Lake workforce is from northern Saskatchewan communities and 90 percent of these workers are Aboriginal people. Cogema's training initiatives have contributed significantly to the success of its mining operations and have been a major factor in the company's ability to meet its commitment to maximize the hiring and advancement of northern people in its operations.

The Stores Training Program at The North West Company

The North West Company has invested $1 million to date on the development of a comprehensive Store Training Program for its chain of *Northern* stores. The training program incorporates user-friendly and culturally-sensitive learning materials and is designed to provide training to local Aboriginal people so that they can increase their jobs skills, increase their career potential and prepare for management positions in the store operations.

The training program is based on training modules that have been specifically developed for training in the north and geared for development of people in the community. Materials and support structures encourage local Aboriginal staff and new recruits to progress into management positions.

The North West Company is the largest private employer of Aboriginal people in Canada. The Stores Training Program is part of a comprehensive set of initiatives by The North West Company to promote employment and business development opportunities for Aboriginal people. Other initiatives include opening new *Tomorrow* stores on a joint venture basis with Aboriginal development corporations, with profits shared between the retailer and the Band, and the preferential use of Aboriginal-owned transportation businesses, whenever possible. The North West Company also makes significant corporate contributions to social, cultural and educational programs that benefit customers, staff and the communities that it serves. Half of all contributions are targeted at programs run by Aboriginal organizations.

The North West Company is Canada's largest private employer of Aboriginal people. The Stores Training Program is part of a comprehensive set of initiatives promoting Aboriginal employment and business development.

The North West Company

The North West Company is the leading retailer of food, family apparel and general merchandise in small northern communities in Canada. The company operates 156 *Northern* stores in Canada and 21 *AC Value Center* stores in Alaska. The company's headquarters are located in Winnipeg, where the major distribution centre is located. The company is the largest marketing agency of Inuit art in the world.

The North West Company has a total of 3700 employees. Of these, 1700 are Aboriginal employees, making the company the largest private employer of Aboriginal people in Canada.

The North West Company is the first major non-Aboriginal corporation to publicly support the entrenchment of Aboriginal self-government as an inherent right.

Objectives

In 1991, The North West Company introduced a new Stores Training Program for its *Northern* stores. The program was developed with two objectives in mind. It was designed to reduce staff turnover in its *Northern* stores, a problem that exit interviews identified was caused in large part by insufficient and outdated training. It was also designed to provide the opportunity for all employees to develop the skills to grow and advance in the company.

The Stores Training Program is designed to enable the company's staff members to learn and practice while on the job.

Learning materials are culturally-adapted and exercises are based on on-the-job training.

Modules are written to allow for different learning speeds, education levels and take into consideration that English is often a second language in the North.

Key Features of the Training Program

The Stores Training Program is designed to enable the company's staff members to learn and practice while on the job. The training program is based on a series of about 120 functional, departmental and management-specific training modules, with some supporting videos. Each training module explains a particular procedure, program or function related to the operation of the stores. They are grouped into different sections such as food, general merchandise, office functions and management.

The training program incorporates a number of significant features.

- Learning materials are culturally-adapted and exercises are based on on-the-job training. Since 70 percent of the company's staff and the majority of its customers are Aboriginal, the information in the training modules has been developed to reflect the communities in which the company operates. This includes the use of Aboriginal names; describing situations that happen in stores in local northern communities; and using Aboriginal staff and company store locations in the videos. Relevant social changes are incorporated in some of the training modules (for example the Healthy Living Training Module explains changing eating patterns in the North).

- Materials are grouped into structured and progressive levels. Assignments are based on the individual's position in the store, experience and career goals.

- Modules are written to allow for different learning speeds, education levels and take into consideration that English is often a second language in the North. The material is targeted at a Grade 8 reading level to ensure that it is understandable to a large portion of staff.

- The training program allows for staff to take an active role in directing their progress and monitoring their own results.

- Module content, materials and support structures encourage Aboriginal staff and new recruits to progress into management positions. Management training skills are built into the system as an integral part of the practical components of a number of modules to mimic real life situations.

- Progress will be rewarded through certificates, recognition awards and advancement to progressively senior levels of responsibility.

The program is continually reviewed and updated. A committee was formed in mid-1995 to examine how the program could be modified and improved.

The Learning Process

Most training modules have four parts or steps that an employee will progress through. These include an instruction book, a quiz book, a practical exercise, and a final test. There are some variations to this pattern, depending on the module.

The Instruction Book helps set company standards and procedures for a large workforce that is spread across the country.

- The Instruction Book provides the basic information related to the task or policy. It tells the student why and how the company does things in a certain way. Staff members are able to work through the material at their own speed. It also helps set company standards and procedures for a large workforce that is spread across the country.

- The Quiz Book enables staff members to test their understanding of the topic by answering a number of self test questions as they work through the technical information in the Instruction Book. At the end of the Quiz Book is a self quiz to prepare them for the final test.

- A Practical Exercise is given by the employee's manager and provides the opportunity for the staff member to demonstrate that they not only understand the procedure or task, but can do it properly.

- The Final Test is designed to certify that the student remembers much of the important information that they have learned.

As each module is successfully completed, a *Northern* icon is affixed by the employee and his or her manager next to the employee's name on a wall chart hanging in every store. The chart lists the name of each staff member and every training module available. Progress will be rewarded through certificates, recognition programs and awards.

Development of the Training Modules

The original module list was compiled based on suggestions from approximately 100 staff members. This included store staff, Retail Operation staff in Winnipeg, marketing staff etc. The objective was to provide training material for all levels and types of positions in all the company's stores.

Modules are categorized into twelve groups.

Modules are now categorized into twelve groups: The North West Company, Customer Service, Food, General Merchandise, Accounting, Loss Prevention, Maintenance and Safety, Environmental Issues, Management, Human Resources, Lifestyle, and Quick Stop (fast food).

Store and head office personnel, and professional and trade experts are involved in the compilation, editing and final review of the resources to make sure that they meet the company's distinct needs and particularly those of Aboriginal employees.

The Stores Training Program is beginning to produce significant results. Participation in the program has increased dramatically over the past three years.

Results

The Stores Training Program is beginning to produce significant results.

Participation in the program has increased dramatically over the past three years. Almost 90 percent of managers in the *Northern* stores, 88 percent of full-time employees and 40 percent of regular part-time employees participated voluntarily in the Stores Training Program in 1994.

Participation in the Program			
	1992	1993	1994
# of Participating Stores	38	145	151
# of Participating Staff in Stores	104	986	1524
# of Participating HO Staff	-	44	80
# Modules Completed by Staff	236	3090	6884

Staff Response has been very positive towards the program, as the typical reactions indicate.

- "Everything is explained in simple terms. The Quiz Book helped me understand more than if I just read an explanation."

- "This (Markup) module helps to make my work in the store easier and gives me confidence."

- "I think it is important because before I didn't know anything about cost, markup or retail. Now I know what they are and can be more useful around the store."

- "This (Snowmobile Program) module is easy to understand. I didn't know what to do, but now I have completed this module I know what to do."

The company feels that the Stores Training Program has had a significant positive impact in reducing management turnover and increasing the percentage of Aboriginal people in management positions.

The company feels that the Stores Training Program has had a significant positive impact in reducing management turnover and increasing the percentage of Aboriginal people in management positions.

- Store management turnover saw a 9 percent reduction between 1991 and 1994.

The company also anticipates that there will be a number of longer-term benefits including greater employee job satisfaction and contributions to the growth and profitability of the company.

- In 1992, there was a 55 percent increase over 1991 in the number of Aboriginal staff appointed to the store supervisor level (which is the entry level store management position). Across all store management positions, The North West Company achieved a 22 percent increase in the number of Aboriginal people promoted to management positions.

- Aboriginal management staff has increased 32 percent from 1991 to 1994. In 1991 there were 50 Aboriginal people in management positions; by 1994 this had increased to 66.

The company also anticipates that there will be a number of other benefits from the training program. Longer-term benefits should result in increased cooperation and teamwork from all staff; better sharing of ideas and suggestions to improve the business; more effective decision-making and problem-solving throughout the company; greater job satisfaction with reduced stress at work and, therefore, at home; and contributions to the growth and profitability of the company.

TD Bank's Nakoda Circle of Aboriginal Employees

The Nakoda Circle was created to provide a focal point for addressing issues related to Aboriginal employment and business development within the bank.

The Nakoda Circle was created by TD Bank in 1994 to provide a focal point for addressing issues related to Aboriginal employment and business development within the bank. The Nakoda Circle brings Aboriginal employees from across Canada to advise senior managers in the bank about Aboriginal employment and business development issues.

As a result of the first meeting in May 1994, a series of short and medium-term action plans was developed to enhance the recruitment and development of Aboriginal employees, strengthen communications, and promote business development with Aboriginal communities. Several of the action plans were implemented within the first year. The second meeting of the Circle took place in Shuswap Territory in June 1995.

The Nakoda Circle has already resulted in tangible steps towards increasing Aboriginal employment in the bank and promoting business opportunities with First Nations. It has become an important part of TD Bank's Aboriginal relations strategy.

Context for the Initiative

In the two years prior to the creation of the Nakoda Circle, the representation of Aboriginal people in the TD Bank's workforce had remained flat at 0.6 percent of the bank's total workforce. Like many employers, this was well below census labour market availability. While the bank had taken steps to attract and hire Aboriginal employees, retention was an issue. At the same time, the bank was increasing its efforts to work more closely with Aboriginal communities and to enhance the banking services it was providing.

In early 1994, the human resources division canvassed senior Aboriginal employees to obtain their views about what steps the bank should be taking to increase Aboriginal employment. A range of perspectives emerged, pointing to the value of bringing people together to explore options and set priorities. The decision was made to form a national Aboriginal circle.

TD Bank

The Toronto-Dominion Bank was formed in 1955 through the amalgamation of The Bank of Toronto and The Dominion Bank.

TD Bank ranks as the fifth largest Canadian bank. The bank has a network of approximately 975 branches and offices across Canada as well as international locations.

At the end of 1994, TD Bank had a workforce in Canada of about 25,500 employees, of whom 191 (or 0.7 percent of the total workforce) had self-identified as being of Aboriginal ancestry.

The model of a circle was selected because it reflects Aboriginal values and traditions.

A group of fourteen Aboriginal employees from different regions were invited to become members of the Circle. The Nakoda Circle is coordinated by the bank's Employee Relations group.

The First Circle

The first meeting of the Circle was held in May 1994 in the Nakoda Lodge Business Conference Centre in Morley, Alberta. This site was chosen, in part, because it would provide non-Aboriginal participants with the opportunity to go to a reserve community. Nakoda also has a research facility and resource centre, which would enrich the knowledge and experience of all participants.

A total of 20 people from six of the bank's divisions participated in the meeting at Nakoda. Senior executives were involved, including a Vice Chairman of the bank, the Senior Vice President of the Alberta Region and Vice Presidents of Human Resources and Financial Services. The meeting was facilitated by the bank's Vice President of Human Resource Development.

The meeting took place over two days, with the first day focusing on cultural and awareness building activities. The Nakoda community played an important role in the first day.

The meeting took place over two days, with the first day focusing on cultural and awareness building activities and the second day dealing with business issues. The Nakoda community played an important role in the first day. The son of the Chief guided participants on a four-hour nature walk. He talked about the history of the community and described many of its traditional teachings, such as for example traditional medicines, the medicine wheel and the sweat lodge. In the evening of the first day, an elder joined Circle participants in a traditional dinner. The elder shared an inspirational message with the group. A film about the Nakoda people and community was shown, describing treaties, economic and agricultural development programs as well as cultural aspects of the community. There was an opportunity for questions and discussion after the film as well as to review the resources in the community's Resource Centre.

The second day was designed as a business meeting. Three key topics were examined: communications; hiring, development and retention of Aboriginal employees; and development of Aboriginal business with the bank.

The second day was designed as a business meeting. The session opened with a welcome by the Vice Chairman of the bank. The Associate Vice President of National Aboriginal Banking Services, as the most senior Aboriginal banker in the Circle, also welcomed members and reviewed the purpose of the session. Prior to the meeting, members of the Circle had identified their individual priorities and from this information, an agenda had been developed. After a round table discussion, during which members examined the challenges facing them as TD employees, the agenda was modified and it was agreed that three key topics would be further examined in break-out groups. These were:

- communications;

- hiring, development and retention of Aboriginal employees; and

- development of Aboriginal business with the bank.

Members of the Circle indicated which group they wished to join. Each group was asked to develop specific goals for the bank in the next three to five years, as well as personal goals for each member. Plans were presented to the Circle as a whole and responsibilities for action assigned. During the year following the Nakoda meeting, each of the groups continued to work together through tele-conferencing.

Results in the First Year

The bank has undertaken initiatives and achieved results in each of the three areas addressed by the Nakoda Circle.

Strengthening communications on issues related to Aboriginal employment and business development was one of the most significant outcomes of the first meeting of the Nakoda Circle.

Strengthening communications on issues related to Aboriginal employment and business development was one of the most significant outcomes of the first meeting of the Nakoda Circle.

- The Circle had identified the importance of building a respectful work environment for Aboriginal employees. The group reviewed communications materials that had been developed by the bank and distributed to management on the issue of respect in the workplace. Shortly after the Nakoda meeting, the bank republished some of this information in its employee newsletter about how individual employees could take positive action to create a respectful environment and reduce friction in the workplace. The newsletter was sent to every employee. In 1995, building on ideas from the Nakoda Circle as well as from the bank's Employment Equity Advisory Committee, a new employee communications initiative will focus on valuing diversity of all employees.

- The bank is also taking steps to increase awareness of the diversity of Aboriginal people. At the Nakoda session, both Aboriginal and non-Aboriginal participants became aware of the diversity of the Aboriginal population. As a result, the bank has been taking steps to increase its knowledge about historical, cultural and language differences within the Aboriginal population and to reflect these in both internal and external communications.

Three key initiatives were undertaken to enhance the hiring and development of Aboriginal employees.

- The Nakoda Circle had emphasized the importance of working with Aboriginal youth and providing information that would help them to find jobs and make informed choices about their futures. The bank sponsored the preparation of a brochure targeted at Aboriginal job seekers. The brochure, which is called Job Works, provides quick tips on getting a job. A companion video was also produced. This initiative was launched at the 1995 Nakoda Circle meeting.

- Mentoring initiatives were increased as a result of the meeting at Nakoda. A number of members of the Nakoda Circle made personal commitments to act as mentors to Aboriginal employees in their individual regions. Regional circles have been created in a number of TD Bank's regions. The regional circles provide Aboriginal employees across Canada with opportunities to come together, thereby facilitating the mentoring process.

- A new tracking mechanism was developed to help the bank increase the recruitment and retention of Aboriginal employees. The idea for this had been developed, in response to concerns raised in 1994, by one of the bank's operating divisions and brought to the 1995 Nakoda Circle meeting for further development. The system tracks information about branch activities, market development, human resources and succession planning. While it has been built specially to address issues related to Aboriginal hiring and development, it can be adapted for a variety of community banking purposes.

To enhance business development, the bank has modified its Aboriginal Financial Services marketing materials to reflect the diversity of the Aboriginal population. During the year, TD Bank also responded to a request from the Saskatchewan Indian Equity Foundation to joint venture the first Aboriginal bank in Canada. In a competitive process, TD Bank was chosen as a partner in this new venture. The advice of the Nakoda Circle on Aboriginal issues was instrumental in this process and will continue to be so in the future.

Moving Forward

The second meeting of the Nakoda Circle was held in June 1995 at the Quaalot Lodge in the Shuswap Territory in British Columbia. There were 30 participants, with all of the bank's divisions represented.

Like the first year, the session took place over two days, with the first day focusing on building cultural awareness and understanding. Members of the Shuswap community played a very active role with members of the Circle. An elder from the community accompanied the group throughout

Mentoring initiatives were increased as a result of the meeting at Nakoda.

TD Bank was chosen by the Saskatchewan Indian Equity Foundation to joint venture the first Aboriginal bank. The advice of the Nakoda Circle on Aboriginal issues was instrumental in this process.

The second meeting was held in the Shuswap Territory in British Columbia.

The Nakoda Circle has emerged as a network for bringing together the small, highly dispersed and diverse population of Aboriginal employees and creating opportunities that otherwise would not have been possible.

the day. A sunrise ceremony took place and a sweat lodge was organized for both male and female participants. Lunch was held at a residential school, with members of the local Aboriginal business community joining the group as guests. Children from the Kamloops Indian Band School gave the Circle a demonstration of their traditional games. During the first day, a great deal of discussion took place on traditional Aboriginal ways and how these continue to survive over time.

The business meeting took place on the second day. Members of the Circle, in a group session, examined priorities and reaffirmed that the three key areas for action should continue to be communication; hiring, development and retention of Aboriginal employees; and development of Aboriginal business with the bank. Break-out groups were formed and action plans were developed. A significant difference from the first year was that the Nakoda Circle recommended setting fewer goals that can be achieved in a shorter period of time.

In two years, the Nakoda Circle has become an important part of TD Bank's Aboriginal relations strategy. It has emerged as a network that brings together the small, highly dispersed and diverse population of Aboriginal employees and that creates opportunities that otherwise would not have been possible.

Canadian Heritage's Aboriginal Working Group

The Aboriginal Working Group is an employee-driven group. It focuses on identifying positive measures and working collaboratively with departmental managers to enhance Aboriginal employment in Canadian Heritage.

The Aboriginal Working Group in the Department of Canadian Heritage was created in 1994. It is an employee-driven group whose mandate is to advise managers in the department on how to enhance the employment situation of Aboriginal people, to provide a support group and mentors for Aboriginal employees, and to increase awareness of Aboriginal culture.

The group has undertaken several initiatives since it was created, including the development of an employment equity action plan for Aboriginal people which has been approved by senior management in the department. The group has organized and participated in events to increase awareness. It has also collaborated in the development of specific training initiatives for Aboriginal students and employees.

Aboriginal Working Group

The Aboriginal Working Group in the Department of Canadian Heritage had its origins in 1992, when a group of Aboriginal employees in the former Department of Communications approached the department about providing a forum for working together. After a preliminary session, the group was set up and began working on an action plan, as well as a number of other initiatives such as cross-cultural awareness workshops.

With the reorganization of the federal government in 1993, parts of the Department of Communications were transferred to the newly-created Department of Canadian Heritage. Some of the employees who had been active in the original working group were interested in continuing to work together in the new department. In 1994, the Aboriginal Working Group was constituted as one of four employment equity advisory committees in the Department of Canadian Heritage.

All departmental employees who had self-identified as being of Aboriginal ancestry were notified of the creation of the Working Group and were asked if they were interested in becoming a member of the group or in participating in other ways. The group now has

---

Department of Canadian Heritage

The Department of Canadian Heritage has been established to work with Canadians to strengthen their shared sense of identity while respecting the diversity of Canada's land and people.

The department's responsibilities include: managing programs related to national parks and other national historic sites; developing cultural affairs and broadcasting policy and assisting cultural industries and organizations; managing programs related to the multicultural character of Canadian society; encouraging and developing amateur sport; and advancing the equality status and use of official languages.

In March 1995, the department had about 6500 employees, of whom 218 (or 3.3 percent) had identified themselves as being of Aboriginal ancestry.

eighteen members, who are Canadian Heritage employees working in a variety of occupations and locations. Members of the group include people of Indian, Inuit and Metis ancestry.

The Aboriginal Working Group focuses on identifying positive measures and working collaboratively with departmental managers to enhance Aboriginal employment in Canadian Heritage. Its mandate is as follows.

- To provide Canadian Heritage managers with advice, strategies and recommendations on how to increase the recruitment, promotion and retention of Aboriginal peoples.

- To provide a support group to meet and share work-related experiences and provide mentors as needed.

- To increase awareness of Aboriginal culture.

The Aboriginal Working Group is employee-driven, setting its own objectives and priorities. At the same time, the group has the strong and visible support of senior management in the department. The Deputy Minister wrote to all employees, recognizing the contribution that employee committees make in improving departmental policies and practices. The message also emphasized the importance of cooperation by managers and supervisors in supporting employees in these activities.

In addition to the National Working Group, there are regional working groups in each of the department's six regions. The regional groups deal with local issues. There is also a National Mailing List, comprised of people who want to have direct information about the group and its initiatives.

The group meets quarterly by tele-conferencing and once a year in person. The annual meeting is organized to take place on a weekend. The meetings are held in departmental offices and the department pays for members' travel costs. The Working Group makes extensive use of E-mail as a means of keeping its members informed about issues of interest to Aboriginal people and providing other people in the department with easy access to information about the group's initiatives.

Aboriginal Employment Equity Plan

One of the most important activities that the Aboriginal Working Group has undertaken is the development of an employment equity action plan for Aboriginal people within Canadian Heritage.

The group held a two-day Action Plan Workshop in Winnipeg in March 1995. The group reviewed a draft of the department's employment equity action plan. The department's plan is in two parts. First, a situation analy-

The group has the strong and visible support of senior management in the department.

The Working Group makes extensive use of E-mail as a means of keeping its members informed and of providing others with information about its initiatives.

One of its most important activities has been the development of an employment equity action plan.

sis of the current state of employment equity and training in Canadian Heritage forms the basis for setting targets. The second part sets out necessary action steps of how to improve employment equity. The department's plan contains initiatives for enhancing the employment of all four designated groups.

The purpose of the Action Plan Workshop of the Aboriginal Working Group was to validate issues and add to or modify the action plan as the group determined necessary. The Working Group broke into four smaller groups, with each one addressing a different aspect of the plan, namely recruitment, promotion, retention and general issues. Overall, over 40 recommendations were developed, dealing with a wide range of issues affecting Aboriginal employment. The Working Group presented the plan to the department's senior management and to the Human Resource Management Committee. It was well received and the Working Group was asked to identify its priority areas for action.

The Employment Equity Action Plan for Aboriginal People has become an element of the department's Multi-Year Diversity Plan, which strives to achieve equitable representation and distribution of designated group members in the department's workforce. Several specific recommendations that were identified in the Aboriginal Working Group's employment equity plan have been incorporated directly into the departmental diversity plan. These include:

The Employment Equity Action Plan for Aboriginal People has become an element of the department's Multi-Year Diversity Plan.

- ensuring, wherever possible, the presence of designated group members on selection boards when considering designated group candidates;

- sensitizing members of employment equity committees, at both headquarters and in regions, to employment equity issues;

- maintaining a departmental inventory of qualified designated group members; and

- maintaining and improving an information tracking system to provide regular updates on designated group members' employment and career progress.

Implementation of the recommendations made by the Working Group will take place over time. Responsibility for implementing some of the recommendations will rest with the department's human resources branch. Others will be implemented in conjunction with departmental managers. The co-chair of the Aboriginal Working Group, who is also an Assistant Deputy Minister in the department, has committed to sponsoring the implementation of three of the group's recommendations within his branch

Members of the group have been directly involved in several initiatives to raise awareness of Aboriginal people and issues within the department.

and has undertaken to seek similar commitments from other departmental executives. The Working Group itself will be directly involved in implementing a number of its recommendations, such as recommendations to address attitudinal barriers through increased awareness of Aboriginal culture.

Awareness Building Initiatives

Members of the Aboriginal Working Group have been directly involved in several initiatives to raise awareness of Aboriginal people and issues within the department.

- Members of the group have participated in the federal government's Aboriginal Awareness Week, which takes place each May. They have helped to organize discussion sessions about Aboriginal people and have invited elders to talk about Aboriginal history and spirituality. In 1995, the group sponsored a Talking Circle with an elder.

- Group members have participated in delivering Aboriginal awareness training in different regions of the country. One example is a training project in Atlantic Canada which was conducted in cooperation with Micmac Nations for 30 participants.

- The Working Group is also involved in the Aboriginal Career Symposium, which is held in the National Capital Region each November. It is attended by Aboriginal students from areas around the National Capital Region. For the 1995 symposium, the group will operate a booth and will have people available to talk about the Department of Canadian Heritage and the work that is being done to promote Aboriginal employment and awareness.

The Working Group has taken steps to increase awareness of the special employment problems faced by Aboriginal women.

The Working Group has taken steps to increase awareness of the special employment problems faced by Aboriginal women.

- The group met with a researcher studying Aboriginal women in the labour force for the Royal Commission of Aboriginal Peoples. Some of the major issues being addressed included outreach to Aboriginal women in the labour force; getting more Aboriginal women into management positions; public education campaigns to deal with racism and sexism; childcare issues; and cross-cultural training done by Aboriginal women themselves.

- One of the members of the Working Group also sits as a representative of the Public Service Alliance of Canada on the Canadian Labour

Congress (CLC). She has kept members of the Working Group informed of how the CLC is addressing issues affecting Aboriginal women in the workplace and examining the potential for changing the wording of collective agreements to reflect aspects of Aboriginal culture (such as leave for hunting or leave because of illness in the extended family).

A package of material on Aboriginal women in the workplace has been developed and recommendations specifically addressing Aboriginal women's issues were incorporated into the Working Group's employment equity action plan.

Training and Development Initiatives

The Aboriginal Working Group has assisted the department with an Aboriginal summer student project.

The Aboriginal Working Group has assisted the department with an Aboriginal summer student project. In 1994, the Department of Canadian Heritage hired eight Aboriginal students. The objectives of this project were to provide a work experience opportunity and network for the students as well as to create awareness about Aboriginal employment in the workplace. Members of the Working Group provided advice to the Human Resources branch on the development of the evaluation questionnaire, which would be completed by the students at the end of the summer. The members of the Working Group ensured that the questions would be respectful of and acceptable to the students.

The Aboriginal Working Group has also assisted in the development of a park warden training program for Aboriginal people. A needs analysis was conducted in 1994/95 to address the recruitment, retention and career development of Aboriginal employees in the warden service of Parks Canada and a proposal for a *Training in Partnership Program* was developed. The Working Group was consulted as part of this initiative.

Looking Forward

The Aboriginal Working Group intends to continue its efforts to enhance Aboriginal employment in Canadian Heritage. It will continue to play a role in the implementation and monitoring of its employment equity action plan. Specific initiatives that it plans to focus on include expanding regional and local working groups; establishing a mentoring program for Aboriginal employees; and participating in a departmental initiative aimed at facilitating changes in corporate culture.

The group hopes to expand its capacity to provide information and build awareness of Aboriginal issues using technology. Its departmental E-

The group plans to expand regional and local working groups; establish a mentoring program for Aboriginal employees; and participate in a departmental initiative aimed at facilitating changes in corporate culture.

mail system has proven to be an effective vehicle for reaching departmental employees across the country. Not only has the group been able to provide information on its activities and plans, but it has been able to use the system to disseminate information of general interest to Aboriginal employees. Over time, the group hopes to use the Internet to promote the exchange of information with a much wider audience.

Within the department, the benefits of an employee-driven advisory committee such as the Aboriginal Working Group have already been clearly acknowledged. The Director General of Human Resources acknowledged the value of the advisory committees to senior managers throughout the department, noting that "the establishment of advisory committees which represent the four designated groups constituted without question the most remarkable achievement in the first year (of the new department's employment equity action plan).... 'Employee driven' committees play a very important role in the department. Not only are they offering support to members of the designated groups, but they also act as an advisory body to management. Their existence has a very positive influence on the way we assume our responsibilities regarding employment equity in the department".

PART FOUR

BUSINESS
DEVELOPMENT

Manitoba Hydro's Procurement Policies for Northern Manitoba Aboriginal Businesses

The Proposed Purchasing, Employment and Training Policies for Northern Projects are instrumental in Manitoba Hydro's efforts to improve relationships with Aboriginal people.

Manitoba Hydro has committed to improving relationships with Aboriginal people, especially in Northern Manitoba where most of Manitoba Hydro's generating, transmission and associated facilities have been constructed, and are now operated and maintained.

The corporation's *Proposed Purchasing, Employment and Training Policies for Northern Projects* (issued in 1991) are instrumental in Manitoba Hydro's efforts to improve relationships with Aboriginal people. The policies, coupled with a commitment to sustainable economic development, are facilitating greater access and involvement of Northern residents in the corporation's northern activities. The specific procurement policies, which have been developed to enhance opportunities for northern Aboriginal residents and businesses, have resulted in more than 300 contracts awarded to Aboriginal businesses in the province over the past few years.

Manitoba Hydro has also introduced other initiatives to help put northern residents in a better position to provide ongoing services to the corporation. For example, the corporation's Employment Equity program is creating a diverse workforce representative of the province's population. Aboriginal employees now make up 6.5 percent of Manitoba Hydro's total staffing, a proportion equal to the percentage of the Aboriginal labour force in Manitoba. But while about 20 percent of Hydro's workforce in northern Manitoba is Aboriginal, this is still well below the percentage of the Aboriginal population (57 percent) or of the Aboriginal labour force (37 percent) in that region. In addition, the Summer Work Experience program annually places a number of Aboriginal youth in career-related positions with the corporation at various locations across the province. Bursaries are awarded to a number of Aboriginal students entering first year studies in a university or college program related to engineering or technology.

Manitoba Hydro has also placed high priority on settling outstanding obligations with First Nations resulting from previous project impacts on their lands. It is expected that the funding and

---

Manitoba Hydro

Manitoba Hydro is a Crown corporation owned by the provincial government. With fixed assets in service of over $6.4 billion, the corporation is the fourth largest electrical utility in Canada.

It produces electricity by operating 12 hydraulic generating stations, two thermal generating stations and 12 diesel plants. Power is distributed to 385,000 customers throughout Manitoba, except for the central portion of the City of Winnipeg.

Manitoba Hydro has 4,000 employees involved in its generating, transmission and distribution activities. Approximately 6.5 percent of its workforce is Aboriginal. Manitoba Hydro's head office is in Winnipeg. It also has four regional offices and 71 district offices through the province.

other assistance provided to First Nations in the settlement agreements will enable northern Aboriginal businesses and communities to take further advantage of Manitoba Hydro's purchasing, employment and training policies.

Background

In anticipation of undertaking construction of the then proposed Conawapa Generating Station and related facilities in northern Manitoba, Manitoba Hydro strengthened existing policies designed to enhance opportunities for northern Aboriginal residents and businesses. The policies were, in part, based on the experience gained during the construction of the Limestone project in the late 1980s. The Limestone experience had demonstrated that changing strategic policies and programs could be instrumental in increasing the level of economic participation by Manitoba companies in the project.

Although the Conawapa project was postponed in 1992, the northern purchasing guidelines are being applied to smaller projects and ongoing construction and maintenance work in the north. The policies remain as draft policies because the process of seeking community input has taken longer than expected and is just now being completed. However, those provisions were implemented on a test basis during the past four years while the consultation process was underway.

The feedback received from Aboriginal leadership and businesses generally has been positive with the exception of concerns about funding and the need for pre-employment training. On the issue of training, Manitoba Hydro has expressed the view, from the outset, that pre-employment training is the responsibility of the Aboriginal community, the federal government and the provincial government. The corporation has agreed that on-the-job training, when needed, is a reasonable cost of the project, thereby further facilitating Aboriginal participation.

The key business issues which have emerged from the consultation have related to training and the establishment of joint ventures. The processes surrounding the formation of joint ventures is new to all participants and has provided challenges to Aboriginal businesses, non-Aboriginal businesses and Manitoba Hydro staff responsible for construction and operations. These are part of the learning curve that is needed to broaden business opportunities in the north.

The policies are intended to provide direct and increased benefits to the residents and the local economy within the province's Northern Affairs boundary.

The Policy Commitment

In 1991, Manitoba Hydro issued its *Proposed Purchasing, Employment and Training Policies for Northern Projects*. These are intended to provide direct and increased benefits to the residents and the local economy within the

The public tendering process continues to be the cornerstone of Manitoba Hydro's purchasing policy. Within this framework, special provisions assist Aboriginal business with their development.

province's Northern Affairs boundary. The proposed policies place particular emphasis on involving northern Aboriginal people in Manitoba Hydro work. Recognizing the desire of Aboriginal people to have increased participation in business opportunities, Manitoba Hydro is giving preference in project purchasing to northern Aboriginal business.

The policies establish common rules that give preference for project opportunities first to northern Aboriginal residents and businesses, second to other northern-based residents and businesses, and third to other Manitoba residents and businesses. Only after this preference system is applied will project benefits go outside the province.

The cornerstone of Manitoba Hydro's purchasing policy continues to be the public tendering process. However, within this framework, special provisions are implemented for Aboriginal business to assist with their development. In the absence of specific policies, participation of small northern businesses could continue to be limited because larger companies tend to deal with sub-contractors and material suppliers with whom they have developed pre-existing long-term business relationships. The long-term plan is to revert to the public tendering method when Aboriginal businesses are positioned to compete in the open market process.

The Procurement Provisions

Northern Aboriginal Businesses or Northern Aboriginal Joint Ventures are defined as businesses that are at least 50 percent owned by Aboriginal residents or organizations based in the Northern Affairs region. The special procurement provisions directed to northern Aboriginal business are as follows.

The special procurement provisions include breaking contracts into smaller packages and setting aside some contract opportunities exclusively for northern Aboriginal business.

- Information on purchasing policies and upcoming contracts is provided early enough to allow adequate preparation time.

- Contracts are broken into smaller packages or "scoped", where feasible, to make them more compatible with capabilities of northern Aboriginal businesses.

- Some contract opportunities are set aside exclusively for northern Aboriginal business. This is done early in the process to enable Aboriginal businesses to plan and organize for the work. The three key criteria in this provision are reasonable price, quality and ability to meet schedule requirements.

- When identifying set aside opportunities, preference is given to businesses located in the vicinity of the project.

- Contracts which have been set aside are awarded through negotiations and/or a restricted tendering process.

- Manitoba Hydro may waive bid and performance bonding for northern Aboriginal businesses.

- All other tenders are required to identify Aboriginal sub-contract opportunities as part of the Manitoba content provisions.

Manitoba Hydro's policies have been widely distributed to interested parties. In addition, Hydro staff discuss this information with Aboriginal leaders and residents during community visits.

Initiatives to Assist Northern Manitoba Aboriginal Businesses

Development initiatives assist northern Aboriginal businesses to participate fully in procurement opportunities.

Manitoba Hydro is taking a number of development initiatives to assist northern Aboriginal businesses to participate fully in procurement opportunities.

Implementation of these initiatives is by the line management staff of the Regions (Northern, Western, Eastern), the Northern Production Division and the Construction Division. These divisions are directly responsible for negotiating contracts and for sharing the details of projects with community representatives. On projects where environmental approvals are needed, these divisions will participate with Environmental and Purchasing staff at open houses and other community meetings to explain the projects and seek input. These are some of the first steps in a series of direct interfaces with the communities.

For example, Manitoba Hydro staff assess the capabilities of Aboriginal businesses and describe the needs related to each specific project. Project requirements such as equipment, job descriptions, training and work procedures are discussed through presentations and follow-up meetings.

Manitoba Hydro offers technical support, as required, to assist northern Aboriginal business in understanding estimates, specifications and requests for proposals.

Joint ventures involving northern Aboriginal business and non-Aboriginal business broaden Aboriginal access to contracts and facilitate skill transfer.

Manitoba Hydro supports existing or new joint ventures involving northern Aboriginal business and non-Aboriginal (preferably Manitoba) business. This is designed to broaden Aboriginal access to contracts and facilitate skill transfer.

Results

Since 1991, Manitoba Hydro has awarded millions of dollars in more than 300 contracts to Aboriginal businesses. The breadth and variety of these contracts demonstrates the effectiveness of specific elements of the policy, such as scoping, set asides, joint ventures, Manitoba content and negotiated contracts.

- 81 percent of the contracts with Aboriginal businesses were negotiated contracts; 10 percent were tendered contracts and 9 percent were restricted tendered contracts.

- More than 65 Aboriginal businesses have been awarded contracts under the northern purchasing guidelines. Approximately 25 First Nations and Metis communities have participated in contract opportunities.

Since 1991, Manitoba Hydro has awarded millions of dollars in more than 300 contracts to Aboriginal businesses.

Northern Aboriginal businesses have provided Manitoba Hydro with a wide range of services over the past few years. These have included construction services, security services, waste management services, equipment and machinery rentals, rights-of-way clearing, site preparation, road construction, consulting services, refuse removal services, snow clearing, janitorial services, supply and delivery of bulk fuels, and soil remediation services.

Manitoba Hydro: Examples of Contracts with Northern Manitoba Aboriginal Businesses

Type of Work	Value
Construction of the Cross Lake Weir	$7,500,000
Clearing of Kelsey-Split Lake transmission line	640,000
Construction of Kelsey-Split Lake transmission line	2,500,000
Diesel site remediation work and clean up	900,000
Supply and haulage of bulk diesel fuel and oils	575,000
Salvage work for 35 km of distribution line	165,000
Clearing for 230 kV transmission line	1,500,000
Supply waste management services	220,000

Source: Manitoba Hydro 1995

The Split Lake Project (which involved the construction of a 48 kilometre transmission line) provides a good example of how Manitoba Hydro's policies created business and employment opportunities for local Aboriginal people. Clearing of the right-of-way was carried out by Split Lake Construction, the First Nations construction company located in the vicinity of the project. Construction of the transmission line was done by Split Lake-Comstock, a joint venture between the local community and the non-Aboriginal contractor, Comstock Construction. Both parts of the work were set aside for the Aboriginal business and contracts were subsequently negotiated reflecting the criteria of quality, schedule and reasonable price.

During the project "wrap-up" meeting, community representatives advised that their leadership was very happy with the outcome of the project and the joint venture. This project was honoured as the 1993 Best Project by the jury of the Corporate Humanist Awards.

Looking Forward

The Split Lake Project was honoured as the 1993 Best Project by the jury of the Corporate Humanist Awards.

The recent approval of the North Central Project will provide new business, employment and training opportunities for northern Aboriginal people. The project, which is funded by Canada, the Province of Manitoba and Manitoba Hydro, includes the construction of transmission and distribution services to provide unrestricted electrical supply to seven First Nations and two non-status communities currently served by diesel generators. The majority of the work on power line clearing and construction, and on civil work for transformer stations, has been set aside for the Aboriginal communities. Contracts will be negotiated either directly with Aboriginal businesses and/or with Aboriginal-based joint ventures. The approximate value of these contracts is expected to be in excess of $38 million. The communities are also expected to participate in related business opportunities and to benefit from direct and indirect employment, both before and after the scheduled in-service dates of 1997 and 1998.

Finally, one of Manitoba Hydro's high priorities is to settle outstanding obligations with First Nations resulting from previous project impacts on their lands. The process has taken many years and has now reached the stage where all five First Nations affected by northern flooding have agreed to Comprehensive Settlements or "Agreements in Principle". As agreements are concluded, they are submitted to Band members for ratification. It is expected that the funding and other assistance provided to First Nations in these settlement agreements will enable northern Aboriginal businesses and communities to take further advantage of Manitoba Hydro's purchasing, employment and training policies.

Westcoast Energy's Initiatives to Create Business Opportunities for Aboriginal Communities and Contractors

A key focus of Westcoast's Aboriginal Affairs program has been creating business opportunities for Aboriginal communities and contractors.

Since 1991, Westcoast Energy has followed a strategy of building a stake for Aboriginal people in the company's success. It has done this by acknowledging Aboriginal concerns about environmental, cultural and economic issues and by developing solutions that take into account the social, political and economic conditions of the Aboriginal communities with which it interacts.

A key focus of the company's Aboriginal Affairs program has been creating business opportunities for Aboriginal communities and contractors. Westcoast has created opportunities for Aboriginal people in B.C. through its own operations (and those of its subsidiaries, such as Centra Gas). The pipeline contracts to the Cowichan Band on Vancouver Island provide a good illustration of this approach. Westcoast has also taken a leadership role in collaborative initiatives with other resource developers, government agencies and educational institutions and the Aboriginal community at large to develop initiatives that provide a diversity of entry points for Aboriginal people into the industrial economy. This has been a key element in Westcoast's activities in Northeast B.C..

Although Westcoast's partnerships with Aboriginal people have had their largest impact in Northeast B.C. and on Vancouver Island, the company also has extensive relationships with Aboriginal communities throughout the province.

Westcoast Energy

Westcoast Energy is a major company in the natural gas industry. It holds core assets in natural gas pipelines, gas processing and gas distribution. Westcoast is building related business activities in power generation, gas services and international energy ventures. The company has annual revenues of $4 billion and assets of $6.5 billion.

Westcoast's pipeline division owns and operates the mainline gas transportation system in B.C. which processes and transports gas throughout B.C. and the U.S. Northwest. Westcoast's gas distribution activities are carried out by Union Gas, the Centra Gas companies and Pacific Northern Gas.

Westcoast Energy's headquarters are in Vancouver, B.C.. The Westcoast group of companies employs more than 6200 people, of whom 1100 are located in B.C.. The bulk of the company's Aboriginal employees in B.C. work for Westcoast's pipeline division where they account for 1.9 percent of the workforce.

Westcoast's Relationships with Aboriginal Communities

Westcoast uses a diverse set of methods to address challenges and fulfil the company's commitment to providing a stake for Aboriginal people in Westcoast's success. These have focused on business development, education and training, and environmental alliances.

Westcoast uses business development, education and training, and environmental alliances to fulfil the company's commitment to provide a stake for Aboriginal people.

The environmental program is based on strategic alliances that are to the mutual benefit of both Aboriginal communities and the company.

Westcoast has taken steps to provide opportunities for Aboriginal people to enter the industrial economy. It has done this through employment and business dealings. The nature of Westcoast's relationships with Aboriginal communities has been defined by the type of work in the area. In northeast B.C., the company's activities are construction based. This is in marked contrast to the south of the province where construction is much more limited and where issues relate more to company facilities or rights-of-way within reserve boundaries. Westcoast's subsidiaries also operate on or within the vicinity of reserve communities in the northwest of the province and on Vancouver Island.

The company, in showing respect for land related issues, also has become involved in the broader issue of community development. The environmental program is based on strategic alliances that are to the mutual benefit of both Aboriginal communities and the company. Westcoast has been active in creating employment opportunities for Aboriginal people through its Aboriginal Environmental-Inspector Training Program. The company is also working with bands and other stakeholders to develop a program that incorporates indigenous knowledge in the restoration and revegetation of rights of way. For example, it has initiated discussions with the Chetwynd Environmental Society to undertake a joint native species reclamation and restoration project in which the participation of Aboriginal groups and producers will be sought.

One of the company's biggest challenges is raising the skill level of Aboriginal people to match existing employment opportunities. In some regions, many Aboriginal people do not have the education and skills to access existing employment opportunities with the company or its contractors. As a result, there have been situations with more opportunities than qualified Aboriginal people to take them. Education and training are needed to move from having marginal representation of Aboriginal participation in low skill jobs to having Aboriginal employees distributed throughout company operations. At present, Westcoast provides educational funding, tuition support and summer employment opportunities that are targeted at Aboriginal communities with which Westcoast has direct relationships.

Westcoast's Aboriginal contracting initiatives are complemented by its employment equity program which is designed to increase the representation of Aboriginal people (and other designated groups) in the workforce of its pipeline division. Westcoast has been active in increasing the number of Aboriginal people hired for construction projects. Westcoast also provides ongoing internships and work experience placements to Aboriginal people and has developed a pilot on-the-job training program to increase the number of Aboriginal people in its gas processing and transmission facilities.

Centra Gas's Pipeline Contracts with the Cowichan Band

Pipeline contracts to Khowutzun Pipeline Constructors, a joint venture between the Cowichan Band and Northern Pipelines, have created significant, ongoing opportunities for Aboriginal people.

The pipeline contracts to the Cowichan Band on Vancouver Island provide a good illustration of how Westcoast has created significant, ongoing business opportunities for Aboriginal people in B.C. through its own operations (or those of its subsidiaries, such as Centra Gas).

The people of Cowichan First Nation on Vancouver Island have been instrumental in installing natural gas mains and connections for Westcoast's Centra Gas subsidiary. As Centra Gas expands its distribution system on Vancouver Island, much of the work is being done by Khowutzun Pipeline Constructors Corp (KPC), which is a joint venture between the Cowichan Band and a U.S.-based construction company, Northern Pipelines.

The joint venture is the outcome of discussions that began in 1989 when Centra was seeking rights-of-way for its natural gas transmission line on the Island. When permission was sought to cross the Cowichan Reserve, Westcoast's Chief Operating Officer and the Band Chief met to discuss ways in which the project could offer long-term business opportunities for the Band. It was agreed that if the Band was to participate in the construction of distribution lines, it would need partners who could provide financial backing and the technical expertise necessary to satisfy the safety and performance criteria required in pipeline construction.

A suitable partner was found and by January 1991, Khowutzun Pipeline Constructors was established with Cowichan Band members forming the majority of its workforce. Skilled and experienced instructors were brought in to provide much of the training for employees of the new company. Classroom instruction was given on weekends, with courses on safety, fusing, the operation of underground locating systems, boring equipment and pipe pushers. The training programs emphasized job quality as the top priority rather than speed, which would come with experience. Since then, training has been on-going and is considered to be an essential element in the success of the company.

The competitiveness of Khowutzun's tenders has resulted in a steady increase in the amount of work for the company.

Khowutzun was successful in winning its first contract from Centra Gas in the spring of 1991. A year later, the term of the contract was extended to February 1994 and Khowutzun was awarded a second contract for service in the Saanich Peninsula. It has since competed for and won further contracts and KPC is now involved in 70 percent of Centra Gas' work on Vancouver Island and currently has revenues of about $10 million each year.

KPC's work has satisfied the quality standards of Centra Gas. The competitiveness of KPC's tenders over the past few years has resulted in a steady increase in the amount of work tendered to the company. Khowutzun Pipeline Constructors has grown from one crew in 1991 to between 16-20 crews today, depending on the amount of work underway.

Westcoast's business development activities in Northeast B.C. illustrate the effectiveness of combining company activities with collaborative initiatives involving other industry and government participants.

Westcoast's Construction Division has been active in helping Aboriginal contractors in Northeast B.C. get started.

At present, there are between 120 and 150 employees on the payroll. The majority of employees are members of the Cowichan Band, with other employees from other bands on Vancouver Island. A number of the foremen are Aboriginal people.

Business Development in Northeast B.C.

Westcoast Energy's business development activities in Northeast B.C. illustrate the effectiveness of combining company activities with collaborative initiatives involving other industry and government participants.

A major focus of Westcoast's Aboriginal Affairs program in recent years has been in Northeastern B.C., an area under dominion treaty. The South Foothills area is the most active oil and gas development region in Canada. There are several Treaty 8 bands in the region, as well as non-status Indians and the only Metis community in B.C..

Westcoast has been instrumental in the development of the Northeast B.C. Industry Group which is an ad hoc group of resource companies, government agencies and Aboriginal communities to promote business and employment opportunities for Aboriginal residents in the region. The Group has delivered in excess of $12 million in training, employment and business opportunities to Aboriginal people in northeast B.C.. Much of this total has been through Westcoast's efforts.

Westcoast's Construction Division has provided most of the opportunities through issuing clearing contracts to band-based contractors and has been active in helping Aboriginal contractors in Northeast B.C. to get started.

- It has assisted band contractors in acquiring lines of credit.

- It has organized skill development workshops that have been put on by Westcoast employees.

- It has assisted Aboriginal companies to write their company profiles.

- It has provided guidance and directed Aboriginal business owners to appropriate sources of management and administrative support services.

Westcoast's experience in northeast B.C. has been positive. More than a dozen clearing contracts have been issued to Aboriginal contractors in the last 3 years. The total value of these contracts is in excess of $9 million. However, more emphasis will be placed in future on shifting the focus from clearing businesses to encouraging a greater diversity of band-based businesses and employment opportunities. This will involve the creation of a roster of contractors from northeast B.C. communities who can bid on a range of projects throughout the region and working with them to develop their business skills.

Results

The results of Westcoast's partnerships with Aboriginal people have not been limited to Northeast B.C. and Vancouver Island. The company has also developed a diverse set of relationships with Aboriginal communities throughout the province. For example, in southern British Columbia, where Westcoast's mainline traverses the lands of nine bands, the company has taken steps to establish educational funds and provide employment opportunities during the company's summer employment program. Westcoast instituted education funds worth $5000 annually with the Cheam and Lower Nicola Bands. Westcoast has begun the process of developing a long-term working relationship with the Cheam Band to explore business, employment and training opportunities related to company operations.

Aboriginal communities have not only benefitted from the employment and business development opportunities from Westcoast's initiatives: they have also benefitted from the support and training that the company has provided, under its multi-dimensional approach, to make the opportunity successful. Communities have been strengthened by the skill development that has resulted from workshops provided, from assistance given to community business owners on how to write a company profile, and from requiring the community to write its own socio-economic study for proposed company projects.

Westcoast has benefitted from its Aboriginal relations program in a number of ways. Westcoast's Aboriginal Affairs initiatives have provided a useful base for developing a workable consultation process for proposed projects. Under the auspices of the Northeast B.C. Industry Group, Westcoast commenced discussion in late 1994 with the Treaty 8 Tribal Association and relevant ministries to develop a consultation model that will be acceptable to Treaty 8 communities, provincial ministries and the oil and gas industry.

Other activities have contributed to the company developing more effective ways to conduct some aspects of its business. The pilot reclamation project for example has involved working with the Aboriginal community, a local environmental group and other resource development companies with the result that improved reclamation practices are emerging.

Westcoast's partnerships with Aboriginal people have embraced communities in all parts of the province.

Westcoast's Aboriginal Affairs initiatives have provided a useful base for developing a workable consultation process for proposed projects.

Canada Post's Service Partnerships with Northern Communities

For many years, Canada Post faced the challenge of maintaining sufficient numbers of trained personnel to provide good postal service to smaller communities in northern Canada.

Canada Post has set up a number of service partnerships with Aboriginal community organizations and Aboriginal businesses to provide more effective postal service to isolated, northern, largely Aboriginal communities which, to this day, depend on mail delivery by air for correspondence and goods.

This initiative has been spearheaded by Canada Post Corporation's Northern Services Division which was created in April 1989 to improve postal service in the North and gradually turn over its northern operations and management functions to the indigenous population.

The service partnership concept has proved to be very successful and agreements are now in place with 149 communities in Canada's north.

Canada Post also works in other ways to provide opportunities for the education and development of Aboriginal people. The corporation offers college scholarships, sponsors various literacy, sports and business events and is an active member of the Canadian Council for Aboriginal Business.

Developing the Service Partnership Concept

Canada Post's Northern Services Division

Canada Post Corporation's Northern Services Division was created in April 1989 to improve postal service in the North and, gradually, turn over its northern operations and management functions to the indigenous population.

The Northern Services Division has been divided into five areas in order to ensure that the postal service requirements of various Bands and municipalities are more adequately met. Area offices are located in Whitehorse for the Yukon, Yellowknife for the Northwest Territories, Winnipeg for northern Saskatchewan and Manitoba, Thunder Bay for northern Ontario, and Val d'Or for northern Quebec and Labrador.

The retail network is made up of 149 partner-operated post offices and 115 post offices run by Canada Post employees. Well over 75 percent of the partners are Aboriginal. The Northern Services Division provides full-time employment for 259 people and part-time employment for 73 people. Over 35 percent of employees are of Aboriginal ancestry.

For many years, Canada Post faced the challenge of maintaining sufficient numbers of trained personnel to provide good postal service to smaller communities of 200-500 people in northern Canada. Turnover of postal employees was very high for a variety of reasons. Successive rapid staff changes resulted in work procedures and methods frequently becoming skewed, since it was incumbent upon the outgoing employee to train the new personnel. Problems would only be discovered months later during the audit process.

Postal service improvements followed when Canada Post adapted its delivery network, policies and procedures to the specific needs of northern communities, especially through the introduction of service partnerships between the corporation and northern communities.

The concept of service partnerships evolved from on-site meetings between the General

The concept of service partnerships evolved from on-site meetings between Canada Post and individual Mayors and Band Chiefs.

Manager responsible for Canada Post's Northern Services and individual Mayors and Band Chiefs. At the very outset, the General Manager visited over half of the isolated communities in the Northern Services region. At meetings held in Northern Quebec and the Northwest Territories with Canada Post representatives, local officials requested more frequent and more reliable mail pick-up and delivery schedules and the addition of vital services such as Cash on Delivery (C.O.D.), money orders, courier service and individual postal boxes. It also became evident many hamlets would prefer operating their post offices themselves.

Canada Post agreed to consider partnership contracts under which the bands or hamlets would hire their own employees and Canada Post, in turn, would compensate them through fees for service. The corporation also provides funds for the provision of adequate facilities for mail services and provides all the necessary training.

Implementing the Partnership Agreements

Once the concept of partnerships between Canada Post and local authorities had been developed, it was implemented through on-site negotiations with Mayors or Band Chiefs and their officials. The resulting partnership agreements were usually contained in simple three-page, open-ended postal service contracts which could be terminated at any time with due notice by either party. However, Canada Post could end such contracts if the partnership did not provide proper mail service or failed to follow proper procedures.

Under the partnership contracts, the bands or hamlets hire their own employees and Canada Post provides a fee for service.

Under the partnership contracts, the bands or hamlets hire their own employees and Canada Post provides a fee for service. The Corporation provides remuneration according to the workload involved. In determining the fee, Canada Post takes into consideration a variety of factors such as the number of customers being serviced, the frequency of air carrier service bringing mail, the number of institutions and businesses in the area and the degree of isolation of the communities. With the partnership contracts, fees in the north became significantly higher than those being paid in areas to the south for equivalent work.

Canada Post also provides funds for the provision of adequate facilities from which to provide mail services. In most cases, this consists of a shared locale such as a band or municipal hall. This is partly for security reasons and also because limited postal operations and revenues could not justify erecting a separate building to house a post office. In the shared building, Canada Post completes the necessary renovations and provides the required equipment such as postal boxes.

Training is an important element underlying the effectiveness of the agreements. Since one of the clauses in the contracts stipulates that there

Training is an important element underlying the effectiveness of the agreements.

When the partnership agreements were signed, Canada Post set out to recruit Aboriginal candidates to be trained as Retail Representatives.

has to be a responsible band or hamlet official appointed to supervise postal employees, Canada Post provides training for both the employees and the supervisors.

Employees undergo a five-day Northern Postmaster Course on the operation of a post office. The courses are sometimes conducted in formal classroom settings (such as Arctic College facilities) or with the instructor training the employees at some other convenient location in the community. The courses deal with all the basic procedures and services of postal operations. There is a special emphasis on cash accounting and other financial operations which were vital following the introduction of money orders for payment of Cash on Delivery parcels. This is the most needed feature of postal operations in isolated Northern communities where there are virtually no banks. Large amounts of money now flow through with the increasing popularity of COD parcels and money orders.

When the partnership agreements were signed, Canada Post set out to recruit Aboriginal candidates to be trained as Retail Representatives who would become responsible for the postal operations in a number of communities. Part of the training for successful candidates consisted of them working for a couple of weeks at counters set up in a specially designated post office. They also spent two weeks being trained by Canada Post internal auditors on how to carry out audits. Their year-long on-the-job management training consisted of working side-by-side with experienced area managers. It also included week-long planning/training sessions with Canada Post Northern Services' senior management. More than 180 northerners were trained either in classroom settings or one-on-one.

Program Modifications and Improvements

The present achievements and momentum did not come easily or without the occasional setback. For instance, some of the hamlets under contract initially experienced cash losses on money order transactions, with some incidents involving losses of between $20,000 and $40,000. It was discovered, that, in many instances, appointed supervisors of employees were not familiar enough with cash transactions themselves and tended to leave postal employees on their own.

Over the two-year period between 1992 to 1994, a number of improvements were made to the system. These included special risk-sharing agreements with insurers covering the hamlets, as well as increasing the number of audit visits to three or four in higher risk communities. Northern Services' personnel at head office established an accounting system which provided close monitoring on incoming cash accounts from the community postal partners.

Between 1992 to 1994, a number of improvements were made to the system, including special risk-sharing agreements and the production of videos on service procedures.

It became evident that while adequate training had been provided to the employees, close monitoring of their operations was required over a period of months to ensure customers were receiving proper services on a continuing basis. This resulted in the production of basic videos on service procedures, The videos, which were presented as refresher training tools, were well received by the various Northern postal outlet operators. The videos were written and produced by the Area Managers and Retail Representatives who also played feature roles in the videos.

In addition, and with the consent of the postal partners themselves, a number of agreements, particularly in northern Quebec and the Northwest Territories, were transferred to the local Co-operative stores. These stores had been increasingly interested in the post office as an additional service for their customers. They were competing with Northern stores of The North West Company, another major partner with Canada Post in the North.

Results

The Northern Service Division has signed upgraded agreements in over 149 communities from the Yukon to the coast of Labrador.

The Northern Services Division has signed upgraded agreements in over 149 communities from the Yukon to the coast of Labrador. The majority of northern postal operations are now handled by bands, hamlets, co-operatives or other businesses, the bulk of which are Aboriginal. The results of this approach, over the five years since inception of the partnership concept, are most encouraging.

Sharing the potential financial risk with other partners through umbrella agreements with the Cooperative Federations has proven to be useful and effective for everyone as the partnerships evolved and matured. Canada Post has four umbrella agreements in place. These vary from partner to partner. For example, in the hamlets in the Northwest Territories, the financial risk of loss due to the activities of the hamlet employee operating the postal outlet are limited to $25,000. Any losses above this ceiling are covered by Canada Post. The more effective controls that Canada Post has put in place in these situations, plus the more frequent visits to high risk offices, makes this risk acceptable.

In other instances, the umbrella organization (such as Arctic Co-operatives Limited) purchases pooled risk insurance and provides additional internal management controls and monitoring. An additional fee is paid to the umbrella organization for these services. In these situations, Canada Post is not required to audit as often.

That part of the Northern Services Division mandate which calls for Canada Post's operations and management in the North to be turned over gradually to the indigenous population is on track. Of the five Area Managers, three are Aboriginal. Four of the nine Retail Representatives, each of whom is responsible for approximately 25 Northern Communities, are also Aboriginal.

Approximately 90 percent of the 180 people trained to date are Aboriginal, of whom approximately 15 percent are Canada Post employees. Most of the Canada Post employees are Managers, Retail Representatives or Postmasters of larger offices.

Building on the successful partnership approach, Canada Posts' Northern Services Division has, since 1991, strengthened its relationships with local communities. It has formed the Northern Postal Service Customer Council. Members of the Council, who are active high-profile residents of various Northern communities, have provided Northern Services - and Canada Post generally - with valuable advice on policies and service and have acted very successfully as third parties for unresolved customer concerns.

Cooperative Ventures between Interfor and First Nations in B.C.

Interfor's cooperative ventures with Aboriginal people in British Columbia, include contracting initiatives, cooperative arrangements and joint business ventures.

Interfor has entered into a number of cooperative ventures with Aboriginal people in British Columbia. These cover a wide variety of business relationships, ranging from contracting opportunities to cooperative arrangements to joint business ventures, with First Nations in the province.

For example, Interfor and the Toquaht Band on Vancouver Island have entered into a joint business venture on the west coast of Vancouver Island. Interfor and the Sechelt Indian Band have entered into a number of cooperative ventures. Interfor's Helifor operations has had an ongoing contract with the Nisga'a Band to provide a helilog rigging crew.

These projects are examples of an increasing number of cooperative ventures which demonstrate that there is significant scope for forest industry and Aboriginal groups to work together for mutual benefit.

Interfor's Approach to Developing Cooperation with Bands and First Nations

Interfor's commitment to working with Aboriginal people in a cooperative manner is based on a number of considerations.

International Forest Products Ltd.

Interfor, which was incorporated in 1963, is one of Canada's major forest companies with logging, sawmilling and forestry operations throughout British Columbia. The company has 59 logging areas and eight sawmills in the south coastal region of B.C. and one logging operation and one sawmill in the central interior region of the province.

Interfor's major products are lumber, logs and woodchips. Interfor had sales of $776 million in 1994. Interfor employs approximately 4000 people, including approximately 900 people through logging contractors operating under its direction. The International Woodworkers of America is the certified bargaining unit for approximately 3000 people engaged in Interfor's logging and manufacturing operations in the coastal region.

- A key motivation is the company's need for ongoing access to a large supply of logs to feed its multi-million dollar investment in mills. To this end Interfor is willing to undertake a range of cooperative arrangements, including joint ventures, with any Aboriginal community or organization that holds cutting rights.

- Interfor also recognizes that other advantages of cooperative arrangements can arise from operating economies, cost savings and improved quality of work. Interfor, along with other forest companies, can benefit from the greater involvement of First Nations in the forest industry, since this gives Aboriginal people a stake in its success and encourages

Interfor has identified a three-step process in establishing and developing cooperative relations with Aboriginal Bands and First Nations.

their support for strategies to maintain forest industry activity as a key component of B.C.'s economy. Increased Aboriginal employment creates individual economic self-sufficiency and also ensures community stability.

Interfor has identified a three-step process in establishing and developing cooperative relations with Aboriginal Bands and First Nations.

- The first step is contact. It is no longer a viable option to operate without contact with neighbouring Aboriginal communities. Initial contacts can be difficult and will often result in the airing of a variety of complaints, many of which the forestry company may be hearing for the first time.

- Two-way communications is the second step. Communication is important for forest companies to understand the Band or First Nation's history, culture and perspective on resource development. For their part, Aboriginal people can benefit from a better understanding of the history, culture and structure of the individual companies, how they do business and how they carry out cooperative ventures.

- Cooperation is the third step. This begins with a willingness to address and resolve issues and irritants that have been raised by the two sides through the communication process. The resulting action plans are a precursor to more detailed joint cooperative efforts.

Cooperative Business Arrangements

Interfor's forestry and logging operations interact with 30 Bands or First Nations in B.C.. Interfor has found that there are innumerable business opportunities for cooperative arrangements with Aboriginal people ranging from simple contracts to Aboriginal contractors for small forestry projects to Interfor contracting to harvest timber limits held by Aboriginal communities.

Interfor provides a large number of contracting opportunities for Aboriginal businesses. For example, since 1993, Interfor has provided brushing, planting and environmental contracts to crews from at least nine Bands or First Nations.

Interfor has entered into more complex economic relationships with some Bands, especially where this involves access to Band timber or cutting rights.

- In situations where Aboriginal people have timber or cutting rights and Interfor owns the only equipment or infrastructure which can

In situations where Bands have timber rights, Interfor has developed innovative business arrangements that have benefitted both the company and the Band.

be used to harvest timber (roads, dry land sorts, log dumps, booming grounds, etc.), the company has been prepared to develop innovative arrangements to the advantage of both the company and the Bands. For example, in one case, Interfor rented a steel spar to an Aboriginal crew to harvest timber from the Band's woodlot. On the same operation, Interfor contracted to do the loading, hauling dumping and booming on behalf of the Band.

- In another situation, Interfor has cooperated with the Toquaht Band in the construction and operation of their sawmill at Macoah and the marketing of their lumber.

- In some instances, Interfor has supplied facilities and equipment to Aboriginal entrepreneurs and it will continue to do this.

Interfor has also entered into discussions with a number of Aboriginal Bands and First Nations to discuss prospective joint development projects.

- A joint Working Group has been established between Interfor and the Tla-o-qui-aht Band to review development proposals.

- Interfor has had discussions with the Anderson Lake Band on a proposed feasibility study for a sawmill.

Helifor's Contracting Arrangements with the Nisga'a Band

Interfor's subsidiary, Helifor Industries, provides helicopter logging services to harvest trees from locations that are either economically or environmentally inaccessible. Helifor provides contract logging services to Interfor and to other forest product companies.

When Helifor was contracted to do the helilogging for a large timber sale from Nisga'a land, Helifor entered into a supplementary contract in which it agreed to employ a number of experienced heliloggers from the Nisga'a Band over the term of the agreement. As a result, Interfor's Helifor operations has had an ongoing contract for the past two years with the Nisga'a Band to provide a helilog rigging crew of about 10-12 persons.

Joint Business Venture with the Toquaht Band

The Toquaht Band holds a non-replaceable 10 year Forest Licence, a qualification for which involves a secondary manufacturing component. In exchange for the right to purchase up to 70 percent of the 110,000 cubic metres of timber available over five years, Interfor financed a new perma-

In exchange for the right to purchase timber from the Toquaht Band, Interfor financed and helped with the construction of a new permanent sawmill.

nent sawmill, helped with its construction and is providing ongoing assistance with sales, marketing and general management. A minimum of 30 percent of the wood logged is guaranteed to the mill.

The project, which is the culmination of a strategic decision taken many years ago by the Toquaht Band to become active participants in forest development, took much patience, persistence and active leadership on the part of the Chiefs. The Forest Licence took about seven years to acquire and significant challenges, such as accessing the isolated sawmill and securing a regular and reliable workforce, also had to be overcome.

The formal contract was signed in August 1993. Construction of the sawmill was done in the fall of 1993 and operations commenced in March 1994. Seven people were employed in the construction of the mill. Interfor provided specialists such as a mechanical superintendent and electrician; other workers were either Band members or local non-Aboriginal people with strong ties to the Band. The mill operation employs seven people. Local Aboriginal people were offered first opportunity for the jobs.

The joint business venture has resulted in mutual gains. For the Toquaht Band, the project provides employment and an opportunity to make profit. The sawmill, which is on reserve land, enables the community to be re-established on its traditional territory. The project also provides an opportunity for the Toquaht to put into action their commitment to improve environmental practices in the forest industry. For its part, Interfor acquires the right to purchase up to 70 percent of the 110,000 cubic metres of timber available over five years.

The relationship between Interfor and the Toquaht Band has been characterized by mutual frankness and honesty.

The relationship between Interfor and the Band has been characterized by mutual frankness and honesty and a willingness by the company to help. The essential success factor was a well-conceived, well-executed business plan. This involved setting realistic objectives, continually assessing performance, and modifying plans and operations as required in the face of changing circumstances. Other important elements contributing to the success of the partnership included mutual respect and understanding, communication and commitment. The commitment of the Chief to the project's objectives and his active involvement in problem-solving was important. The fact that the Chief was previously employed in the forest industry meant that he understood the industry.

Cooperative Initiatives with the Sechelt Band

Interfor and the Sechelt Band have been working cooperatively on a number of joint initiatives in the forest sector. In total, Interfor has undertaken 16 different cooperative initiatives with the Sechelt Band.

Interfor and the Sechelt Band have worked cooperatively on 16 different joint initiatives in the forest sector.

The most important initiative has been the agreement between Interfor and the Sechelt Band on a joint stewardship and economic alliance covering lands in the Sechelt area, which was signed in 1994. The agreement gave Interfor the right to build logging roads and provided it with continued access through timber on reserve lands. In return, the Band was able to purchase Vancouver Bay land from Interfor, together with a lodge and other facilities, which it wished to use initially for a youth rehabilitation program and which it plans to develop into a major tourism centre. Under the agreement, the Band also participates on a joint planning committee which reviews all the company's five year plans in the area, as well as its silviculture and reclamation initiatives.

Interfor has assisted the Band in feasibility studies for complementary milling opportunities in Sechelt. Interfor has provided technical advice to the Sechelt Band on a project to set up a value-added mill in the area. The project is being finalized and decisions to purchase the machinery and acquire the industrial land are expected shortly.

Under a joint stewardship and economic alliance agreement, the Sechelt Band participates on a joint planning committee which reviews all the company's five-year plans in the area.

Interfor has also assisted in training several fisheries and forestry crews and has hired them to work on Interfor projects. In particular, Interfor has provided opportunities for practical training through demonstration contracts.

The success of these relationships between Interfor and the Sechelt Band is the result of a number of factors.

- The Sechelt Band has found that it shares a compatible long-term vision with Interfor.

- The partnerships provide the Sechelt Band with substantive, not nominal, involvement.

- The Sechelt Band has taken a very pragmatic, strategic approach towards becoming a full and equal partner in the regional economy. It is receptive to developing alliances with forest companies as a means of strengthening its economic base and ensuring its ongoing stewardship over the environment.

- The nature of the partnerships have been mutually beneficial "win-win" situations for the company and for the Band which have enabled them to do more together than they could alone.

Success Factors

These cooperative ventures between Interfor and Aboriginal people in British Columbia demonstrate how the forest industry and Aboriginal groups can work together for mutual benefit.

As the benefits of cooperative ventures become more widely understood by the Aboriginal community and forest industry, more arrangements will be formed.

The projects demonstrate that the Aboriginal partners can realize significant direct benefits from a range of cooperative ventures, including opportunities for employment, skill development, development of business and management skills, revenues and profits. Forest companies benefit from improved access to timber and to local workers and contractors. These types of ventures also are important to forest companies as the process of land claims and self-government unfolds in B.C..

Interfor has found that the success of these arrangements depends on three key factors.

- There must be clear potential for mutual benefit.
- The two parties must bring together a mix of capital, human resources, business skills and technology to ensure that the arrangement is profitable.
- The relationship must be characterized by mutual respect and trust.

The company expects that, as the benefits of participating in cooperative ventures are more widely understood in both the Aboriginal community and in the forest industry, this will provide powerful incentives for more arrangements to be formed.

Regional Aboriginal Relations Initiatives in Northeast B.C.

The Northeast B.C. Industry Group is an ad hoc group to promote cultural understanding and develop business and employment opportunities for Aboriginal residents in the region.

The Northeast B.C. Industry Group is an ad hoc group of resource developers, Aboriginal people, government ministries, educational and financial institutions and service agencies that meet regularly to promote cultural understanding and to develop and promote business and employment opportunities for Aboriginal residents in the region.

The South Foothills area is the most active oil and gas development region in Canada. There are seven bands in the region with a total population of just over 2000. There are also an equal number of non-status Indians living in the area, as well as the only Metis community in B.C.

The Northeast B.C. Industry Group operates with no executive and no constitution. Member companies take turns in sponsoring, chairing and organizing meetings. Despite its informality, the Group has been successful in creating significant new business and employment opportunities for the local Aboriginal people over the past few years.

Membership and Evolution

The Northeast B.C. Industry Group was created in 1990 as a forum to discuss opportunities and expectations between members of the Treaty 8 bands and gas companies involved in exploring for and producing natural gas in the region. The Group came together to help address the deep mistrust felt towards the industry by Aboriginal people in the area. Since there was no distinction made between companies or between the various sub-sectors of the industry, a coordinated effort was needed by the industry.

The Northeast B.C. Industry Group began when a few representatives from energy companies and government ministries got together to consider how best to approach Aboriginal issues in the region. Companies involved in the initial phase of the Industry Group's establishment included Canadian Hunter Exploration, Talisman Energy, Amoco Canada and Shell Canada.

The Industry Group was launched on the premise that although individual companies

---

Northeast B.C. Industry Group

The Northeast B.C. Industry Group was formed in 1990. It is an ad hoc group of over 200 organizations that includes resource developers, Aboriginal contractors, band councils, local businesses, government ministries, educational and financial institutions and service agencies that meet regularly to promote cultural understanding and to develop and promote business and employment opportunities for Aboriginal residents in the region.

The large industry members are Amoco, Canadian Hunter, Westcoast Energy, Petro-Canada, Canfor, Mobil, Talisman and Shell.

do not have the ability to resolve political issues, they do have the ability to address employment issues and, thereby, the economic conditions of Aboriginal people. Employment and business opportunities could be provided independent of, but with respect towards and recognition of the political goals of the Tribal Association and member bands.

Membership in the Group includes the majority of resource companies that operate in the area and each of the seven First Nations.

Membership in the Northeast B.C. Industry Group now includes the majority of resource companies that operate in the area and each of the seven First Nations. The Group has grown to include utilities and forest sector companies, as well as government ministries and educational institutions.

In 1992, joint task teams were developed to address specific educational, training and business development opportunities for the Aboriginal people and businesses in the region.

Objectives

The Northeast B.C. Industry Group has set the following specific objectives.

- To improve each company's knowledge of Aboriginal concerns about industry.
- To improve Aboriginal knowledge about industry concerns.
- To respect traditional land concerns in the development of industry.
- To increase Aboriginal employment and business opportunities.
- To provide two-way communications.

Joint Task Teams

Joint task teams were formed to help achieve the objectives of the Group. Each team works to develop and deliver practical initiatives that will promote Aboriginal self-reliance.

Joint task teams have been formed to help achieve the objectives of the Group. The concept of forming teams was introduced when the number of participants grew too large for interactive dialogue between everyone attending meetings. The Group decided to organize into teams, each of which would address an area of need within the local Aboriginal community. Group participants are free to select which team they wish to work within. People usually select a team in which they have a specific interest or expertise.

The Industry Group meets regularly from September until June of each year. In September, each team decides the tasks they will undertake to complete between then and the following June. There is no prescribed way of doing things. What is done and how it is done is left to the judgement of team participants. Each of the teams works to develop and deliver practical initiatives that will promote Aboriginal self-reliance. The teams endeavour to develop and implement initiatives that are practical, cost effective and strengthen rather than duplicate programs by other agencies and institutions.

Three task teams have been formed to date: a business development team, an education, training and careers team, and a communications team.

The Business Development task team was formed to increase the number of Aboriginal businesses and contracting companies in fields required by industries operating in the area.

The Business Development task team was formed to increase the number of Aboriginal businesses and contracting companies in fields required by industries operating in the area.

- This team has assessed and redefined the purpose of a business registry.

- It has identified and conducted a series of "how to" workshops and courses that will increase the operating knowledge of business principles among Aboriginal businesses. These have included presentations on basic contract operating procedures and courses on book-keeping.

The Education, Training and Careers task team is working to increase the number of Aboriginal people qualified to enter the industrial workforce and progress to technical and managerial jobs. It has undertaken several initiatives.

The Education, Training and Careers task team is working to increase the number of Aboriginal people qualified to enter the industrial workforce and progress to technical and managerial jobs.

- The task team is working to establishing a local Aboriginal Joint Apprenticeship Board that will enable the regional Aboriginal population to enter apprenticeable trades.

- It is identifying blockages to funding for adult education and training and preparing a plan to address the blockages.

- It is establishing an Aboriginal employment registry and taking steps to maximize summer student hiring. It is also facilitating a number of other specific education and training projects such as contributing to the North Peace Adult Education Task Force inventory; promoting stay in school initiatives and career fairs; and supporting an Aboriginal Women in Business conference.

The Communications task team was established to increase mutual knowledge and understanding.

- This entails increasing knowledge within industry, including among industry leaders, about the values and organization of the Aboriginal community.

The Communications task team was established to increase mutual knowledge and understanding. Moose School is a joint initiative between the Northeast B.C. Industry Group and the Elders' Council of Treaty 8.

- The Communications task team is working to increasing knowledge in Aboriginal communities and their leadership of the work and organization of industries.

- Moose School is a joint initiative between the Northeast B.C. Industry Group and the Elders' Council of Treaty 8. Moose School is a camp in which skilled elders, trappers, hunters and women of the Treaty 8 tribes of northeast B.C. instruct urban and industrial people in Aboriginal land values and traditions. The camps are held in the traditional hunting territories of the Aboriginal people in northeastern B.C..

- The Communications task team is also taking steps to recruit wider participation from industries, businesses and Aboriginal communities in the work of the Northeast B.C. Industry Group.

The Northeast B.C. Industry Group member companies, represented by the Canadian Association of Petroleum Producers, together with representatives of Westcoast Energy and government ministries, commenced discussion in late 1994 with the Treaty 8 Tribal Association to develop a consultation model which will be acceptable to Treaty 8 communities, provincial ministries and the oil and gas industry.

Accomplishments

The combined efforts of the Northeast B.C. Industry Group has resulted in over $12 million in business and employment opportunities to the Aboriginal residents of the region over the past few years. Slashing contracting has become the most prevalent form of business activity by the local population.

The Group's combined efforts have resulted in over $12 million in business opportunities to the Aboriginal residents. Accomplishments include the creation of a Native Construction Contractors Association.

Other accomplishments with respect to business development include the creation of an increasingly open dialogue in roundtable format and the creation of a Native Construction Contractors Association to better represent the Aboriginal contractors in the area. Participating gas companies are changing the way in which they subcontract construction work to create improved opportunities for these contractors.

Specific job training has been provided to individual Aboriginal workers. The Group has also provided 12 industry-relevant workshops and training sessions. It has entered into a six month cost sharing arrangement with the Treaty 8 Tribal Association to hire an Economic Development Advisor who will assist member bands and companies in accomplishing Northeast B.C. Industry Group objectives. In addition to Group workshops, individual Industry Group member companies have organized and sponsored a number of workshops and training sessions.

To date, approximately 30 people have attended the Moose School. The program has been a very effective medium for conveying the Aboriginal land use ethic to people who work in resource industries. Its has also benefitted Moose School teachers who have gained a better understanding of resource industries through the process.

The Group has organized northeast B.C.'s first Aboriginal career days. It has organized and facilitated annual information sessions for potential summer students and employers. The Group is in the process of promoting the formation of the province's first Aboriginal Apprenticeship Board. The concept for a Northeast Aboriginal Joint Training Board was formally presented to the B.C. Provincial Apprenticeship Board in mid-1995. If the proposal is implemented as a three-year pilot, it will differ from other joint training boards in that it will be able to indenture virtually any apprenticeable trade and possibly indenture apprentices who are being trained under company-specific training programs.

Success Factors

The key to the success of the Northeast B.C. Industry Group is that it brings people together by working on initiatives that focus on commonalities rather than differences.

The key to the success of the Northeast B.C. Industry Group is that it brings people together by working on initiatives that focus on commonalities rather than differences. Other success factors are as follows.

- The needs of the Aboriginal community are acknowledged in their entirety (social, economic and cultural).

- There is no distinction made between status and non-status people.

- Task teams endeavour to develop and implement initiatives that are practical and cost-efficient, and strengthen rather than duplicate existing social services, agencies and institutions.

- Efforts are oriented towards assisting individuals meet their specific employment or business development goals.

Next Steps

The Group must now progress to developing initiatives that widen and deepen local Aboriginal participation in the industrial economy.

The Group has accomplished its initial objectives and must now progress to developing initiatives that widen and deepen local Aboriginal participation in the industrial economy. Expanding to the next level of employment and business opportunities will involve action on a number of fronts, including:

- the increased participation of secondary industries in the Group;

- greater Aboriginal participation in surveying and heavy equipment operation;

- increasing opportunities for Aboriginal participation in contracts tendered at field locations, such as painting, janitorial work and road maintenance; and

- development of permanent employment opportunities.

Some of these initiatives will be undertaken collaboratively (with several companies, organizations and training institutions working together). Others will be done on a company-specific basis.

PART FIVE

COMMUNITY RELATIONS

Hydro-Québec's Negotiated Agreements with Aboriginal Communities

Negotiated agreements provide the mechanism whereby Hydro-Québec can reconcile the fulfilment of its mandate with the objectives of the Aboriginal nations, on the basis of mutual respect and understanding.

Over the past 20 years, Hydro-Québec has signed major agreements with a number of Aboriginal nations. Hydro-Québec's responsibilities for generating, transmitting and distributing electricity throughout Quebec has meant constant contact with the Aboriginal nations of the province. Negotiated agreements provide the mechanism whereby Hydro-Québec can reconcile the fulfilment of its mandate (such as the development of hydro resources) with the objectives of the Aboriginal nations, on the basis of mutual respect and understanding.

The nature of the negotiated agreements has evolved since the James Bay and Northern Quebec Agreement was signed in 1975. Today, Hydro-Québec's policy is to try to achieve **integrated** agreements with Aboriginal people that deal with remedial measures as well as measures for community, economic and cultural development.

Hydro-Québec has achieved substantial progress in its relationships with the Aboriginal peoples of Quebec. Many of Quebec's Aboriginal nations, particularly Cree, Inuit, Atikamekw, Montagnais and Naskapis peoples, have benefitted to varying degrees from the multi-million dollar economic spin-offs of the utility's construction and operation activities. In addition, several Aboriginal nations have signed agreements that contain joint remedial works corporations. These are funded by Hydro-Québec, but jointly controlled by Hydro-Québec and the Aboriginal signatories. The agreements provide the mechanism to undertake specific mitigation, research, monitoring and remedial works related to the project. Under its new integrated agreements, Hydro-Québec also funds community development and socio-economic initiatives.

Hydro-Québec's Approach to Aboriginal Relations

As a result of its presence throughout Quebec, Hydro-Québec believes it can contribute to the

---

Hydro-Québec

Hydro-Québec ranks among North America's largest utilities in terms of assets and volume of sales. In 1994, Hydro-Québec had revenues of $7.3 billion. It generates, transmits and distributes most of the electricity in Quebec and also sells and purchases both power and energy under agreement with neighbouring systems in Canada and the United States.

Hydro-Québec was constituted by an act of the Quebec legislature in 1944. In 1981, it became a joint stock company with a single shareholder: the Quebec government. The company's headquarters are in Montreal and it is active in all parts of Quebec.

Hydro-Québec has about 20,500 permanent employees, 200 of whom (or about 1 percent) are Aboriginal peoples. Aboriginal people work for the company as clerical workers, managers, engineering technicians, apparatus electricians, line workers and customer service representatives.

goal of self-sufficiency for Aboriginal peoples. To do this, the utility must meet two challenges.

New relationships between Aboriginal and non-Aboriginal people should be built, in part, on negotiated agreements. Negotiating and signing agreements constitutes a de facto recognition of a degree of self-government.

- First, it must make sure that the impacts of its structures on traditional ways of life are mitigated as far as possible. This must always be done in consultation with the nations and communities affected.

- Second, it must ensure that the design, execution and operation of its activities enable Aboriginal nations to diversify their economy, train the Aboriginal workforce and participate fully and as equals in Quebec's economy.

Hydro-Québec believes that new relationships between Aboriginal and non-Aboriginal people should be built, in part, on negotiated agreements. Negotiating and signing agreements constitutes a *de facto* recognition of a degree of self-government, even if this is not yet defined in law. For Hydro-Québec, negotiated agreements help provide the ongoing framework for the relationship between the utility and Aboriginal peoples. Because negotiations are ongoing, there are often multiple agreements with various Aboriginal communities.

Each negotiated agreement is based on a process of rigorous preparation that is designed to define the real needs of the First Nations and communities affected by a project. For example, before the signing of the La Grande (1992) - Opimiscow Agreement, Hydro-Québec and the Crees formed a number of joint committees whose task was to collect opinions and data on specific needs of the Chisasibi and Weminji communities. The actual negotiations were then used to give form to the conclusions drawn from the data collection and impact study process.

Negotiated Agreements with First Nations

The practice of negotiating agreements for projects affecting Aboriginal peoples stems from the provisions of the James Bay and Northern Quebec Agreement signed in 1975.

The practice of negotiating agreements for projects affecting Aboriginal peoples stems from the provisions of the James Bay and Northern Quebec Agreement signed in 1975. Hydro-Québec is a signatory to this agreement (as well as the Northeastern Quebec Agreement of 1978 which was based on it) along with the Grand Council of the Crees, The Northern Quebec Inuit Association, the Government of Canada, the Société d'énergie de la Baie James, and the Société de développement de la Baie James, as well as with the Naskapis in the case of the Northeastern Quebec Agreement.

These agreements have had a significant influence in defining and shaping Hydro-Québec's relationships with Aboriginal people throughout the province.

- The negotiation of project undertakings has its origin in the James Bay Agreement.

- The concept of mitigating the environmental impact of projects through remedial corporations jointly managed by Hydro-Québec and Aboriginal communities is inspired by the Agreement.

- The support for traditional economic activities follows the example of the special funding program for Cree hunters and fishermen established by the James Bay Agreement.

- The James Bay Agreement also led to the establishment of an administrative unit in Hydro-Québec to serve as an ongoing and effective communications link between Aboriginal people and the corporation's senior management. In 1985 the position of Vice President of Indian and Inuit Affairs was created (which became Vice President, Aboriginal and Community Affairs in 1994).

Since 1975, Hydro-Québec has also participated in the conclusion of eight complementary agreements to the James Bay and Northern Quebec Agreement which have the effect of amending and clarifying it.

Hydro-Québec also has signed an additional nine specific agreements with Aboriginal nations or communities in Quebec and has arrived at an agreement-in-principle with the Inuit with respect to the proposed Great Whale Complex.

Hydro-Québec's Agreements with Aboriginal Nations and Communities

Agreement	Year
James Bay and Northern Quebec Agreement	1975
Northeastern Quebec Agreement	1978
Chisasibi Agreement	1978
Sakami Lake Agreement	1979
La Grande (1986) Agreement	1986
The Mercury Agreement	1986
Atikamekw/Hydro-Québec Agreement	1988
Kuujjuaq Agreement	1988
Mashteuiatsh/Hydro-Québec Agreement	1990
La Grande (1992)/Opimiscow Agreement	1993
Mashteuiatsh/Hydro-Québec Agreement	1993
Uashat mak Mani-Utenam/Hydro-Québec	1994

Source: Hydro-Québec 1995

Hydro-Québec's agreements with Aboriginal nations include a number of measures to stimulate economic development. The economic spin-offs arise from specific construction projects as well as from ongoing operations.

Economic Development

Hydro-Québec's agreements with Aboriginal nations include a number of measures to stimulate economic development. This approach is consistent with the corporation's broader corporate policy, which is designed to favour the purchase of local goods and services and hiring of local workers in each of its operating regions.

The economic spin-offs arise from Hydro-Québec's specific construction projects as well as from ongoing operations. Construction projects, such a building generating stations, as well as substations and power transmission lines, provide opportunities for Aboriginal contractors and Aboriginal project workers.

Hydro-Québec has adopted a number of measures to ensure that Aboriginal communities and Aboriginal businesses obtain construction, maintenance, renovation and service contracts. For example, the utility defines the scope of the contracts so that a portion can be carried out by Aboriginal suppliers. Hydro-Québec also conducts information campaigns with communities to make them familiar with its commercial practices and administrative procedures, as well as its construction and service contract needs. It also supports the creation of joint ventures to enable an Aboriginal company to acquire experience in new fields.

Remedial measures are important elements of the negotiated agreements. Several rely on specifically-created, jointly-managed remedial works corporations to carry out these measures.

Mitigating and Enhancement Measures

Remedial measures are also important elements of the negotiated agreements. Hydro-Québec recognizes that projects in areas where Aboriginal people carry out their traditional activities may have negative impacts on their way of life and their social and economic structures. As a result, specific measures are needed to circumscribe or offset the negative effects. Hydro-Québec has negotiated several agreements that rely on specifically-created, jointly-managed remedial works corporations to carry out the mitigating and enhancement measures needed to address the negative impacts.

The first remedial works corporation (SOTRAC) was created in 1975 pursuant to the James Bay Agreement. This corporation, named La Grande Complex Remedial Works Corporation, was set up to manage the environmental impacts on hunting, fishing and trapping among the Cree. It was a joint non-profit corporation which received $30 million from Hydro-Québec to invest in such projects as relocation and intensive trapping of beaver in the reservoirs before they were impounded, the reorganization of traplines and adaptation of activities associated with hunting, fishing and trapping to new conditions.

The Development of Integrated Agreements

In December 1993, Hydro-Québec adopted an integrated enhancement and development policy to resolve problems that arise when land required for generating and transmitting electricity is also used for other purposes. Under this policy, Hydro-Québec recognizes that some impacts of its projects cannot be mitigated and will remain after the project has been completed.

Negotiated agreements now deal with remedial issues and issues relating to community, economic and cultural development in an integrated fashion.

Negotiated agreements now deal with remedial issues and issues relating to community, economic and cultural development in an integrated fashion. The utility provides funds, over and above the project budget, that can be used to support environmental enhancements, alleviate the impact on traditional hunting, fishing and trapping activities, and promote the economic development of regions and Aboriginal communities or nations. The amounts made available can reach a maximum of 2 percent of the total project budget.

Remedial works corporations have emerged as an important element in all Hydro-Québec's new integrated agreements with Aboriginal peoples. They have become a vehicle for mitigating the negative effects of Hydro-Québec projects on Aboriginal communities. All remedial corporations are jointly controlled by Hydro-Québec and the Aboriginal signatory to the agreement. Some SOTRACs have funding for up to 50 years.

In 1994, Hydro-Québec signed two integrated agreements with Montagnais (Innu) communities: one for a transmission line project and the other for the Sainte-Marguerite hydro project. The utility has also reached an agreement-in-principle with the Inuit of Quebec on the proposed Great Whale project.

The Uashat Mak Mani-Utenam (1994) Agreement

The Uashat Mak Mani-Utenam Agreement provides an example of a new integrated approach to negotiated agreements. It was signed in 1994 between the Band of the Montagnais (or Innu) of Uashat-Maliotenam and Hydro-Québec regarding the project to develop a hydro-electric station on the Sainte-Marguerite River.

The Agreement is designed to reduce the negative impacts of the project on the Montagnais and to maximize the positive impacts by promoting community, economic and cultural development opportunities for the Montagnais. There are a number of elements in the Agreement.

- Commitments which promote employment and business development opportunities for the Montagnais are a key element of the Agreement. During the construction period the provisions of the

The Uashat Mak Mani-Utenam Agreement is designed to reduce the negative impacts and maximize the opportunities for the Montagnais.

Agreement call for Hydro-Québec and its contractors to provide opportunities for the Montagnais workforce from Uashat-Maliotenam. Hydro-Québec will also favour the award of contracts to Montagnais enterprises when it is possible to do so. Contracts have already been awarded to partnerships formed between the Montagnais and other local companies for fuel supply (Petro-Innu) and road construction (Uisht Construction). When the project is operational, a strategy will be developed that facilitates the hiring of Montagnais in Hydro-Québec's local workforce and provides systematic opportunities to Montagnais contractors through the use of restricted tenders for the first five years.

- The establishment of a corporation and fund to undertake environmental and remedial measures is another element of the Agreement. The remedial corporation (SOTRAC) will be jointly managed by Hydro-Québec and the Montagnais. Remedial activities will be funded by a $10 million Remedial Works Fund which will be used to adapt the project to respond to the particular needs of the Montagnais, preserve the quality and productivity of the environment, and assist the regeneration of habitats. The works that SOTRAC recommends will be carried out, to the extent possible, by Montagnais enterprises.

- The Agreement provides for the establishment of a $7 million Economic and Community Development Fund to pay for community infrastructure projects.

- It also provides for the establishment of an *Innu aitun* Fund (which means "Innu at work") to alleviate the impacts of the project on the hunting, fishing and trapping activities of the Montagnais. This will involve 50 annual payments by Hydro-Québec of just over $300,000, indexed annually. The fund may be used for the improvement of trappers' installations, the relocation of animals and the creation of fish spawning areas. This enables the Band Council to provide people who pursue traditional activities with better equipment, better traps, radios for emergencies and improved transportation into and out of the bush. The Fund has also helped re-launch and consolidate programs for young school dropouts by taking them to "a school of the land" where experienced instructors show them how to live off the land and regain their physical and mental health.

- Commitments to protect, to the extent possible, the archaeological and burial sites discovered during the construction of the project are included in the Agreement. These measures are paid for by Hydro-Québec.

Results

Hydro-Québec has achieved substantial progress through the relationships it has developed with the Aboriginal peoples of Quebec.

Between 1973 and 1994 Hydro-Québec and its subsidiary, the Société d'énergie de la Baie James (SEBJ), have signed agreements that have resulted in payments to Aboriginal nations in Quebec worth $410 million. These payments have been used to help Aboriginal nations meet their socio-economic and community development needs, to ensure protection of the environment and to provide financial compensation for residual impacts.

Between 1973 and 1994 Hydro-Québec signed agreements that resulted in payments to Aboriginal nations in Quebec worth $410 million.

- Some of the funds have been invested to set up regional Aboriginal enterprises in diverse sectors, such as air transport, construction, and commercial services.

- Some of the funds have been invested in financial markets for the benefit of future generations and needs.

- Remedial works funds have been used to preserve the quality and productivity of the environment and assist with the regeneration of habitats.

- Socio-economic funding has also been directed at alleviating the impacts of projects on hunting, fishing and trapping activities and promoting cultural development.

In addition, the spin-offs from Hydro-Québec's activities for some of the Aboriginal nations in Quebec have been substantial. In the period from 1989 to 1993, Hydro-Québec and SEBJ granted contracts worth over $300 million to Aboriginal contractors, suppliers and workers. Many contracts are won in an open bidding procedure. Most of Quebec's Aboriginal nations (most notably Cree, Inuit, Atikamekw, Montagnais and Naskapis) have benefitted to varying degrees from the economic spin-offs of the utility's construction and operation activities.

- Cree companies and workers were awarded $214 million in contracts and wages over the five year period.

- Inuit organizations and workers received $50 million in contracts, salaries and wages.

- Montagnais businesses and workers received contracts and wages worth over $12 million.

- Naskapis businesses and workers received contracts and wages worth $7 million.

- Almost $10 million flowed to Atikamekw suppliers.

Hydro-Québec has noted that the experience gained in undertaking contracts for the utility has enabled Aboriginal companies to train workers, improve their general competence and better position themselves in bidding on open calls for tender.

Falconbridge's Approach to Community Relations at the Raglan Project

Community relations with local Inuit people have been an important element in the development of Falconbridge's Raglan Project. The project needs the support of the local communities to be successful over the long term.

Community relations with local Inuit people have been an important element in the development of Falconbridge's Raglan Project in the Ungava region of northern Quebec. A mining development in such a remote and fragile area is of great importance to the people who live there. Even with legal authority to proceed, the Raglan project needs the support of the local communities to be successful over the long term.

Working closely and openly with the local communities has been a priority from the beginning. The company has worked to build trust through ongoing consultations with the local people and by incorporating their concerns into Falconbridge's planning process. Since the key concerns of the local Inuit people centred around employment and environmental impact, Falconbridge has emphasized these two areas.

Wherever possible, the company has taken steps to deliver benefits to local communities. Recognizing that local communities have long-term economic interests, Falconbridge has undertaken considerable planning to ensure that Inuit participation in the Raglan project is maximized over the long term, both in terms of direct jobs and through contracting opportunities. Falconbridge has signed an agreement with Makivik Corporation that gives priority to hiring and training qualified Inuit workers for the project, provides contracting opportunities for Inuit enterprises and sets up a Trust Fund for the local Inuit people. Falconbridge has also taken specific action to address environmental concerns and is committed to using the best environmental technologies and practices.

Falconbridge Limited

Falconbridge is an international mining company with operations in Sudbury, Timmins, Norway and the Dominican Republic. The company mines and processes nickel, ferro-nickel, cobalt, copper and zinc. The company had revenues of almost $2 billion in 1994.

Falconbridge is a publicly traded company. Its majority owner is Noranda Inc of Toronto which owns 46 percent of the company.

Falconbridge employs 6300 people in its worldwide operations.

The Raglan Project

Raglan is a nickel-copper property on the Ungava Peninsula in Northern Quebec. It is one of the best undeveloped nickel deposits in the world. The property is located about sixty kilometres west of the Inuit village of Kangiqsujuaq and one hundred kilometres south east of Salluit. The focus of Falconbridge's exploration work has been at Katinniq, the largest ore body in the centre of the property.

The mine should be in operation in 1998. Capital expenditures of $486 million are planned and about 4000 direct and indirect jobs are expected to be created.

One of Falconbridge's main goals has been to ensure that the Inuit know what the company is doing at Raglan and feel comfortable expressing their views.

Falconbridge has been working at Raglan intermittently since the late 1960's. In addition to exploration activities, a significant amount of other work has been done to build infrastructure. The airstrip and roads have been upgraded, retaining dykes for fuel tanks have been built and a new camp was constructed. Extensive baseline and environmental impact studies have also been completed.

The decision to develop the mine project was made in early 1995. Now that all the necessary government approvals are in place, Société Minière Raglan Limitée, Falconbridge's wholly-owned subsidiary, is proceeding with project development work. The mine should be in operation by March 1998. Capital expenditures of $486 million are planned and approximately 4000 direct and indirect jobs are expected to be created, of which 350 will be full-time jobs on site.

Falconbridge's Approach to Community Relations

Falconbridge's long-standing approach to the Raglan project is that it can only be a success if it is viewed as a positive development by the local Inuit people. When the decision was made to proceed with advanced exploration and development work at Raglan in the late 1980s, the company was conscious of the interests of the Inuit people and their concerns about the potential for industrial development in their vicinity. The harsh arctic climate and the fragile permafrost environment bring some unique challenges to the Raglan project. The Inuit rely heavily on the land and water for their food needs, making any industrial development a cause for concern.

One of Falconbridge's main goals has been to ensure that the Inuit know what the company is doing at Raglan and feel comfortable expressing their views. Falconbridge has taken a number of steps to acquaint local people with the project and understand their concerns.

- With the advice and assistance of the Makivik Corporation (which oversees the political, social and economic development of the Nunavik territory) and others, Falconbridge retained an Inuit advisor in 1991. The role of the advisor has been to act as a liaison between the company and the communities. He has keeps Falconbridge abreast of people's sentiments towards the Raglan development, reports back on local rumours, and identifies concerns that local people feel have not been adequately addressed by the company. He also helps to identify workforce candidates.

- Other initiatives have included visits to the communities and meetings with mayors and councillors; radio shows in which Falconbridge's local advisor updates the status of the project; the production and airing of a television documentary on Raglan; and visits by key community leaders to both Raglan and other northern operating mines.

The initial consultation with the villages of Salluit and Kangiqsujuaq highlighted two key Inuit concerns, namely employment and environmental impact.

The initial consultation with the villages of Salluit and Kangiqsujuaq highlighted two key Inuit concerns, namely employment and environmental impact.

- Many Inuit expressed interest in developing their communities and expanding into a wage-based economy that would lead to greater diversification and lower dependence on government. The Raglan project was seen as a potential source of local, well-paying jobs and long-term employment for the villages. At the same time, significant concern was expressed that the communities be able to embrace a wage sector economy without abandoning their dedication to the traditional pursuits of hunting and fishing.

- Environmental concerns also emerged as important issues to the people of Nunavik. While supportive of economic diversification, it was clear that the communities believed that this could not be achieved without some perceived cost to the environment. With Raglan, the key environmental issue of local concern is water quality.

Employment Initiatives

Falconbridge's goal is to maximize Inuit participation in the Raglan project over the long term.

Falconbridge's goal is to maximize Inuit participation in the Raglan project over the long term.

In the summers of 1991 and 1992, Falconbridge employed up to 100 people on the Raglan site. Between 10 and 20 percent of the employees were from the villages of Kangiqsujuaq and Salluit. The jobs held by local people ranged from heavy equipment operators to truck drivers, custodians, geological assistants and general labourers. In general, the work experience was extremely positive. Some differences in work culture did emerge, including occasions where local employees wished to leave camp to hunt during a shift. The company recognizes that differences in work culture will take time to resolve and that over the long-term, training and flexibility will be the key considerations in developing a large indigenous workforce.

A workforce strategy to maximize Inuit involvement is being developed in cooperation with the communities, the Kativik Regional Employment and Training Committee and Inuit employees. The strategy addresses the low supply of local job-ready labour and the need to develop training programs and educational initiatives for Inuit still in school. Other issues include establishing educational equivalents for local employees and developing realistic approaches to a labour pool dispersed over a wide geographic area.

In February 1995, Makivik Corporation (which represents local Inuit) and the Société Minière Raglan Limitée signed an agreement to promote Inuit training and employment. The Raglan Agreement gives priority employment opportunities to Inuit in the two closest communities, followed by Inuit from the region as a whole and then other Inuit from Nunavik.

Société Minière Raglan is working with the Kativik Regional Government and the Kativik School Board to ensure that on-site and off-site training is made available so that Inuit employment can be maximized over the longer term. The Kativik Regional Government and the Kativik School Board have contracted four heavy equipment operator training programs to train up to 60 Inuit over the next four years. The Kativik Regional Government will identify candidates and Société Minière Raglan will select candidates for the program. Other training initiatives (on and off-site) will cover academic upgrading, languages, orientation and safety, common core mining skills, operations and maintenance, trades leading to certification, and train-the-trainer programs. Trainers from Falconbridge's Kidd Creek division are seconded to the site as required.

Initiatives to facilitate Inuit integration into the work environment will include career counselling, a full-time Inuit advisor and an employee assistance program. Since many Inuit expressed concern that being away from their family for the usual 4 week rotation would make it difficult to accommodate their family's hunting and fishing needs, Falconbridge has offered the option of a two week rotation (two weeks in, two weeks out). Although safety considerations made it impossible for Falconbridge to accommodate the request by Inuit workers for rifles on-site to hunt for food, the company agreed to bring in country foods (including wild meat) and is providing kitchen facilities to prepare it. Falconbridge implemented a policy of prohibition of drugs and alcohol to meet Inuit priorities. Local communities indicated that it was very important to them that the Raglan camp be dry.

Contracting Opportunities

Inuit businesses will be actively involved during the development and operation phases of the Raglan Project, with specific opportunities for Inuit enterprises that supply air transportation services, hotel and catering services, public works, and road transportation of goods.

Building the infrastructure for the mine site will take no more than two to three years, whereas the operations stage is expected to last at least fif-

The Raglan Agreement gives priority employment opportunities to Inuit in the two closest communities, followed by Inuit from the region as a whole and then other Inuit from Nunavik.

There will be specific opportunities for Inuit businesses that supply air transportation services, hotel and catering services, public works, and road transportation of goods.

teen years. As a result, the most significant contracting opportunities for Inuit businesses will be linked to the lengthier operations phase of the project. This will allow time for the people in the region to create new businesses and position themselves for the emerging opportunities.

Establishment of a Trust Fund

To ensure that the Inuit of Nunavik, and more particularly those living in the villages of Salluit and Kangiqsujuaq, benefit fully from the project's economic spin-offs, Société Minière Raglan will make guaranteed contributions of $14 million over an 18-year period into a Trust Fund, established for the benefit of the Inuit. This amount will be added to a portion of the profits generated by the Raglan project, calculated on a profit-sharing basis and evaluated at approximately $61 million. If the life span of the project exceeds 18 years, profits and guaranteed contributions would be adjusted accordingly.

The Raglan Trust, which was created to manage payments to the Inuit, allows flexibility in the distribution of compensation to individuals as well as to Makivik and the Landholding Corporations. The Trust has three distinct sets of beneficiaries: Salluit, Kangiqsujuaq, and the Region. There are also sub-classes of beneficiaries (all residents, students, elders, the Landholding Corporations, etc.) which allows the flexibility to benefit one group one year and another group another year.

Environmental Initiatives

Raglan is being designed to meet the highest environmental standards from the outset. Falconbridge is consulting with local stakeholders on environmental issues as it proceeds.

Raglan is being designed to meet the highest environmental standards from the outset and Falconbridge is consulting with local stakeholders on environmental issues as it proceeds. The company has completed an extensive environmental baseline study of all aspects of the physical environment in the region including the climate, aquatic and plant life, archaeology, land use patterns and the numbers and migratory patterns of land and sea mammals. The study shows the natural environment before any mining operations begin and gives a benchmark against which to measure any impact the project may have on the environment. If a negative impact is detected, action to correct it can be taken immediately.

Specific environmental initiatives that address local concerns include the following.

- To ensure minimal impact on water quality from tailings, the tailings disposal system is designed to minimize the formation of acid from sulphides and to allow progressive restoration during operations.

There will be no seepage from the tailings and spring run-off will be held in a pond for re-use or treated prior to discharge into the environment.

- Windblown dust from the tailings will be minimized by winter snow and by controlling its moisture content.

- The greatest volume of solid waste produced by the mine comes from waste rock. Since sulphide-bearing rock could generate acid if it is stored on the surface, most waste rock will be returned underground as backfill. Sulphide-bearing rock will have a priority as backfill.

Next Steps

Ongoing community relations will be spearheaded by local management of the mine as part of its operational responsibilities. The company will continue to provide the local people with up-to-date information on what the company is doing.

A Raglan Committee has been set up and will serve as the formal forum between Société Minière Raglan and the Inuit. Three of the six members will be local Inuit.

A Raglan Committee has been set up and will serve as the formal forum between Société Minière Raglan and the Inuit. Three of the six members will be local Inuit. The Raglan Committee will follow up on environmental matters and will work to solve any potential problems that might arise. An external consultant will analyze and make recommendations to the Raglan Committee on any environmental issues. An Inuit guide will monitor any environmental changes and will report them to the Raglan Committee.

Parks Canada's Cooperative Management Arrangements with Aboriginal Peoples

Aboriginal people currently participate in the management of five national parks and national park reserves.

Parks Canada has entered into a number of successful agreements with Aboriginal communities to cooperatively manage certain national parks. Under these agreements, park-level officials and local Aboriginal communities cooperate in advising the Minister of Canadian Heritage on the management of the national park. The Aboriginal community has equal representation on the park's management board, which is the equivalent of a board of directors.

The management board operates within the parameters of the *National Parks Act*. If the board has been set up through a comprehensive land claims agreement, provisions of that agreement as it affects the national park, prevail. The board sets the overall site-specific policy and objectives, is involved in the development of a park management plan, and deals with issues that have an impact on the economic situation of the people in the community. This might involve workplans, budget allocations, recruitment and employee training. The implementation of the park management plan and day-to-day operations are the responsibility of the Superintendent and park staff.

Aboriginal people currently participate in the management of five national parks and national park reserves. These agreements have demonstrated that Parks Canada and Aboriginal peoples can achieve significant shared objectives over protected spaces through cooperative planning and management of park lands. Parks Canada anticipates that there will be more such agreements in the future and discussions are also underway for cooperative management boards to be set up to assist in the management of certain national historic sites administered by the department.

Evolution of the Arrangements

Cooperative management arrangements between Parks Canada and Aboriginal peoples

---

Parks Canada

Parks Canada is part of the Department of Canadian Heritage. Parks Canada is responsible for managing a system of national heritage areas and programs (national ports, national historic sites, national marine conservation areas, historic canals, heritage rivers and heritage railway stations) in ways that encourage public understanding, appreciation and enjoyment of this heritage while ensuring long-term ecological and commemorative integrity.

Canada's national parks system comprises 36 national parks and national parks reserves. The system has been established to protect representative examples of the Canadian landscape. To this end, Parks Canada has divided the country into 39 natural regions, each with distinctive natural characteristics such as vegetation, physiography and environmental conditions. The goal is to create a national park to represent each of the 39 regions by the year 2000. Twenty-three regions are currently represented and work is underway to establish new parks in the remaining 16 natural regions.

Cooperative management arrangements between Parks Canada and Aboriginal peoples date back to the 1970s.

date back to the 1970s. The first such arrangement was put in place at Wood Buffalo National Park (the second largest national park in the world that straddles the Alberta-Northwest Territories border) when a Hunters and Trappers Association was put in place to set limits on the number of harvesting permits issued. When the park was created in 1922, Treaty Indians who had hunted and trapped in the park were allowed to continue these activities by permit, as were a number of non-Treaty Indians and Metis hunters and trappers. Access to a permit, that originally applied to some 80 people, became a hereditary privilege. By the 1970s, over 600 people were eligible to obtain a permit. Over time, game resources were being depleted and hunters and trappers and park officials worked cooperatively to address the problem.

A more formal framework for cooperative management has come about through the land claim process. In negotiating comprehensive claims, it became apparent that this process could involve the creation of national parks which could be beneficial to the Aboriginal claimant group in whose traditional territory the park is situated. Set aside to encourage natural heritage understanding, appreciation and enjoyment by all Canadians, these parks provide a protected area where local Aboriginal people have the right to continue their traditional harvesting activities of hunting, trapping, fishing and gathering. The claims agreements also set out the formal structure for cooperative management.

A number of such parks have been created since the comprehensive claims process began in the 1970s, bringing local Aboriginal people into the management process. A management board involving equal numbers of Aboriginal people and appointees of the Minister provides the forum for community representatives and parks officials to discuss the management of the park, especially its wildlife population.

A park management board provides the forum for community representatives and parks officials to discuss the management of the park, especially its wildlife population.

Parks Canada adopted a formal policy to negotiate these types of cooperative management arrangements in 1979. In 1994, Parks Canada issued a statement of *Guiding Principles and Operational Policies* which provides the framework for its present programs and future initiatives. A number of these policies address relations with Aboriginal people. In particular, these principles make it explicit that existing Aboriginal and treaty rights of the Aboriginal peoples of Canada will be honoured. In areas subject to existing Aboriginal or treaty rights or comprehensive land claims by Aboriginal peoples, the terms and conditions of park establishment will provide for continuation of renewable resource harvesting activities and will set out the nature and extent of Aboriginal peoples' involvement in park planning and management.

Parks Canada has also made commitments to foster employment and business opportunities for local residents, including neighbouring Aboriginal communities, in areas related to the operation of national parks.

Cooperative Management Arrangements

Through the *National Parks Act,* Parliament has decreed that the Minister of Canadian Heritage is responsible for the overall control, management and administration of all national parks. Each national park in Canada is required to have a park management plan. These plans provide the framework for the long-term development and operation of the park and are essential for the direction of park managers. The plans include a park conservation plan specifying the type and degree of resource protection and management needed to assure the ecological integrity of the park and the management of its cultural resources. They also include a park service plan which defines the type, character and locale of visitor facilities, activities and visitor services, and identifies target groups. Each plan also details how the park will protect its region. Management plans are developed with active public involvement at the national, regional and local levels.

The cooperative arrangements with Aboriginal people go beyond the usual public participation in the park planning process.

The cooperative arrangements with Aboriginal people go beyond the usual public participation in the park planning process. The cooperative management board provides a formal mechanism to work with community representatives on an ongoing basis.

The agreements also enable Parks Canada and Aboriginal peoples to achieve significant shared objectives through cooperative planning and management of park lands, including:

- protection of representative natural areas and critical wildlife habitat;

- continuation of traditional resource harvesting by local Aboriginal people in a way that preserves the ecological integrity of the region;

- protection and presentation of archaeological and historical sites and themes relating to Aboriginal peoples; and

- ongoing economic opportunities for local communities.

Aboriginal people currently participate, to varying degrees, in the management of five national parks and national park reserves. These are Wood Buffalo National Park, Ivvavik National Park, Aulavik National Park, Mingan Archipelago National Park Reserve in Quebec, and Gwaii Hanas National Park.

A portion of the Yukon North Slope was established as a national park and the Inuvialuit attained rights to hunt, fish and trap within it and to participate with the government in managing the area.

The Ivvavik National Park Example

The Ivvavik National Park provides a good example of the range of cooperation that is occurring between Parks Canada and Aboriginal peoples in managing national parks.

Ivvavik National Park was created under the Inuvialuit Final Agreement (IFA) of 1984. The Agreement sets a precedent both for Aboriginal people and for the management of national parks. Under the agreement, a portion of the Yukon North Slope was established as a national park and the Inuvialuit attained rights to hunt, fish and trap within it and to participate with the government in managing the area.

Several clauses in the agreement empower the Inuvialuit in managing the park. For example, the agreement states that any change in the character of the national park requires the consent of the Inuvialuit. The agreement also requires that a Wildlife Management Advisory Council, with an equal number of Aboriginal and government members, be established to advise on park planning and management and to recommend a management plan for the national park.

Cooperative management of the park takes place in a number of ways.

- The park management plan was prepared by a planning committee consisting of 2 Park representatives, 2 Inuvialuit people and representatives from the Wildlife Management Advisory Council.

- Specific implementation plans are developed cooperatively. For example the Ecosystem Management Plan is being developed by Parks staff working with the Hunter and Trappers Group, elders, and community representatives. Once it is developed, it will be presented to the Wildlife Management Advisory Council for approval.

- Some of the regulations for the park will be developed cooperatively. For example, the department is examining how to develop regulations for subsistence use in the National Parks in the Settlement Region on a collaborative basis. The process is managed by a steering committee consisting of senior Park officials and a selection of the Chairs of the co-management committees.

The Inuvialuit Final Agreement stipulates that the predominant number of persons employed in the operation and the management of the national park should be Inuvialuit.

Employment and training provisions are included in the Inuvialuit Final Agreement. The agreement stipulates that the predominant number of persons employed in the operation and the management of the national park should be Inuvialuit. Inuvialuit must be given appropriate training to assist them in qualifying for such employment.

There has been some progress toward achieving these objectives in Ivvavik National Park.

- Four Inuvialuit were on staff in 1991-92. That has increased to 8 in 1994-95.

- In 1994, two local Aboriginal people were hired into term positions as research assistants for the regional ecologist and archaeologist.

- Inuvialuit now account for almost half the workforce in the Settlement area.

- A variety of staff training is provided, ranging from on-the-job training to formal courses. Patrolpersons participate in cooperative training sessions with the staff of Ivvavik National Park. Staff also have participated in a number of training programs including whitewater rafting, search and rescue, first aid/CPR, wilderness travel and various resource management courses. This training has benefitted Aboriginal people by providing them with advancement opportunities.

The agreement also seeks to provide business development opportunities for Aboriginal people.

The Inuvialuit Final Agreement also seeks to provide business development opportunities for Aboriginal people. The agreement specifies that to the extent that the management plans of the national parks provides for economic activities, opportunities should be provided to the Inuvialuit on a preferred basis.

Rafting is the predominant commercial activity in Ivvavik National Park. The Park Superintendent has negotiated a memorandum of understanding with the Inuvialuit Regional Corporation and the Aklavik Regional Corporation for managing rafting on the Firth River. The memorandum represents a working agreement and a commitment of cooperation and understanding between the Inuvialuit and Parks Canada to establish a strong outfitting industry on the Firth River and to optimize the economic benefits to Inuvialuit individuals from Inuvialuit and non-Inuvialuit commercial operators.

- Ten of the 20 licences for commercial trips on the Firth River are reserved exclusively for Inuvialuit businesses and are allocated through the Aklavik Community Corporation.

- The remaining 10 commercial licences will be allocated through a public competitive application process and are available to either Inuvialuit and non-Inuvialuit businesses who provide the greatest net benefit (through employment, purchasing, training, joint venture opportunities, etc.) to the Inuvialuit of Aklavik.

The agreements that are now in place have demonstrated that Parks Canada and Aboriginal peoples can achieve significant shared objectives through cooperative planning and management of park lands.

• For the non-reserved licences, Parks Canada will undertake all reasonable measures to ensure that qualified Inuvialuit firms have the opportunity either to compete for them or to otherwise participate in them through sub-contracting or joint venture arrangements.

The first licences were awarded for the period 1994 to 1998. At the end of each year, the Inuvialuit benefits resulting from commercial rafting activities are to be reviewed by Parks Canada, IRC and the Aklavik Community Corporation.

Looking Forward

The agreements that are now in place have demonstrated that Parks Canada and Aboriginal peoples can achieve significant shared objectives through cooperative planning and management of park lands.

Parks Canada anticipates that there will be more such agreements in the future. At least four more national parks will have such cooperative management boards within the next few years. These are Kluane, Vuntut, Auyuittuq and Ellesmere Island.

Negotiations are also underway for the establishment of cooperative management boards at Batoche National Historic Site and Pukaskwa National Park. Boards are being considered for the proposed parks at Churchill in Manitoba and Tuktut Nogait in the Northwest Territories. As comprehensive land claim negotiations proceed in British Columbia and Labrador, boards will likely be established at a number of national parks in these regions.

Ontario Hydro's Approach to Resolving Grievances with Aboriginal Communities

Grievance resolution as a very important element in strengthening relationships with Aboriginal communities. Addressing past grievances is often a first step in fostering positive working relationships for the future.

Ontario Hydro has taken steps to build positive, enduring and mutually beneficial business relationships with First Nation communities. This has involved adopting a corporate policy for Aboriginal relationships, developing a set of principles for resolving past grievances and using facilitated, non-adversarial processes to resolve past differences.

Ontario Hydro views grievance resolution as a very important element in strengthening relationships with Aboriginal communities: addressing past grievances is often a first step in fostering positive working relationships for the future. To this end it has adopted a cooperative process of healing with First Nations. Ontario Hydro has found that its approach to addressing and resolving Aboriginal issues through joint problem-solving teams, using a neutral facilitator, has been effective in resolving grievances with a number of First Nations.

Historical Context

Past experiences with Hydro have often been viewed by Aboriginal people as negative, both in terms of environmental impact as well as economic and employment development. In a keynote address to the *Doing Business with First Nations* conference in Toronto on March 1, 1993, Ontario Hydro Chairman Maurice Strong described the legacy of past Hydro actions with regards Aboriginal peoples as follows:

> "Many First Nations people in Ontario were victims of past practices, which, while strictly legal at the time ... were also unfair, unfeeling, uncaring and institutionally discriminatory. We realized that we could not begin to forge enduring and mutually beneficial partnerships with First Nations until we had adequately addressed past grievances."

Ontario Hydro

Ontario Hydro is Ontario's largest Crown agency. In 1994, it had assets of over $44 billion, annual revenues of $8.7 billion and a workforce of 22,500 people. Ontario Hydro's head office is located in Toronto.

Ontario Hydro was created in 1906 by a special statute of the Province of Ontario. The corporation is regulated under the *Power Corporation Act*, which stipulates that Ontario Hydro must generate, supply and deliver electricity at cost throughout Ontario, as well as provide energy conservation programs.

Ontario Hydro operates 80 hydro-electric, fossil-fuelled and nuclear generating stations and an extensive transmission and distribution system across the province. Hydro sells electricity to 306 municipal utilities, which then sell this power to customers in their service area. In addition, the corporation directly serves more than 103 large industrial users and another 954,000 industrial, commercial, residential and farm customers mostly in rural and remote areas.

First Nations were dissatisfied with the legalistic approach Ontario Hydro had used in the past and sought a new approach.

Many of these concerns are unique to the geographic location of a particular community and sometimes to its historical relationship with Ontario Hydro. For example, the impact of diverting rivers and the flooding of some First Nations by Ontario Hydro in the 1940s and 1950s has never been resolved to the satisfaction of the Aboriginal communities affected. Ontario Hydro has also built transmission lines, sometimes over land regarded as sacred, without any consultation or approval from the people directly involved.

In the past, Ontario Hydro used a legalistic approach to deal with issues affecting First Nations and addressed most of these issues indirectly by arrangements made through the federal government. First Nations were dissatisfied with agreements reached in this manner and sought a new approach that adequately addressed the full scope of their concerns. Ontario Hydro, sharing the desire for a new approach and recognizing the critical influence of First Nations in the approval of new projects, took steps to develop mutually beneficial relationships with First Nations and, to that end, to create lasting solutions to past grievances for which Hydro is responsible.

Policy for Aboriginal Relationships

In 1990, Ontario Hydro made a Board-level commitment to ensure that the corporations's relations with Aboriginal peoples reflected their interests.

In 1990, Ontario Hydro made a Board-level commitment to address these issues and ensure that the corporations's strategic focus and direction in its relations with Aboriginal peoples reflect their interests. As part of this commitment, the Board of Directors of Ontario Hydro endorsed a set of guidelines to ensure positive relations with Aboriginal communities in Ontario. In 1991, the Aboriginal and Northern Affairs Branch was created to address concerns of Aboriginal and northern communities and to build positive, lasting relationships.

In May 1993, Ontario Hydro's commitment was strengthened further when the Board approved a Corporate Policy for Aboriginal Relationships. The governing principle of this policy is that Ontario Hydro recognizes the distinct legal, historical and cultural status of Aboriginal peoples, including specifically those rights of First Nations described in the Statement of Political Relationship (which was signed by Ontario and the First Nations of Ontario in August 1991), and will reflect these rights in all its relationships with First Nations, including the resolution of historical grievances against Ontario Hydro, the conduct of current business and planning for the future.

The policy, which applies to all managers whose responsibilities include business relationships with Aboriginal peoples or the development of policy governing such relationships, also sets out specific decision rules. These rules state that:

The governing principle of the Corporate Policy for Aboriginal Relationships is that Ontario Hydro recognizes the distinct legal, historical and cultural status of Aboriginal peoples.

- Ontario Hydro will work with First Nations to review their historical grievances against Ontario Hydro and seek mutually acceptable solutions.

- Ontario Hydro is committed to achieving long-term benefits for Aboriginal communities whose traditional lands are affected by its projects and facilities.

- Ontario Hydro accepts that First Nations' agreement is a critically important part of the process of obtaining approval under the Environmental Assessment Act of Ontario for construction and operation of facilities which impact on their lands or livelihood.

The rationale for this policy states that Ontario Hydro's policies governing business relationships with Aboriginal peoples are grounded in the Constitution, federal and provincial legislation and treaties signed between Canada and First Nations, government-to-government. Although power-sharing between levels of government is not yet defined in the case of First Nations, Hydro owes the First Nations the consideration and respect due to governments. Among other things, this means that Ontario Hydro cannot assume that First Nations are to be treated as special interest groups.

To build positive relationship with Aboriginal peoples, Hydro must deal with their grievances concerning past activities, enter new and respectful relationships in its day-to-day business, and include them in the planning of the corporation's future facilities.

Principles for Resolving Past Grievances

As an alternative to adversarial, legalistic processes, Ontario Hydro has developed a team-based, problem-solving approach for resolving First Nations' grievances.

As an alternative to the adversarial and legalistic processes previously used to resolve grievances, Ontario Hydro has developed a team-based, problem-solving approach for resolving First Nations' grievances that involves representatives both of Hydro and of the First Nation or Nations directly involved. This approach seeks consensus and is non-adversarial. It relies on developing understanding between the parties as to the physical, environmental, economic and cultural effects of Ontario Hydro's activities on reserves and traditional land use areas and on the First Nations peoples who occupy or use these areas.

The aim of this approach is to reach consensus on appropriate action to be taken, including compensation for impacts, and to achieve settlements that are sensitive to First Nations traditions and culture and to Ontario Hydro's corporate needs and responsibilities to customers.

Ontario Hydro does not view the goal of the process as simply negotiating a signed settlement at the lowest possible cost. It approaches the

Ontario Hydro's principles for resolving past grievances were approved by the Board of Directors in April 1994.

negotiating process to listen and to learn and to address First Nations concerns in a broad and lasting way. It is committed to finding agreement on the basis of shared values, including a respect for nature and a concern for the environment.

Ontario Hydro has adopted the following principles as the basis for resolving past grievances. The principles were approved by the Board of Directors in April 1994.

- Ontario Hydro shall work with an individual First Nation or group of First Nations to resolve all past (historical) grievances.

- Ontario Hydro shall pursue consensus-seeking, non-adversarial processes for resolving past grievances in a manner which respects the First Nations' traditions and cultures and which facilitates the timely resolution of these grievances and the development of effective future relationships. As a demonstration of its commitment, Ontario Hydro shall pay all reasonable costs of the processes.

- Ontario Hydro shall acknowledge the past impacts it has had on a First Nation through an apology where this is appropriate.

- Ontario Hydro shall consider various forms of compensation as means of resolving a grievance if the process determines that there has been a violation of law, including the current interpretation of treaty or Aboriginal rights and/or a breach of fundamental principles of fairness.

- The process to determine the degree and form of compensation shall examine the economic, environmental, physical and cultural impacts on reserves and in traditional land use areas resulting from the development and operation of Ontario Hydro's facilities.

- The degree and form of compensation provided by Ontario Hydro shall relate to the net impacts of Ontario Hydro's actions.

- The form of the compensation shall, to the extent possible, be designed to foster a mutually beneficial future relationship.

These principles have been translated into a generic process of joint problem-solving that involves the formation of Joint Consensus Teams.

Joint Problem-Solving Processes for Resolving Grievances

The principles for resolving past grievances provide the mandate and general framework for resolving specific grievances with individual First Nations. These principles have been translated into a generic process of joint problem-solving that enables specific grievances between Ontario Hydro and First Nations to be resolved.

- The first step is to jointly design a process that suits the needs of the First Nation. Joint Consensus Teams are formed and, if necessary, mutually-agreed independent facilitators assist the process. To select facilitators, both parties propose possible candidates, who are interviewed and selected by consensus.

- The Joint Consensus Team enters into discussions to develop rapport, build and test the commitment to achieve mutually beneficial outcomes and clarify objectives. Based on the results, a Memorandum of Understanding is agreed and signed. A workplan and budget is developed and Ontario Hydro and the First Nation sign a funding agreement.

- The Joint Consensus Team then proceeds to test common ground, conduct research to clarify grievances or issues, discuss differences and explore alternative solutions. The Ontario Hydro team develops the utility's business case for the alternatives and presents it to either the Executive or Board for approval.

- Finally, the Joint Consensus Team confirms common ground, negotiates and ultimately achieves agreement. Ontario Hydro and the First Nation reach agreement in principle and finalize legal agreements, including other parties such as the Department of Indian Affairs and Northern Development as required.

Since 1991, Ontario Hydro has entered into discussions with more than 20 First Nations in Ontario to seek solutions to past grievances and develop positive relationships for the future.

The agreement is signed by the required level of authority in Ontario Hydro. Depending on the value of the settlement, this can range from the Vice President of Aboriginal and Northern Affairs to the Board of Directors. For the First Nation, the agreement is signed by the Chief and Council.

Agreements usually require certain items to be implemented such as, for example, the negotiation of a lease, remedial environmental work, or specific monitoring initiatives. Ontario Hydro and the First Nation establish specific implementation plans and teams to ensure that these are carried out.

Experience to Date

Since 1991, Ontario Hydro has entered into discussions with more than 20 First Nations in Ontario to seek solutions to past grievances and develop positive relationships for the future. Agreements have been reached with six First Nations, namely Wabaseemoong, Dalles, Grassy Narrows, Onegaming, Pays Plat and Mattagami. However, because of the long history of mutual distrust, not all First Nations in Ontario have felt entirely comfortable about "working with" Ontario Hydro toward finding a solution.

Within the process, some First Nations still see themselves as "negotiating against" Hydro. Nonetheless, although all First Nations working with Ontario Hydro in a joint problem-solving process maintain their right to opt out at any time and pursue legalistic processes, this has not happened.

For those that have participated in the joint consensus decision-making process, there have also been a number of challenges for both sides. Differences have emerged in the interpretation of the guidelines. For example, the notion of "reasonable cost" that determines the amount of process funding has been interpreted differently by the parties. Making the transition from the joint identification of issues and data collection to joint resolution has been difficult sometimes because the parties are far apart on possible resolution options. Also, expectations get built through the process which often cannot be met at the end.

The new approach has resulted in a number of specific resolutions with First Nations. Ontario Hydro has adopted a flexible and creative approach to compensation. Agreements often have involved some form of cash payment. However, they may also involve transfer of money to Band trust funds that will be used for cultural projects and land purchases.

- In one situation, compensation has been offered by Hydro for support of the revitalization of Aboriginal language and culture, socio-economic development and environmental efforts.

- In another, at Onegaming First Nation, the community invested part of its settlement with Hydro in the development of an energy management program. The people of Onegaming hope to offer the program to other Aboriginal communities, thereby promoting economic development and creating jobs.

- Other examples of compensation include an educational award program for high school students pursuing post-secondary studies; rehabilitation of a cemetery; construction of housing within the community; and the construction of a community centre.

Ontario Hydro is committed to resolving all outstanding grievances. The corporation believes that it has spoken with most First Nations that have a grievance and anticipates that it has either reached a solution, begun a process or will soon begin a process with all of them. Ontario Hydro intends to continue using the joint problem-solving process that has been developed and to be flexible to the requirements of individual First Nations, with the objective of moving from relationships focused on the past to those that are oriented toward mutually beneficial business dealings, now and in the future.

Ontario Hydro is committed to resolving all outstanding grievances, with the objective of moving from relationships focused on the past to those that are oriented toward mutually beneficial business dealings, now and in the future.

Community Participation in the Peace Arch Project

The Peace Arch Project is a partnership of community, industry and government members designed to increase long-term employment and business opportunities for the Aboriginal residents of the region.

The Peace Arch Project in Alberta has been operating since 1987. It is a partnership of community, industry and government members designed to increase long-term employment and business opportunities for the Aboriginal residents of the region. It is currently jointly funded by the energy, forestry and utility sectors and the provincial and federal governments.

Considerable benefit to area residents has been generated through the Peace Arch Project resulting in employment, pre-employment and on-the-job training, as well as small business development opportunities.

Background

The Peace Arch region in Alberta is bordered by the towns of Peace River and Slave Lake. The area is named after a local geological formation rich in oil and natural gas. The Peace Arch Project was established to create an environment in which opportunities for local employment and business benefits could be generated and sustained. The region includes several Aboriginal communities, including Atikameg, Gift Lake, Cadotte Lake, Little Buffalo, Trout Lake, Peerless Lake and Loon Lake.

Despite the extensive oil and gas exploration and development activity and the large number of major companies operating in the region, local residents were not benefitting from new jobs and business opportunities due to the preference by industry to use established outside services with which they were familiar and comfortable. Several oil companies expressed interest in developing a collective industry approach as a means of responding to these challenges. As a result, discussions were held with the Northern Alberta Development Branch and the Canadian Petroleum Association (now called the Canadian Association of Petroleum Producers) to put an organization and funding in place to manage a project to increase Aboriginal participation in the region's resource development.

The Peace Arch Project began in 1987 and has operated as a non-profit registered society

Corporate Contributors to the Peace Arch Project

Since its inception the Peace Arch Project has been funded by the federal and Alberta governments, the Canadian Association of Petroleum Producers and by individual companies in the energy and forestry sectors. Contributing companies in 1993/94 included:

Petro-Canada
Imperial Oil
International Colin Energy
Unocal Canada Resources
Norcen Energy Resources
Shell Canada Ltd.
Stampeder Exploration Ltd.
Star Oil and Gas Ltd.

Rigel Oil and Gas Ltd.
Alberta-Pacific Forest Industries
Daishowa Marubeni
NOVA Corporation
Alberta Power
Sunset Welding Ltd.

Despite extensive activity in the region, local residents were not benefitting from new opportunities.

The Peace Arch Project began in 1987. It was originally planned as a two-year pilot but has proved so successful that it has been extended several times.

Community representatives elected by the eight northern communities, sit on the Management Committee.

since 1989. It is currently jointly funded by companies in the energy, forestry and utility sectors and by the provincial and federal governments. The project was originally planned as a two-year pilot but proved to be so successful that it has been extended several times.

Project Objectives

The Peace Arch Project was established to create an environment in which opportunities for local employment and business benefits could be generated and sustained. Two principal goals have been set for the project.

- The first goal is to improve communications and relationships between partners. This involves strengthening community involvement in the project; delivery more project training and employment services at the community level; implementing a bursary program for local residents; conducting an annual workshop with community, industry and government representatives; and increasing the project's profile through media promotion.

- The second goal is to increase long-term local employment and business opportunities for residents of the region by finding employment for local residents. This involves building greater commitment from industry participants to provide employment and business opportunities for community residents and expanding the scope of the project to include other employers, such as the forest industry.

Organization

The Peach Arch Management Committee was established in 1989 to direct and advise the project. It operates in consultation with three associate committees, a project coordinator and a training and development coordinator. The associate committees represent the regional communities, industry and government agencies.

The Management Committee normally has 6 members. It is composed of 2 industry representatives, 2 community representatives and 2 government representatives. The project coordinator attends meetings as a resource person. The Chairman of the Management Committee has been an employee of the lead industry company. Since the project began, the lead industry position has been held by Imperial Oil Resources, Amoco and Petro-Canada. International Colin Energy is the lead industry company at present. Community representatives are elected by the eight northern communities.

The Management Committee is assisted by a full-time project coordinator and a training and employment coordinator.

The Project Coordinator is based in the Peace Arch project office in Slave Lake and his salary is paid by the Canada/Alberta Northern Development Agreement. The coordinator's role is to help local individuals and businesses to develop business plans and access government support programs and to work with industry operators and training institutions to develop and implement training programs at the local level.

The training and employment coordinator is based in Loon Lake. His salary is paid by Alberta Advanced Education and Career Development. He works closely with the project coordinator to develop training programs to meet the needs of industry and the communities and help match employable community residents with jobs.

Funding

The project is currently jointly funded by the private companies in the energy, forestry and utility sectors and by the provincial and federal governments (primarily through the Canada/Alberta Northern Development Subsidiary agreement).

The project is currently jointly funded by the private companies in the energy, forestry and utility sectors and by the provincial and federal governments.

Private sector resource companies that have contributed ongoing funding to the project, over the years, have included Petro-Canada Resources, Gulf Canada Resources, Shell Canada, Mobil Oil Canada, Norcen Energy, Unocal Canada Resources, Amoco Canada Petroleum, Chevron Canada, Kerr McGee Canada, Westcoast Petroleum, Alberta Power, Alberta-Pacific Forest Industries, Imperial Oil, International Colin Energy, Daishowa Marubeni, NOVA Corporation, Stampeder Exploration, Star Oil and Gas, Sunset Welding and Rigel Oil and Gas.

Pre-Employment Initiatives

The major pre-employment initiatives that are being carried out under the project are outreach activities with local schools, a bursary program, and pre-employment training programs.

Industry and project representatives have made presentations to Grade 9 students from the local schools. They have addressed the importance of a Grade 12 education for obtaining employment. The presentations start with a video of the Peace Arch project. This is followed by presentations from Aboriginal people working in specific occupations in the oil and gas industry.

The Peace Arch Bursary program was established with a joint financial seed contribution of $10,000 from Norcen and Amoco. The money may be awarded for travel, accommodation or tuition that relates to education or training. A special committee selects the recipients.

Pre-employment initiatives include outreach activities with local schools, a bursary program, and pre-employment training programs.

A training program for local students in oil and gas field maintenance was established through consultation with Fairview College and local industry. Funding was provided under the federal government's Canadian Jobs Strategy program. The course was tailored to the needs of local industry and targeted Grade 12 graduates. In order for students from the communities to access the training, Fairview College set up a field classroom in Red Earth in a leased warehouse. Alberta Vocational College provided 10 weeks of upgrading and pre-trades courses (including prerequisite certification courses) and Fairview College delivered 28 weeks of basic training in the maintenance and operation of oilfield production equipment. The basic training also included 10 weeks of practical work experience made possible with the cooperation of local industry.

The Oil and Gas Field Operation and Maintenance Program ended in November 1992. Since then over 19 different training courses have been provided by the Peace Arch project. A total of 347 industry and community people have participated in the courses.

Business Development

The project coordinator has the key function of facilitating new business development opportunities for Aboriginal suppliers.

In order to create small business development opportunities, the project coordinator holds an ongoing series of meetings with industry representatives in the oil and gas, forestry and utility sectors. These meetings are used to promote consideration of local Aboriginal contractors and subcontractors and to encourage industry representatives to identify potential opportunities early enough that local suppliers can be organized to compete for them.

The project coordinator facilitates new business development opportunities for Aboriginal suppliers.

The project coordinator also provides business direction and advice to prospective business people in the Aboriginal communities. This can involve one-on-one small business advice, counselling and mentorship, such as providing guidance on specific bidding processes. Assistance is provided in addressing barriers (access to financing, access to expertise, lack of profile) that Aboriginal businesses face in competing on contracts for goods or services to the industry. The project coordinator has assisted some local companies to obtain operating loans from the banks to deal with cash flow problems and helped others to get bank financing for the purchase of capital equipment. The project coordinator also works closely with the growing number of community-based businesses that have developed in the region.

In recent years, the project coordinator has put more emphasis on ways to create opportunities for Aboriginal businesses in the forestry sector, especially those related to silviculture and stand tending - areas where equipment costs are relatively low and training is more readily available.

The Al-Pac and Daishowa Marubeni pulp mills are now in operation. Tolko Industries' oriented strand board plant in High Prairie should result in more harvesting, log hauling and silviculture jobs for Aboriginal people.

Employment Initiatives

The training and employment coordinator helps match employable community residents with jobs and acts as a contact point for employers.

The training and employment coordinator's position is maintained at the Loon Lake Employment Office under an annual contract funded by Alberta Advanced Education and Career Development. The coordinator helps match employable community residents with jobs and acts as a contact point for employers. Employers are assisted by advertising available positions, pre-screening job applicants and recommending candidates. The Office maintains an inventory of education and work experience of community members and is often able to provide industry with good potential candidates.

Employment follow-up is important in order to ensure that individuals placed in jobs are comfortable in their positions and are receiving support in the workplace. By following up on job placements, the employment coordinator can address areas of concern in the workplace with the employer and thereby ensure that new employees have a fair chance to succeed.

Results

The Peace Arch Project has generated considerable opportunities for employment, pre-employment and on-the-job training, as well as small business development.

Considerable benefit to area residents has been generated through the Peace Arch Project resulting in employment, pre-employment and on-the-job training, as well as small business development opportunities. An independent evaluation of the project was undertaken in 1993. It concluded that the project has performed well against its objectives. It has helped community members find full-time, seasonal and part-time employment. Employment development has been supported by the enhanced communication between the communities, industry and government. The project has also had a particularly profound and positive impact on identifying the importance of industry-specific training.

Since its inception in 1987, the project has succeeded in identifying, training and placing about 400 Aboriginal people in jobs either with the oil and gas companies operating in the region or with local contractors and service industries. In total, 50 Aboriginal people have been placed in permanent positions and another 345 in temporary positions since the project started. Employers include major oil and gas companies, local contractors and other service industries. Permanent positions filled have included battery and field operators, power saw operators, cooks, secretaries, waitresses, truck drivers, journeyperson mechanics and safety instructors.

Over 266 community people have participated successfully in one or more courses provided through the project. Much of the training has contributed to Aboriginal residents qualifying for full-time jobs or enabling them to participate in contracting opportunities, such as the construction of Alberta Power's powerline from Loon Lake to Panny River.

The Gas/Oilfield Equipment Maintenance Program run by Fairview College at Red Earth was developed jointly with industry and tailored to their needs. Of the 23 students who started, 14 completed the program and seven found permanent jobs upon graduating.

Many communities have started up their own businesses to provide contracting and other services to the oil industry. Examples include Trout River Contractors, Gift Lake Developments, Loon River Contractors, Back Lake Slashing, Trout Lake Forest Contractors, and Woodland Cree Band. These are involved in activities as diverse as slashing and clearing to pipeline fabrication and installation. Local industry has been receptive to trying service contractors from the local communities, and often accepts the risks without prior work experience. Nevertheless many opportunities for greater community participation in industry developments are still being missed.

The project has succeeded in widening the base of industry involvement and sponsorship. New companies in the utility sector, such as Alberta Power and NOVA Corporation, have joined the project. In recent years two major forest sector companies, Alberta-Pacific Forest Industries and Daishowa Marubeni, have become contributing companies.

Community involvement has been key to the project's success. For example, the communities have selected the project coordinator as well as the training coordinator. There is an increased awareness by community members of opportunities surrounding them. Communities are beginning to assert their ownership of the project, showing greater commitment and initiative.

The ultimate goal is to increase the role of communities with a view to their assuming leadership of the project.

Looking Forward

The ultimate goal of the project is to enable communities to pursue their business and employment opportunities independently. Increasing the role of communities with a view to assuming project leadership will help the communities reach that goal.

The current focus and objectives of the project will be maintained until a community based model is established. To this end, the Peace Arch Project plans to facilitate a process to help the communities prepare a business plan by the end of 1995.

CHECKLIST OF CC
PRACT

1. BUILD ORGANIZATIONAL (AND CAPACITY

1.1 Develop and Adopt a Formal Aborig...

- Appoint policy development coordinator/project team

- Establish business case for Aboriginal relations policy/program

- Develop policy in conjunction with Aboriginal and other stakeholders

- Obtain Board-level approval for policy

- Obtain endorsement/support of union

- Hold formal launch to mark adoption of policy

- Communicate policy to internal and external audiences

- Sustain senior management role in promotion of policy

1.2 Allocate Resources to Aboriginal Relations Initiatives

- Appoint Aboriginal affairs coordinator

- Create and staff Aboriginal relations unit (if program size warrants)

- Define mandate and reporting relations to senior management

- Define linkages to and responsibilities of rest of organization

1.3 Integrate Aboriginal Relations into Business Planning Process

- Set realistic long-term goals

- Allocate responsibility for goals among relevant business units

- Set annual targets at business unit level

- Establish accountability framework

- Establish monitoring and reporting system

- Integrate accountability into performance review process for managers

1.4 Build Knowledge and Understanding about Aboriginal Relations

- Communicate policy/program/results to employees on ongoing basis

- Communicate policy/program/results to Aboriginal stakeholders on ongoing basis

- Communicate policy/program/results to external stakeholders on ongoing basis

- Provide Aboriginal awareness training for managers

- Provide Aboriginal awareness training for employees

2. EDUCATION AND TRAINING

2.1 Encourage Young People to Stay in School

- Establish relationships with schools with large Aboriginal populations

- Provide information to students about education and career options

- Provide role models and mentors for Aboriginal students

- Develop educational experience programs

- Offer short-term work experience programs to students

2.2 Provide Education/Training Opportunities and Support

- Develop/support access programs for post-secondary education

- Provide educational awards/scholarships in relevant disciplines

- Develop access programs for employer-based training programs

- Develop/support access programs for skilled trade training programs

- Provide information on skilled trade qualification/certification process

- Develop/support training programs in high skill occupations

2.3 Offer Pre-Employment Programs

- Develop/participate in job-readiness training programs

- Link training to concrete job opportunities

- Guarantee employment for successful program participants

- Offer employment skills workshops

- Provide summer employment opportunities

- Offer short-term work assignments

3.   ENHANCING EMPLOYMENT OPPORTUNITIES

3.1 Develop Aboriginal Employment Strategy

- Establish advisory committee or special task force

- Ensure participation of Aboriginal and other stakeholders

- Set long-term goals for Aboriginal employment

- Set annual targets for Aboriginal employment

- Identify barriers to Aboriginal employment

- Determine necessary modifications to corporate human resource policies

- Define special measures needed to improve employment opportunities

- Develop action plan

- Establish accountability framework

3.2 Target Recruitment Initiatives

- Target outreach activities to organizations with high Aboriginal populations

- Visit Aboriginal communities and training institutions

- Encourage/facilitate visits by Aboriginal people to local offices/workplaces

- Network with Aboriginal education and employment counsellors

- Form partnerships with Aboriginal communities and service organizations

- Keep Aboriginal organizations informed about job opportunities

- Use available inventories of Aboriginal job candidates

- Promote development of inventories of Aboriginal job candidates

3.3 Facilitate Access to Entry-Level Positions

- Ensure Aboriginal representation in recruitment pool

- Include Aboriginal people in selection processes

- Use Aboriginal internship programs

- Negotiate hiring preferences in collective agreement

- Negotiate apprenticeship opportunities in collective agreement

- Create in-house training positions in technical occupations

- Create in-house training positions in skilled trades

3.4 Encourage Career Development

- Provide in-house basic education and literacy program

- Adapt corporate training programs to ensure cultural sensitivity

- Ensure Aboriginal access to management/supervisory development opportunities

- Implement succession planning and ensure Aboriginal representation

- Promote and facilitate mentoring

3.5 Create a Positive Working Environment

- Implement measures to eliminate harassment, discrimination and racism

- Promote workforce diversity as a business benefit

- Use Aboriginal employee advisory groups as resource to management

- Facilitate development of Aboriginal employee support networks

- Encourage buddy systems for new Aboriginal employees

4. ABORIGINAL BUSINESS DEVELOPMENT

4.1 Develop Procurement Policies

- Set long-term goals for Aboriginal business participation

- Set annual targets for Aboriginal business participation

- Adopt procurement policies that target Aboriginal suppliers

- Set aside some contracts exclusively for Aboriginal business

- Allocate set asides through negotiated/restricted tendering processes

- Provide long-term supply contracts to promote business formation/expansion

- Require major suppliers to provide opportunities for Aboriginal participation

4.2 Remove Procurement Barriers

- Break contracts into smaller packages to provide access to small business

- Ensure that Aboriginal contractors are on bid lists

- Provide early notice to Aboriginal communities/businesses on upcoming contracts

- Clarify procurement processes for Aboriginal businesses

- Use pre-qualification process to promote competitiveness of bids

- Inform potential bidders about legal/safety/regulatory requirements

- Assist potential bidders to meet legal/safety/regulatory requirements

- Waive bid and performance bond requirements, if feasible

4.3   Promote Supplier Development

- Develop inventories of local Aboriginal contractors and businesses

- Help Aboriginal businesses compete effectively for contracts

- Foster development of management skills among Aboriginal business

- Encourage joint ventures with non-Aboriginal business to build capacity

- Provide subsidies and financial assistance

- Debrief unsuccessful bidders to help improve future bids

- Create joint opportunities to promote development of large Aboriginal suppliers

4.4   Enter into Cooperative Business Ventures

- Enter into cooperative business ventures with Aboriginal organizations

- Structure business ventures to ensure substantive benefits for Aboriginal partners

- Partner with Aboriginal development agencies to develop commercial complexes

5. COMMUNITY RELATIONS

5.1 Establish Communications with Local Communities

- Establish a community liaison committee

- Establish Aboriginal advisory councils

- Consider representation of community leaders on Board of Directors

- Provide ongoing information through Aboriginal affairs group and other staff

- Produce communication materials in variety of formats and local languages

5.2 Make Resources Available for Community Development

- Assist local communities to define their community development needs

- Assign staff to work with community on economic/business development strategy

- Open up corporate training courses/workshop to community representatives

- Loan equipment for community projects

- Provide funding for community infrastructure

- Sponsor and promote community events and projects

- Allocate corporate donations to Aboriginal communities

- Promote recognition of Aboriginal achievement in broader community

5.3 Develop Collaborative Initiatives

- Establish joint planning and decision-making mechanisms

- Establish joint problem-solving/grievance resolution processes

- Enter into integrated agreements for socio-economic development

- Establish education and training partnerships

- Establish employment development partnerships

- Establish business development partnerships

- Establish joint environmental initiatives

- Enter into collaborative resource management initiatives

About the Authors

Both Pamela Sloan and Roger Hill are Principals of Hill Sloan Associates Inc., an economics and management consulting firm. Over the past ten years, they have undertaken a wide range of complex consulting assignments for corporate and government clients across Canada and have authored numerous publications.

Pamela Sloan is a graduate of McGill University (Faculty of Management) and has an MA in Economics from Cambridge University. She was formerly Vice President of Economic and Public Affairs at the Toronto Stock Exchange and has worked in professional positions with the Royal Bank, Ontario Ministry of Industry and Trade and the federal Department of Finance.

Roger Hill holds an MA in Economics from Cambridge University. He served as Director of Trade Policy as well as Director of Labour Policy for the Ontario Government. He also has worked as a special advisor to the Department of External Affairs on US Trade Relations.

Hill Sloan Associates was formed in 1985. The firm has developed specialized expertise in documenting, analyzing and benchmarking corporate practices, particularly those relating to workforce diversity, workplace training, economic development and Aboriginal relations.